EARLY
FLIGHT

From Balloons to Biplanes

EARLY
FLIGHT

From Balloons to Biplanes

Edited by
Frank Oppel

CASTLE

EARLY
FLIGHT
From Balloons to Biplanes

Printed in the United States of America.

ISBN: 1-55521-227-1

Contents

1.
The Men Who Learned to Fly (1908)

THE MEN WHO LEARNED TO FLY

THE WRIGHT BROTHERS' STORY OF THEIR EXPERIMENTS, THE SENSATIONS OF FLIGHT, AND THEIR ESTIMATE OF THE FUTURE OF THE AËROPLANE

BY

GEORGE KIBBE TURNER

AUTHOR OF "GALVESTON: A BUSINESS CORPORATION"

ILLUSTRATIONS FROM PHOTOGRAPHS

IN 1888 scientific authorities could demonstrate mathematically that a mechanical flying-machine was impossible. Formulae— absolutely fundamental formulae proving this — had remained almost undisturbed since they were proposed by Sir Isaac Newton. Any flying-machine must be too heavy to be supported by the air. Yet, it was also well understood that many birds were a thousand times heavier than the air they flew in.

During the eighties a German mechanical engineer, Otto Lilienthal, studied the mechanics of the flight of birds, and decided we knew very little about the laws of flying. The only way for a man to learn to fly, he believed, was to start flying. In 1891 he began to fly. Using wings built like those of soaring birds, such as the hawk and buzzard, he precipitated himself from steep hills, against strong winds, and glided down through the air into the valleys. In more than two thousand flights — varying from a few yards to a fifth of a mile in length — he established entirely new views concerning the support of moving bodies by the air. In August, 1896,

CHANUTE'S MULTIPLE-WING MACHINE (1896)

Lilienthal's wings gave way in a sudden gust of wind. He fell fifty feet, broke his back, and died the following day.

Percy S. Pilcher of England continued similar experiments in soaring flight. In September, 1899, his wings also broke; he dropped thirty feet through the air, and died of his injuries two days later. With the death of the two leading European experimenters, the principal burden of the discovery of mechanical flight was taken up by Americans.

In 1887–89, Professor S. P. Langley, subsequently of the Smithsonian Institution, by means of experiments with impelled metal plates, established new scientific formulae concerning the support given flying-planes by the air, and published them in 1891; in 1896 he made a small steam-aëroplane which flew three quarters of a mile down the Potomac River. In 1896 Octave Chanute of Chicago, assisted by A. M. Herring and others as active operators and designers, made and tested new and better types of glidingm-achines as the result of experiments on the shores of Lake Michigan.

THE FIRST OF THE GLIDING-MACHINES

LILIENTHAL OPERATING HIS BIRDLIKE AËROPLANE

In 1900 the Wright brothers, two young bicycle-makers of Dayton, Ohio, started experiments in air-gliding in a machine operated on a new principle. In 1903 they added a gasoline-engine to their aëroplane, and began to navigate the air in mechanical flying-machines. It is a well-established fact that they have been flying on mechanically driven aëroplanes for the past four years. Exactly how they do this is not known; they are keeping their method secret, in the belief that this is the only way in which they can secure a financial return from their invention.

The Wright Brothers and their Story

Before the Wright brothers sailed abroad last summer, for the demonstrations of their machines before foreign war departments, they discussed with me for an entire morning their invention, the theories and sensations of flight, and their personal beliefs and ambitions in connection with their discovery — two lean, quiet men in a dingy, commonplace little brick bicycle-shop; pleasant, unassuming, most approachable, but shy and silent under the oppression of the greatest secret of the time.

Orville, of the more social and conversational temperament, did the greater share of the talking — an amiable, kindly-faced man of thirty-five. Wilbur — prematurely bald, about forty, with the watchful eyes, marked facial lines, and dry, brief speech of a naturally reticent man — corroborated or amplified his brother's statements. It would be both unnecessary and impossible to divide the story of their invention between the two men exactly as they told it. Practically their story, like their invention, was the product of one mind — one dual mind. I will tell it as a simple statement of fact, without attempting to reproduce the exact conversation. It is the extraordinary information, and not the method of statement, which is of importance. The story follows:

In 1896 we saw a little press despatch in a newspaper telling of the death of Lilienthal by a fall from his machine. This, and the reading of the "Aëronautical Annual" for 1897, started our first active interest in the problem of aërial navigation. We have been at work at it ever since — first as a mere scientific pastime, but for nearly ten years as the most serious purpose of our

THE WRIGHT BROTHERS' LATEST GLIDER

THE HORIZONTAL POSITION OF THE OPERATOR, THE BALANCING RUDDER IN FRONT, AND THE SLIGHT
CURVES OF THE DOUBLE WING SURFACES SHOWN IN THIS PHOTOGRAPH, REPRESENT THREE
OF THE WRIGHT BROTHERS' CHIEF CONTRIBUTIONS TO THE ART OF FLYING

life. Up to 1900 we had merely studied and made laboratory experiments; in that year we started actual experiments in flying on our gliding-machine.

At that time (1900) there was really only one problem remaining to be solved to make a workable flying-machine — the problem of equilibrium. Men already knew how to make aëroplanes that would support them when driven through the air at a sufficient speed, and there were engines light enough per horse-power to propel the aëroplane at the necessary speed, and to carry their own weight and the weight of an operator. There were plenty of aëroplanes that would fly in still air. What was needed was an air-ship that would not capsize when the wind was blowing.

The Turbulence of the Air

No one who has not navigated the air can appreciate the real difficulty of mechanical flight. To the ordinary person it seems a miracle that a thin solid plane can be driven up into the air by machinery; but for over ten years that miracle has been accomplished. On the other hand, the great problem — the problem of equilibrium — never occurs to any one who has not actually tried flying. The real question of the flying-machine is how to keep it from turning over.

The chief trouble is the turmoil of the air. The common impression is that the atmosphere runs in comparatively regular currents which we call winds. No one who has not been thrown about on a gliding-aëroplane — rising or falling ten, twenty, or even thirty feet in a few seconds — can understand how utterly wrong this idea is. The air along the surface of the earth, as a matter of fact, is continually churning. It is thrown upward from every irregularity, like sea breakers on a coast-line; every hill and tree and building sends up a wave or slanting current. And it moves, not directly back and forth upon its coast-line, like the sea, but in whirling rotary masses. Some of these rise up hundreds of yards. In a fairly strong wind the air near the earth is more disturbed than the whirlpools of Niagara.

Equilibrium—the Real Problem of Flying

The problem of mechanical flight is how to balance in this moving fluid which supports the flying-machine; or, technically speaking, how to make the center of gravity coincide with the center of air-pressure. Now, the irregular action of the air is naturally reflected in the movement of this center of pressure. If a wind should blow against a plane at right angles to it, the center of pressure would be in the center of the plane. But an aëroplane must be sailed at a very slight angle to the direction in which it is moving. That means that the center of air-pressure is well forward on the surfaces of the machine. Every sudden breeze that blows strikes strongly on the front of the plane and very little on the back of it. The result is that the force of every gust of wind is multiplied by leverage in its tendency to tip the plane over. The wind often veers several times a second, quicker than thought, and the center of pressure changes with it. It is as difficult to follow this center of pressure as to keep your finger on the flickering blot of light from a prism swinging in the sun.

Lilienthal balanced himself in his gliding-machine by shifting his weight; his body hung down below his wings, resting on his elbows. In Chanute's machines the operator did nearly the same, swinging below the wings, with his arm-pits supported on little parallel bars.* In both machines the rapid motion of the body was difficult and exhausting work, and the size of the machine was definitely limited by the weight which the operator could carry on his back. In our gliding-machine we introduced

ORVILLE WRIGHT

an entirely new method; we governed the motion of the center of pressure, not by shifting our weight, but by shifting the rudder and surfaces of the machine against the action of the air. Before this can be understood there must be some idea of the wings of our machine.

The Development of Artificial Wings

Lilienthal, in his first flights, copied the wings of soaring birds very closely; later he used wings in two planes, that is, one above another. Chanute experimented with wings of as many as five planes, but, like Lilienthal, secured the best results with the "double-deckers." When we took up our gliding experiments, we believed that these wings in two planes had been shown to be the best type for the aëroplane; they were stronger than any other, allowing the principle of the truss-bridge to be used in their bracing, and they were more compact and manageable than the single-surface wings.

By 1900 we had designed our type of gliding-machine. It was made of cloth and spruce and steel wire, very much after the style of the Chanute double-decker—a little larger than his. But in its principle of operation it was entirely different. The operator, instead of swinging below the wings, lay fore and aft across the middle of the lower wing upon his stomach. In front of him — extended out before the machine instead of behind it — was a horizontal rudder. This guided the gliding-machine up and down. But it did much more than that: it counterbalanced the movement of the center of pressure backward and forward on the main surfaces of the machine; that is, it kept the aëroplane from pitching over backward or forward. For steering and balancing sideways we turned the outside edges of the

*Chanute tested three types of his own, in two of which the wings were automatically readjusted by the wind-pressure. The multiple-wing machine was his first type.

wings against the air-pressure by cords controlled by movements of the operator's body.
The tail used in previous gliding-machines was
given up. Our idea was to secure a machine
which, with a little practice, could be balanced
and steered semi-automatically, by reflex action,
just as a bicycle is. There is no time to be given
to conscious thought in balancing an aëroplane; the action of the air is too rapid.

The shape of the wings offered another important problem. Langley and other experimenters had favored wings set at a dihedral
angle — that is, each
slanting upward
from the center
where they joined.
They hoped to se-
cure a stable equilib-
rium by this. We
believed that this
device would work
well in still air, but
that in the shifting,
troubled air of out-
of-doors it would
add to the danger
of turning over.
These wings are
made after the style
of the wings of a
soaring buzzard —
a bird which avoids
high winds. We
curved ours down a
little at the tips,
after the fashion of
the soaring gull — a
rough-weather bird.
Our wings did not
approach the exact
form of birds' wings
so closely as Lilien-
thal's or Pilcher's.
They were made of
cloth fixed to two rectangular wooden frames,
fastened one above the other by wooden braces
and wires. The cloth surfaces were arched
by ribs between these frames to secure the
curved surfaces of birds' wings, which Lilienthal had shown were essential to the best
results in flying.

Those Animated Aëroplanes, the Birds

We had also worked out a new method of practice with gliding-machines which we hoped to
use. Lilienthal and Chanute had obtained their
experience in flying by the operator's launching
himself from a hill and gliding down on to lower
land. This involved carrying back their apparatus, after a short flight, to the top of the
hill again. Because of the difficulties of this
awkward method, although Lilienthal had
made over two thousand flights, we calculated
that in all his five years of experiment he
could not have been actually practising flying more than five hours — far too short a
time for the ordinary man to learn to ride
a bicycle. It was our plan to follow the
example of soaring birds, and find a place
where we could be supported by strong rising winds.

WILBUR WRIGHT

A bird is really
an aëroplane. The
portions of its wings
near the body are
used as planes of
support, while the
more flexible parts
outside, when
flapped, act as pro-
pellers. Some of
the soaring birds
are not much more
than animated sail-
ing-machines. A
buzzard can be
safely kept in an
open pen thirty feet
across and ten feet
high. He cannot fly
out of it. In fact,
we know from ob-
servation made by
ourselves that he
cannot fly for any
distance up a grade
of one to six. Yet
these birds sailing
through the air are
among the common-
est sights through
a great section of
the country. Every one who has been outdoors has seen a buzzard or a hawk soaring;
every one who has been at sea has seen the
gulls sailing after a steamship for hundreds
of miles with scarcely a movement of the
wings. All of these birds are doing the
same thing — they are balancing on rising
currents of air. The buzzards and hawks
find the currents blowing upward off the
land; the gulls that follow the steamers
from New York to Florida are merely sliding
downhill a thousand miles on rising currents
in the wake of the steamer in the atmosphere, and on the hot air rising from her
smokestacks.

A Plan which Failed

On a clear, warm day the buzzards find the high, rotary, rising currents of air, and go sailing around and around in them. On damp, windy days they hang above the edge of a steep hill on the air which comes rising up its slope. From their position in the air they can glide down at will. Now, we planned to take our gliding-machine, in 1900, to some section where there were strong, constant winds, and try soaring and gliding in the manner of these birds. We calculated, by Lilienthal's tables, that our gliding-machine, which had 165 square feet of surface, should be sustained by a wind of twenty-one miles an hour. We planned to raise the machine — operator and all — like a kite in this wind, men holding ropes at the end of each wing. When the machine had started soaring at the end of the ropes, these would be released and the operator could glide to the earth. In this way we hoped we would avoid the weary dragging back of the machine necessary in the operation of gliding downhill, and could get hours instead of seconds of practice in flying.

Winds of between sixteen and twenty-five miles an hour are not unusual at points on the Atlantic coast, and after a little study and inquiry we located the place we wanted at Kitty Hawk, North Carolina, on the sand-dunes which separate Albemarle Sound from the Atlantic Ocean. There were strong winds there, and steep hills of soft sand for use in gliding from heights, if we found that necessary. In the summer of 1900 we

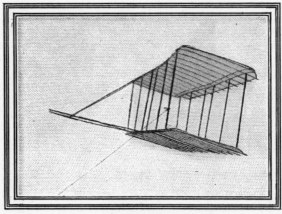

THE FIRST WRIGHT GLIDER (1900)

took our first gliding-machine there for experiment.

We found on this trip that our plan to practise by raising the machine like a kite was impracticable. It required a wind of nearly thirty miles an hour to support our aëroplane at an angle flat or level enough to be of any use in gliding. The surfaces of this first machine were not curved deeply enough, in the first place, but we found also that the tables of the earlier experimenters concerning the lifting power of the wind were not accurate. So we had to give up our plan of soaring, and start gliding from hills, as the others had done. Instead of hours of gliding, as we had hoped, we had only two minutes of actual sailing in the air that year. Nevertheless we came to some very clear and satisfactory conclusions. We found that our new and revolutionary method of steering and balancing by shifting surfaces instead of by weights worked well, and that it promised to work in large as well as in small machines.

A Revolution in the Art of Flying

In 1901 we started gliding again at Kitty Hawk, on a machine nearly twice as large as had been counted safe before. This ma-

THE SECOND WRIGHT GLIDER (1901)

chine had a surface of 308 square feet, whereas Lilienthal's had had 151, Pilcher's 165, and Chanute's double-decker 134. Our new glider was 22 feet from tip to tip, and the main surfaces were 7 feet across and 6 feet apart. It weighed 100 pounds, 240 or 250 with its operator. This machine, like the first one, had no tail. Its trials were so successful that the next year

(1902) we made another on advanced lines. The main surfaces of this were 32 feet from tip to tip and only 5 feet across. In addition to the devices in the former gliders, we used a vertical tail on this, as an additional method of keeping the lateral balance. We made between seven hundred and one thousand glides with this — the longest of which was 622 feet. By the actual tests of flying, we established many points definitely, and made many changes in the tables of calculation for aërial flight.

Eighteen Miles an Hour — the Rate when Flight Begins

We found that a rate of eighteen miles an hour through the air would sustain our aëroplane and its operator in flight. A rate of sixteen miles would sustain it, but at too great an angle to allow progress through the air. A wind of eighteen miles an hour is a good strong breeze, but it is not extraordinary. Half our glides in 1902 were made in winds of twenty miles an hour, and at one time we were gliding in a wind which measured thirty-seven miles an hour. You understand, of course, that these gliding experiments do not mean the mere sliding down an inclined plane in the air. In heavy winds the aviator is sometimes lifted above the point he starts from and often held soaring in one place. If he had the balancing skill of a soaring bird, he could remain there as long as there was enough wind to support him. Indeed, in our experiments we have remained motionless in one position for over half a minute.

December 17, 1903, the First Flying-machine Sails

In these three years of gliding we established enough practical knowledge, we thought, to go on to the next experiment of placing a gas-engine upon our aëroplane and starting work on the real object of our research — mechanical flight. In the next year we experimented in our workshop with models and machinery for this. On December 17, 1903, our first mechanical flier, in a trial at Kitty Hawk, made four

THE THIRD WRIGHT GLIDER (1902-3)

flights, in the longest of which it sustained itself in the air fifty-nine seconds, and moved 852 feet against a twenty-mile wind; that is, it actually moved half a mile through the air. After this first experiment we felt assured that mechanical flight was feasible.

This first flying-machine, with its operator, weighed about 745 pounds. It was run by a gas-engine which weighed 240 pounds complete with fuel and water, and developed 12 or 13 horse-power. The next year another flier was made, weighing, with ballast, 925 pounds, with an engine giving 16 horse-power, but weighing the same as that of the first flier — 240 pounds. With this machine we made the successful experiments in flying of 1904 and 1905, over 150 in number, averaging a mile apiece.

The Trouble Turning Corners

The problem of the real power-driven flying-machine was exactly what we knew it must be — the question of equilibrium. It was no longer necessary for us to have the peculiar conditions furnished by the wind and hills at Kitty Hawk to make our experiments with the mechanical machine. We secured the use of a swampy meadow eight miles east of Dayton, Ohio. On our tests there it became clear that the flying-machine would operate well in a straight line; the difficulty came immediately upon turning corners, as it was necessary to do in the small field. Just what the trouble was we could not tell. Several turns might be made safely; then, all at once, the machine would begin to lose its balance, and must be stopped and brought down to the ground. We kept experimenting to discover the cause of the trouble and the way of dealing with it, and in the latter part of the year 1904 we made some progress. We accomplished a complete circle on September 20, and two flights of three miles each around the course in November and December.

A Practical Working Air-ship

In 1905 we kept making changes in the machine, but made few flights until fall. Finally, about the middle of September, we discovered the way to control the flier in turning corners. The machine was now under practical control. Six flights from September 26 to October 5 averaged over fifteen miles each; on October 5 we obtained a flight of twenty-four miles in thirty-eight minutes, that is, at the rate of thirty-eight miles an hour. As this was on a curved course, the speed would have been over forty miles an hour straight away.

Up to this time we had been able to work and to escape much notice. The local papers were good enough not to print descriptions of our work. There was, in fact, very little understanding locally of what we were trying to do. There was general knowledge that dirigible balloons — like those of Santos-Dumont — were being operated in France, and the local people did not seem to grasp the difference between his experiments and ours. After we had made these long flights we began to attract attention, and we were compelled to give up experimenting in order to keep secret our method of management. We took our machine to pieces and started to plan the 1907 flier. We knew that we had at last secured a practical working aëroplane. Our experiments had been witnessed by a considerable number of reliable men, who constituted a sufficient guaranty that we had made the long flights we claimed, though they did not have technical knowledge enough of mechanics to understand how we made them.

For Sale — An Aërial War-ship

We feel that it is absolutely essential for us to keep our method of control a secret. We could patent many points in the machine, and it is possible that we could make a success of the invention commercially. We have been approached by many promoters on the matter. But we believe that our best market is to sell the machine to some government for use in war. To do this, it is necessary for us to keep its construction an absolute secret. We do not believe that this secret can be kept indefinitely by a government, but we believe that the government which has the secret can hold the lead in the use of the invention for years. It will be able constantly to keep ahead of other nations by developing the special knowledge in its possession.

So far as we can learn, we are able now to give a government a five years' lead in the development of the flying-machine. The recent trials of Santos-Dumont's aëroplane in France confirm us in this belief. Take one point only. He is trying to sustain a 500-pound machine in the air for short flights with a 50-horse-power engine — that is, sustaining ten pounds to the horse-power. We are flying and carrying, at a rate of 30 miles an hour, 925 pounds with 16 horse-power — that is, practically sixty pounds to the horse-power. The comparison speaks for itself concerning the relative efficiency of the two machines.

Like the Bicycle, but Easier

It is impossible, under these circumstances, for us to discuss the exact secrets of control and management which are our only asset in our machine. We have not even drawn working-plans of our machine, for fear they might fall into other hands. But there are general principles of operating our aëroplane of which we make no secret.

It has been a common aim of experimenters with the aëroplane to solve the problem of equilibrium by some automatic system of balancing. We believe that the control should be left in the possession of the operator. The sense of equilibrium is very delicate and certain. If you lie upon a bed three quarters of an inch out of true, you know it at once. And this sense of equilibrium is just as reliable a mile above the earth as it is on it. The management of

STARTING A FLIGHT

our aëroplane, like that of the bicycle, is based upon the sense of equilibrium of the operator. The apparatus for preserving the balance of the machine consists of levers operated by simple uniform movements which readjust the flying surfaces of the machine to the air. The movement of these levers very soon becomes automatic with the aviator, as does the balancing of a bicycle-rider. In fact, the aëroplane is easier to learn and simpler to operate than the bicycle. In all our experiments with gliding- and flying-machines, we have not even sprained a limb; we have scarcely scratched our flesh.

No Danger from Stopping Engines

The only danger in our aëroplane is of turning over. We have purposely made our machine many times heavier than necessary, so that it cannot break. There is absolutely no danger — as might appear at first thought — from the stopping of the engine. The aëroplane is supported by its motion through the air, it is true; but, however high it is flying, gravity furnishes it all the potential energy it needs to get safely

THE GLIDER TURNING IN THE AIR

to the ground. When the power is shut off, it merely scales through the air to its landing. Theoretically, it is safer at a mile above the earth than at two hundred feet, because it has a wider choice of places in which to land; you can choose your landing from 256 square miles from a mile above the surface if descending one in sixteen. As a matter of fact, we always shut off the power when we start to alight, and come down by the force of gravity. We reach the ground at so slight an angle and so lightly that it is impossible for the operator to tell by his own sensation within several yards of where the ground was first actually touched.

The Uses of the Aëroplane

We know that we have made the aëroplane a practical machine, but we are not over-sanguine about its revolutionizing the transportation of the future. It will scarcely displace the railroad or the steamboat; necessarily, its expenditure of fuel will be too great. In a steamship, it is calculated that the heat from the burning of a sheet of letter-paper will carry a ton a mile; you could scarcely expect such results in an air-ship. The air-ship, so far as we can see at present, will have its chief value for warfare, and for reaching inaccessible places — for such uses as expeditions into the Klondike, or to Pekin during its siege a few years ago. The value of an air-ship moving faster than a

railroad train for reconnoitering or dropping explosives upon an enemy in time of war is now obvious to the entire civilized world. The aëroplane may also be of great value in the near future for service like the carrying of mail. When properly developed, it will be quicker than any means of locomotion now in use for direct journeys between two places — unless against hurricanes. There will be no switches, no stops whatever; and the journey can be made in an airline.

Speed Sixty to One Hundred Miles an Hour

The eventual speed of the aëroplane will be easily sixty miles an hour. It will probably be forced up to a hundred miles. Our last machine showed forty miles, and the one we are building now will go considerably faster. At speeds above sixty miles an hour the resistance of the air to the machine will make travel much more expensive of power. Our experiments have shown that a flier designed to carry an aggregate of 745 pounds at 20 miles an hour would require only 8 horse-power, and at 30 miles an hour 12 horse-power. At 60 miles 24 would be needed, and at 120 miles 60 or 75 horse-power. It is clear that there is a certain point of speed beyond which the air resistance makes it impossible to go. Just what that is experiment will determine. Every year gas-engines are being made lighter — a fact which will increase the surplus carrying power of the machine available for fuel and operator and heavier construction; but at present sixty miles an hour can be counted on for the flying-machine. This, of course, means speed through the air.

Fuel for a Thousand Miles

The aëroplane running sixty miles an hour will have surplus lifting power enough to carry fuel for long journeys. Our 1907 machine will carry gasoline enough to fly 500 miles at a rate of some 50 miles an hour. We can, and possibly soon will, make a one-man machine carrying gasoline enough to go 1,000 miles at 40 miles an hour. Moreover, any machine made to move at speeds up to 60 miles an hour can be operated economically, at a cost of not much more than one cent a mile for gasoline.

The aëroplane, while developed originally from the study of the flight of birds, will have a considerably different mechanism for flying. Probably the chief departure comes from the use of the screw-propeller to secure motion. The bird moves forward by sculling with the outer portion of its wings. In some ways this is a more effective mechanism than the screw-propeller, because at each motion the bird secures a grip on new air, while the propeller keeps operating on the stream of air it sets in motion behind it. At the same time, the propeller can go so much faster than any other method of propulsion that it is undoubtedly the device which must be used to propel air-ships.

Better Wings than a Bird's

There is no question but that a man can make a lighter and more efficient wing than a bird's. A cloth surface, for instance, can be produced, offering less surface friction than feathers. The reason for this fact is that a bird's wing is really a compromise. It is not made for flying only — it must be folded up and gotten out of the way when the bird is on its feet; and efficiency in flying must be sacrificed to permit this. The wings of aëroplanes will vary in size according to speed. A slow machine will require a large wing; but the faster the speed, the less will be the supporting surface necessary, and wings for high speeds will naturally be very small. Not only will less support be needed, but the size must be reduced to reduce the friction of the air.

One difficulty with these fast machines will be in launching them at a high enough speed for their wings to support them. There may also be some difficulty in landing. We have launched our machines from an arrangement of wheels, and have landed upon stout skids fastened to the bottom of the machine. The aëroplane will make its journeys, we believe, 200 or 300 feet above the earth — just high enough to escape the effects of the disturbance of the air along the ground — just out of the surf, so to speak. Our experiments have been at a considerably lower level — at some 80 feet or less.

Our idea in our experiments has been to produce a strong, practical motor flying-machine. We have made no great effort to secure extraordinary machinery to furnish power. We found the gas-motor already developed to a point where it was practically available for our purposes. We have applied ourselves to the invention of an aëroplane which would balance safely, could be easily steered, and would move with a moderate expenditure of power. In doing this we have devoted our chief attention to the scientific construction of wings and screws and steering apparatus.

Scientists, not Mechanics

Our hope is, first, to get some adequate financial return from our invention. We are not rich men, and we have devoted our time and what money we could command to the problem for nearly ten years. We do not expect a tremendous fortune from our discovery, but we do feel we should have something that would be an ample competence for men with our comparatively simple tastes. If we do secure this, we are anxious — whenever it becomes possible — to give the world the benefit of the scientific knowledge obtained by our experiments.

We object to the manner in which we have so far been put before the public. Nearly every writer upon our work in current publications has characterized us as mechanics, and taken it for granted — because of the fact that we are in the bicycle business, no doubt — that our invention has come from mechanical skill. We object to this as neither true nor fair. We are not mechanics; we are scientists.

We have approached the subject of aërial navigation in a purely scientific spirit. We are not highly educated men, it is true, but the subject of aërial navigation is not so much a problem of higher mathematics as of general principles; it can be approached by any one possessing a high-school education — which we have had. We have taken up the principles involved in flying, one after another — not only by practical flights, but in constant laboratory experiments in our workshops. We have worked out new tables of the sustaining power of the air.

Discovered Principles of Screw-propeller

Besides inventing a practical flying-machine, we claim to have discovered for the first time the method of calculating in advance the exact efficiency of screw-propellers, which will save the great waste involved in the present practice, by which screws must be made and tested before their efficiency can be accurately learned. This method of ours has been tested in the manufacture of our aëroplanes; our screws were made with only a slight margin of power over what was demanded by our flier, and they have invariably proved successful.

We say frankly that we hope to obtain an ample financial return from our invention; but we care especially for some recognition as scientists, and, whenever it becomes possible, we propose to bring out the results of our investigations in a scientific work upon the principles of aërial navigation.

2.
Early Aeronautics
(1869)

HARPER'S
NEW MONTHLY MAGAZINE.

No. CCXXX.—JULY, 1869.—Vol. XXXIX.

EARLY AERONAUTICS.

FIRST ATTEMPT AT MILITARY AERONAUTICS.

THE obstacle for man in the way of his acquiring the art of flying is not the difficulty of *constructing wings*, but that of obtaining the necessary force to work them. Birds are provided with muscles of large size, packed in their breasts, which are capable of exerting an enor-

BESNIER'S SYSTEM.

mous force—that is, enormous in relation to the size and weight of the body of the bird. By means of these muscles she can strike the air with her expanded wings so energetically as to lift herself from the ground by them, and then to impel herself through the air. If the arms of a man could be invested with an equal power in proportion to the weight of his body, any respectable mechanician could easily adapt an arrangement to them for expanding the surface, so that he could raise and propel himself as easily as any bird.

Thus the trouble is not, as many people have supposed, in *making wings*, but in obtaining the strength to work them.

Perhaps the most ingenious of the plans devised for furnishing man with wings was that of Besnier, a dextrous locksmith who lived in the province of Maine, in France, nearly a century ago, and who was quite distinguished in his day for his mechanical skill. His contrivance consisted of a double pair of wings, as seen in the engraving, to be worked by both hands and feet. The wings on each side were connected together by a stiff though slender bar of wood, the centre of which rested on the shoulder, as its pivot, in such a manner that the two ends, with the wings attached to them, could be brought down alternately by the action of the hands and feet. Each wing was formed of two leaves, which were hinged to the bar in such a manner as to cause them to open and present a large surface to the air in coming down, and then close again in going up.

The contrivance is ingenious enough, and might have succeeded were it not for the want of strength in the arms and legs of any man to work it with force and rapidity enough to make it effective. If we simply look at the figure, and make a mental estimate of the weight of the man, and of the prodigious power and rapidity of the impulses with which such wings must strike the air to lift and propel him, we shall see at once how totally inadequate the human strength must be to perform such a work.

It is said that Besnier did not really expect that he could raise himself from the ground and fly at will through the air by means of this mechanism, but only that, by starting from some elevated place, he could make a kind of fluttering which would have the effect of protracting a little the time of his descent to the ground so as to amuse spectators at a fair or at other country gatherings. At any rate this was all that he accomplished by his contrivance, and it is very probable that it was all that he aimed at.

The difficulty in the way of navigating the air by means of balloons is substantially the same as in the case of wings—the want of *power to propel* the balloon. Many persons have imagined that the difficulty is in *steering* it; and a great many inventions and contrivances have been brought forward, from time to time, for overcoming this imaginary obstacle. But the difficulty is not in the want of means to direct, but of force to propel. If there were a force at our command adequate to drive such a mass as a balloon *in any manner* through the air there would be no difficulty whatever in giving its course any direction that might be desired. But if we had such a force at our command in the air the balloon would be of no use. The best thing that could be done in that case would be for the operator to cast off the immense encumbrance of the bag of gas, and force his way forward, wherever he wished to go, by means of compact and appropriate mechanism.

It is probable, however, that the schemers who have been endeavoring to discover a mode of navigating the air, when they speak of *steering* the balloon, really mean, not merely putting the head of the machine, so far as it has any head, in the right direction, but to include also the making it move on in that direction—which last is really a very different thing. A boat may be headed in any direction by means of an oar at the stern, but whether she will move forward in the line on which she is placed depends not at all upon such steering, but upon there being a *propulsive force*—whether of wind, or water, or oars, or steam—to drive her forward in the direction determined by the oar.

The attempts made to contrive some means to enable man to fly were long anterior to the invention of the balloon, and amidst innumerable failures there were some cases of what might be considered partial success. The famous Blanchard, whose name is so celebrated in the history of aeronautics, after many fruitless attempts to construct wings, by means of which he could raise himself from the ground,

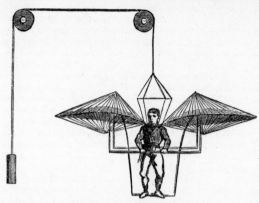

BLANCHARD'S COUNTERPOISE.

and paddling with his hands; and in a gale his power to control the force with which it would be swept along the sky, or even to retard its motion, would be about equal to his ability to stop the progress of a ship going before the wind with all sails spread, by such resistance as he could make in a small boat at the stern, by flapping an umbrella!

The cases would be very different, it is true, in relation to the *nature* of the antagonistic forces, but much the same in regard to the proportion between them.

Blanchard, however, not taking this view of the case into account, concluded that, although he had found that he could not lift himself

determined at last to contrive the means of measuring the degree of approximation that he attained. So he constructed an apparatus for taking off a portion of the weight of his body, by means of a counterpoise, and then undertook to overcome the gravitation of the rest by the action of wings, formed like parachutes, to move vertically, and to be worked by the combined action of his legs and his arms.

The two pulleys over which the cord passes, as seen in the engraving, were supported at a great height by means of a tall mast, not shown. By means of this arrangement, and a counterpoise of *twenty pounds*, Blanchard succeeded in raising himself eighty feet from the ground. Of course, what he really lifted was the excess of the weight of his own body over that of the counterpoise.

As soon as the discovery of the balloon was made, in 1783, Blanchard at once thought that the whole question was solved. The great difficulty, as he understood it, had been the work of lifting the aeronaut from the ground—in other words, the overcoming of the force of gravitation. This work could now be readily accomplished by the balloon. The navigator being once lifted into the air by this means, he supposed that it would be very easy to produce motion in any required direction by means of wings.

He forgot, it seems, that though the balloon might lift the navigator into the air, its vast bulk would occasion an enormous resistance to his motion through it after he was lifted. In a calm the attempt of a man to draw a balloon after him through the air, with any wings which he would have the strength to manage, would be something like his undertaking to tow a ship by swimming before it,

from the ground by means of wings, yet if he had a balloon to lift him he could make them effectual in enabling him to fly. He studied the subject carefully, and some of his drawings are still extant, though all his attempts to carry his plans into effect resulted in absolute failure.

The adjoining engraving of one of his plans illustrates his ideas. The wings by which the whole apparatus, balloon and all, was to be pro-

BLANCHARD'S FLYING BALLOON.

pelled, were to be worked from the car—or as it was then called "the boat"—which was suspended below. Between the balloon and the car was the parachute—a contrivance in the form of an umbrella, which was intended as a safeguard, to let the car down gently to the ground in case of any accident to the balloon.

The history of the origin of the parachute, and of the gradual development of the idea, is very curious. The invention was one of the results of that prodigious intellectual activity in the search for novelties of every kind, which so strongly characterized the people of France, and especially of Paris, in the years immediately succeeding the first French Revolution. The chief inventor of the parachute is generally considered to be Sebastian Lenormand, then residing in Montpellier, a city in the south of France, near the mouths of the Rhone. He had read in books of travels that in some part of the world there were performers among the people who were accustomed, for the amusement of the king, to jump from heights, with an instrument like an umbrella held over their heads to retard their fall. He determined to try the experiment. His first trial was made with two umbrellas, one held in each hand. He chose umbrellas of the largest size, and strengthened them by additional ties within, to prevent their being turned inside out by the resistance of the air. With these in his hands he leaped from the second story of a house, in Montpellier, and came to the ground in safety.

Some one who witnessed this experiment reported it to the Abbé Bertholon, who was at that time a professor of Natural Philosophy at Montpellier. He was much interested in the idea, and sent for Lenormand. Lenormand proposed to repeat the experiment in a new form. He obtained a large umbrella, one about thirty inches in diameter, and suspended a number of animals to it, one after another, and let them fall from the top of the observatory. They all came to the ground in safety.

Lenormand then made a calculation, from the weight of the heaviest animal that he let fall in safety from the tower of the observatory, compared with the size of the umbrella, to determine what must be the magnitude of an expanded surface sufficient to sustain a man. He found that an umbrella about fourteen feet in diameter would be required to retard sufficiently a weight of 200 pounds, which was his estimated weight of the man and of the apparatus, which last would of course be pretty heavy, on account of the necessity of giving great strength to all the parts. He concluded to give the name of *parachute* to his contrivance. Parachute is a word of French construction, equivalent in signification—so far as it can be expressed in an English fashion—to *counterfall.*

When his parachute was finished Lenormand, after some minor trials, leaped with it himself from the top of the tower of the observatory in the presence of a vast crowd of spectators, and came down safely to the ground.

Among the spectators who witnessed the experiment was Montgolfier, the inventor of hot-air balloons, which for a long time were greatly used, and were called by his name, though the hot air has since been almost entirely superseded by hydrogen gas. He at once perceived the importance of this invention as a means of adding interest to the aeronautic exhibitions that he was accustomed to make for the amusement of the people of Paris, and he immediately adopted it. Blanchard also, who used balloons filled with gas, exhibited the parachute in his performances, by letting small animals, such as dogs, rabbits, hens, and cats, fall from great heights in the air.

There were a great many of these public exhibitions of the balloon in its various forms in Paris in those days. The invention itself being novel, and the spectacle being very imposing, it was very natural that the attention of the people of Paris should be greatly excited by the ascensions whenever they took place. Then, besides, very great expectations were entertained in those days in respect to the benefit to be derived from the invention when it should be matured, and multitudes of schemers and projectors appeared with plans by which all difficulties could be removed, and the art of navigating the air made practically useful.

The engraving represents one of these scenes. The balloon is one of the kind called a Montgolfier, that is, one filled with rarefied air, as is evident from the large orifice below, and the smoke issuing from it. In balloons of this class the place for the persons ascending was in a little gallery formed around the orifice.

Whenever an inventor conceived a new idea his first object was to make a public exhibition of his plan, partly in order to obtain funds to aid him in perfecting it. Thus the parachute was exhibited as a new invention; at first, however, only animals were intrusted to it; but in all cases it let them down gently and in safety to the ground.

Among the spectators who witnessed these performances were two men of considerable political standing, who afterward, being sent at different times to the army of the Republic, on the northern frontier, with commissions from the Convention, were each taken prisoner by the allied armies then fighting against France, and confined in fortresses, and who conceived the idea of escaping from the walls of their prison by means of some sort of parachute similar to those which they had seen exhibited in Paris. One of these, whose name was Jacques Garnerin, and who was confined in Hungary, was betrayed by the persons whom he employed to procure the materials for his parachute, and his design was thus discovered before he was ready for his attempt. The other, whose name was Drouet, and whose prison was the castle of Spielberg, in Moravia, attempted to manufacture a parachute out of the curtains of his bed. He succeeded in finishing it, and when the time came he leaped with it from a lofty embrasure.

PUBLIC ASCENSIONS IN PARIS.

But he broke his leg in the fall, and was thus retaken and returned to his confinement. Both these prisoners were, however, exchanged before a great while; and one of them, Jacques Garnerin, afterward distinguished himself by some remarkable performances with real parachutes, as we shall presently see.

It is a curious fact that almost all great inventions are preceded by imperfect, partial, and more or less abortive attempts, involving the same principle, which seem to foreshadow the discovery, as it were, and often give rise to protracted disputes in relation to the true origin of it. This was strikingly the case in regard to the parachute; for a prisoner did actually make his escape by means of a large umbrella to lighten his fall more than twenty years before the time of Lenormand's experiments.

His name was Lavin. He was confined, however, not as a prisoner of war, but as a criminal. His crime was forgery.

He was a remarkably skillful penman, and his extreme dexterity in the use of his pen, and the facility with which he could imitate any writing or printing, tempted him, it seems, to counterfeit certain Treasury certificates—the greenbacks, in fact, of those days. He was convicted of the crime and imprisoned, and he occupied himself in his prison in executing certain specimens of penmanship so wonderful that they were afterward publicly exhibited as almost worthy of being considered works of art. They consisted of portraits of public men, and of high officers of state, whom he hoped in this way to interest in his favor, so as to procure his release and pardon. These performances were the more remarkable from the fact that they were executed with pens which he made from stalks of the straw furnished him in his cell.

These ingenious efforts failing to procure his release, he determined to release himself. The window of his room in the tower in which he was confined overlooked a river, on the banks of which the castle was built, and he determined to make his escape by leaping from the window into the water with an umbrella in his hand. He concluded that the umbrella would materially check the rapidity of his descent, and that if he should acquire too great a velocity, the water would break the force of his fall.

The experiment succeeded. He fell to the water and sank into it without injury. As soon as he rose to the surface he swam to the shore and escaped. The poor man was, however, afterward retaken, and was kept in close confinement for the rest of his life. It is difficult not to experience a feeling of regret at his recapture. And yet the counterfeiter attacks the most vital interests of society by weakening the confidence of men in the authenticity of the written signature, and thus undermining the foundation on which all the great transactions of civilized life are based. He is, moreover, in one sense the greatest of criminals; for he has not either of the two great pleas which may be offered in mitigation of crime—urgent want or sudden passion. He must act calmly and deliberately, for his work requires it. He must have talent, and ability to earn a livelihood in an honest way. His work proves it.

Although Jacques Garnerin, the first of the two prisoners already referred to, was prevented from carrying out his design of escaping from his prison by means of a parachute, he did not dismiss the subject from his mind, but resolved that as soon as he was released he would make the experiment on a grand scale, to show what he would have done in his prison if he had not been betrayed.

He was released in 1797. In the fall of that year he carried his plan into execution. He caused a balloon to be constructed and a parachute to be attached to it. The parachute was folded, but so arranged that the resistance of the air should open it as soon as it should commence its descent.

The place chosen for the experiment was a large open piece of ground on the outskirts of Paris. A large number of spectators assembled to witness the daring feat of a man's letting himself drop from the clouds, and come down to the ground, with only a big umbrella over his head to lighten his fall.

The people gathered around the spot, and looked on in solemn silence while the preparations were made. The balloon was inflated, the parachute, folded, was attached to it. A small car was beneath. There was a cord which descended from the balloon to the car, by cutting which the aeronaut could sunder his connection with it, and let himself and the para-

chute fall. There was also an arrangement by which the gas should be liberated from the balloon at the same time, so that it might also descend to the ground and be recovered.

The fearless adventurer allowed the balloon to ascend until it reached a height of about 3000 feet, more than half a mile. The people below watched the progress of it with intense interest and in solemn silence. At length they saw the parachute separate itself from the balloon, and begin to fall. It soon expanded, and at once began to sway to and fro from one side to the other in frightful oscillations, which, when it had descended far enough to bring the little car in sight, were seen to jerk the car so violently from side to side as to make it very difficult for the man to retain his place. At the same time the balloon turned over on its side, began to collapse, and to follow the parachute in its fall. Both together drifted away before the wind, and so descended to the ground. The balloon reached the ground first.

The car struck the ground with some violence, but without doing Garnerin himself any injury. His balloon had, however, drifted so far by the wind that he was now at some distance from the place where he made the ascent. So he at once mounted on horseback, and rode back with all speed to carry to the crowds of spectators the intelligence of his having accomplished the descent in safety. He was very fortunate in having escaped so well; and, considering the vast height from which he fell, the absolute novelty of his situation, and the terrific surgings of the car as it swung to and fro in the air, we may perhaps consider this descent as one of the most frightful voyages ever made by any human being.

Garnerin obtained great celebrity by this and by some other aeronautical exploits, and as balloon ascensions became soon after this objects of such general interest among the people that some spectacle of the kind became almost an essential part of the celebration on all days of public rejoicing, the government created an office for the superintendence and management of these spectacles, and Garnerin was appointed to fill it. He retained the position of government aeronaut for many years.

A great number of ascensions were made by different performers during those years in safety, but in some cases they led to the most disastrous results. One of the most terrible of these accidents was that which resulted in the death of Madame Blanchard. Her husband, who has been already referred to in this article, was one of the most intrepid and most successful aeronauts of his day. Indeed, he acquired a large fortune by his public exhibitions. He made more than sixty ascensions in all, one of which took place in New York. He received large rewards from the government for certain discoveries and improvements that he made.

At last, however, he became involved in some political complications, in consequence of which he lost all his property, and was re-

GARNERIN'S DESCENT.

duced to such a state of destitution that he told his wife on his death-bed that she could have her choice of hanging herself or drowning herself after he was gone, but that that seemed to be all the choice that would be left to her.

She, however, after his death found that she was not inclined to accept either alternative. Instead of this she resolved to adopt and carry on her husband's profession, which she did with great success. She made a great many ascensions and acquired extraordinary skill; and she became at last so intrepid that she exposed herself to the greatest dangers. This of course only increased the interest which the public felt in her ascensions and added to her profits.

She met with many extraordinary adventures, and had several hair-breadth escapes.

At one time she lost the control of her balloon and it came down with her into a bog, where it got caught among the trees and was dashed about with great violence, while there was no firm ground on which she could stand. It was thought that she must have perished if some of the country people living near had not come to her aid.

She made between fifty and sixty ascensions, varying them by a great number of different exploits which she performed in connection with them, until at length, in 1819, she conceived the idea of letting off fire-works in the skies for the amusement of the people at a fair in Paris. The fire-works were what are called Bengal lights. They were attached to the balloon in such a manner that Madame Blanchard from her car below could reach them by means

DEATH OF MADAME BLANCHARD.

of a long pole with a torch at the end of it, and then detach them so that they might fall burning through the air watched by the people below.

That any person should conceive the idea of ascending several thousand feet into the air by means of an immense volume of one of the most combustible substances known, and contained in the thinnest possible envelope formed of a substance scarcely less combustible, there to set off fire-works by means of a torch at the end of a pole, and that person a *woman*, would seem to be one of the most desperate conceptions that could possibly enter a human brain.

As might have been anticipated, by some want of steadiness in hand in holding the long pole, or by some sudden and unexpected swaying of the balloon or of the car, the fire, either from the torch or from the fire-works, reached

the hydrogen, and the lower portion of the balloon was immediately enveloped in flames.

The balloon began immediately to descend very rapidly. The cords by which the car was attached to it were burned off, and Madame Blanchard was thrown out and fell upon the roofs, and from the roofs to the ground. She was killed upon the spot.

In some respects the most remarkable ascension that ever took place was one made by an apprentice boy of twelve years old named Guerin, who was taken up by the action of the balloon itself without his consent, and without any intention that he should go up on the part of any other person. It was a rarefied air balloon. The car was in the form of a boat, and was to be suspended from the balloon by cords attached to each end of it when the balloon was filled. There was also an anchor suspended by a cord from the bottom of the boat, which was intended to catch upon the ground and hold the balloon when it should come down.

After the balloon was filled and was ready to go up some of the assistants held it by cords, while others went to work to attach the car to it. They had secured one end, and were then going to secure the other, when, by some means or other, the balloon broke away from those holding it and began slowly to rise, and at the same time to drift along with the wind, dragging the car and the anchor over the ground. It happened that, as the anchor was thus drawn along, and was beginning to rise, it passed so closely over this boy—who was sitting quietly near by with his companions, not dreaming of being any thing but a spectator of the proceedings—as to catch the fluke in the waistband of his pantaloons, and as it continued to ascend it took him up with it.

The boy uttered piercing screams and cries and calls for help; and there was, perhaps, no harm in this so long as he held on bravely. Of course no help was possible except calls to him from below to hold on. He found that the waistband began to give way, and he instinctively grasped the rope above his head with both hands, and so sustained himself. The strength of his hands, without the aid of the hook in his waistband, would not have been sufficient to sustain his weight many minutes; and the waistband was not strong enough without the hands. Both together, however, answered the purpose.

It was very fortunate for Guerin that it was a Montgolfier, that is, a rarefied air balloon and not one filled with hydrogen, that was running away with him; for in the latter case the gas within would have continued to expand as the outside pressure upon it diminished by the increasing elevation; and as there would have been no possibility of opening the valve, as is usually done, to relieve it, the balloon would have burst and collapsed, and the poor boy would have fallen a thousand feet or more to the ground with full force. But being a Montgolfier, the ascending power gradually diminished as the air grew cool, until at length, after floating a moment in equilibrium, it began slowly to descend. As the balloon descended, the rope which had begun to untwist under the influence of the boy's weight, turned more and more rapidly; and inasmuch as a person suspended from a balloon is never conscious of his own motion—the illusion which makes the motion seem to be in the earth and not in the balloon being perfect—as it is indeed on a smaller scale to a person going up in the elevator of a hotel

—it appeared to Guerin that the earth was spinning round beneath him in a vast and most frightful gyration. Guerin was more terrified than ever. As he drew near the ground, or rather, as it appeared to him, as the ground and the concourse of spectators upon it came whirling up to him, he cried out to the people to save him. They called to him in reply not to be afraid, that he was all right; and, receiving him in their arms as soon as he came within reach, they at the same moment stopped the spinning of the earth and unhooked him from the anchor.

The incident of course created a great sensation at the time; and, as the account of it became a part of the history of aerostation, the story will be repeated in all coming time. Guerin found himself very suddenly famous. As

YOUNG GUERIN TAKEN UP.

PHILOSOPHY IN THE AIR.

he was only in the air about fifteen minutes, it is very probable that this boy acquired historical immortality at an earlier age, and in a shorter time, than any other human being.

Notwithstanding the high hopes which were entertained at the first invention of the balloon, that the system, when developed, would become the means of rendering great service to mankind, and which are still entertained by many people, no results have yet been realized of any serious importance; nor is there any present prospect that any ever will be realized. The balloon has been from the beginning little more than a philosophical toy, although it must be confessed that it is a very grand and imposing one. The difficulty is simply the want of *power*, and the seeming hopelessness of obtain-

ing the means of procuring, in the air, any *great power with little weight in the appliances to furnish it and employ it.* Where we see that we have power, or have a source at our command from which we can procure it, there is no limit to the hopes we may entertain in respect to the objects, however complicated or difficult, which may be accomplished by it. Man can and does make *fire sew.* Fire is power, and through the intermedium of the steam-engine and the sewing-machine he can make it sew, or do any thing else, however intricate, for which he can devise the proper means of applying it. But he can not make the lightest wheel turn itself, or one force overcome another, in the smallest degree greater.

When man can contrive a way to take heat

enough into the air, in connection with mechanism so light that the power of the heat can lift and operate it, then, and not till then, so far as we can now see, will he be able to navigate the air.

Many attempts have been made to derive some practical benefit from the use of the balloon in various ways. Among these the one which has most nearly attained success is the use of it as a means of making reconnoissances in time of war. Attempts to employ the balloon in this way were first made by the French Government, in the time of the first republic. A regular aeronautic corps was organized, and a system of drill and of signals established, and other arrangements devised by means of which ascensions could be made by a reconnoitring party, information communicated to the commanders below, and the balloons, ready charged, be transported from place to place, wherever they might be required. The engraving at the head of this article represents a body of men in those days manœuvring a balloon in the field.

The operation of the system was, however, attended with so many practical difficulties, and the results were so uncertain, that it never became established as a regular element in the art of war. One of the chief sources of embarrassment was the trouble of transporting so cumbrous a mass as an inflated balloon across the country. To empty the balloon when it required to be moved, with a view of refilling it where the next ascension was to be made, would have very partially remedied the difficulty, as it would have rendered it necessary to transport the chemical apparatus and materials for producing the gas, and involved the difficulty, uncertainty, and delay of a tedious chemical process at every station from which a reconnoissance was to be made.

The use of the balloon was attempted to some extent in the late war in this country, but with no very conspicuous success.

The balloon has, however, been made practically useful in a certain sense—or, rather, it has been made practically conducive to the attainment of theoretic ends—by being employed as an instrument of scientific investigation. The engraving opposite represents an ascension made by Gay Lussac and Biot, two distinguished French philosophers. The special object of this expedition was to determine certain questions in respect to certain phenomena of electricity and magnetism, as affected by distance from the surface of the earth. The nature of these questions, and the results which the philosophers obtained, can not be here explained. The results were somewhat unexpected, and were of great importance, and the ascension formed a memorable event in the history of science. It was one of the first of its kind, though many others of a similar character have since been made.

Every one is familiar with the toy hydrogen balloons, so common at the present day, formed by inclosing hydrogen in a globular bag, consisting of a thin film of caoutchouc. The defect of this arrangement arises from a difficulty which greatly embarrassed the French engineers in their attempts to employ the balloon for purposes of war, and that is, the incapacity of the film of caoutchouc to prevent the transpiration of the gas through its pores. Hydrogen is of so extremely subtle and tenuous a nature that it is impossible to find any thin and flexible substance which will long contain it. The balloons of the French army were made of silk or cotton textures, and thoroughly varnished; but the gas would ooze through. It was said that they at last discovered a remedy for the difficulty, but that the remedy was afterward lost.

It is not difficult for any ingenious young persons to construct a toy Montgolfier, or hot-air balloon, to be filled by the heated air ascending from a lamp or from a gas flame, and made to ascend to the ceiling. The best material for a balloon of this size is tissue paper. It ought to be nearly or quite three feet in diameter, which would make the circumference nine feet, and the gores on each side four and a half feet. But as the gores, instead of coming to a point at the lower end, may be shortened there, and made square, to allow for the opening for the admission of the hot air, four feet will be long enough. About this length can be obtained by dividing each sheet of paper into two parts, and pasting them together, end to end.

From the long sheets thus obtained the gores can easily be cut, a pattern being first made in stiff paper. The general form of the gores is shown in the engraving. The precise form, except so far as having them all alike is concerned, is not material, unless it is desired to make the balloon perfectly spherical, or to give it some other precise determinate character.

When the gores are cut the first is to be placed upon a table, and the second laid upon it in such a manner that the edge of the lower one on one side, say upon the *right* side, may project about half an inch beyond that of the one above it. This edge is then folded over and pasted down upon the other. The third gore is then to be laid on, and placed in such a manner as to leave the *right*-hand edge of the second projecting beyond that of the third, and this edge must then be folded down and pasted. In the same manner all the gores in succession are to be laid on and pasted, alternately, on the two sides. When the last gore is reached, which must be one to be pasted on the *right* side, and must be made somewhat wider than the rest, the left-hand edge, after the right-hand edge is pasted, must be carried around

FORM OF THE GORES.

HEROIC SELF-SACRIFICE.

under all the other left-hand edges, and pasted to the left-hand edge of the first one.

Thus the balloon will be completed, and as thus completed it will lie folded upon the table. During the process of pasting, however, a short piece of twine, or narrow tape, should be inserted in each seam, at the top of the balloon, in such a manner that the ends may project about six inches or more above, to be afterward tied together to form a loop by which the balloon may be suspended. A continuous tape is also to be put along the lower edges of the gores, and pasted there by folding the edge over it. This tape is to strengthen the border of the orifice left at the bottom for the admission of the hot air.

The balloon, when thus complete, is to be held suspended by means of a pole, and then opened a little by inserting the hand under it below. It is then to be cautiously held over the lamp or gas flame, or other source of heat, taking care to hold it at such a distance above as not to endanger it. As the hot air ascends into it the top, supported by the pole, must be gradually lowered, to allow of the swelling out of the sides of the balloon. When it is found to be sufficiently full to sustain itself the pole is to be withdrawn, and the balloon held by means of the tape forming the circumference of the orifice, or by cords previously attached to it for this purpose. When it is released it will mount to the ceiling, if the experiment is made in a room, and a great deal higher if it is tried, on a calm day, in the open air.

Its flight may indeed be considerably protracted by attaching to it, below the orifice, by means of wire, a sponge saturated with alcohol, and then setting the alcohol on fire just as it is about to commence its ascent.

We close this discussion by narrating an incident which occurred in London in 1824, and which belongs rather to the realm of sentiment and romance than to that of science and philosophy. There was an exhibition of a balloon ascension to be made by an English aeronaut named Harris, at Vauxhall, a celebrated public garden. Harris, to give greater *éclat* to the spectacle, invited a young woman to whom he was engaged to be married to accompany him. The departure and the ascent were accomplished without any difficulty; but when high in the air the cord communicating with the valve at the top of the balloon, used for discharging any excess of hydrogen, or the valve itself, became disarranged, so that Harris, after opening it when he had reached the proper altitude, in order to prevent any farther ascent, found, to his consternation and horror, that he could not close it again. Of course, as the gas continued to issue from the opening, the balloon descended with greater and greater rapidity every instant. Harris threw out all his ballast, and every thing else that he could lay hand upon, to arrest the descent. He took off his own and the lady's outer clothing, and threw it over. All was in vain. He finally concluded that by throwing himself over he might save her, as the balloon might perhaps have buoyancy enough left to sustain the weight of one. He accordingly kissed her farewell, and leaped into the air. She saw him go down, and immediately fell fainting into the bottom of the car.

When she came to herself she found herself in the midst of a crowd of eager spectators, some pressing around her to see, others doing all in their power to revive and to support her. She soon recovered sufficiently to be taken home, and she sustained no permanent injury from her awful adventure.

It is needless to say what was the fate of her devoted and heroic lover.

3.
Worm's-Eye Views of Flying Men

⊛⊛⊛

The Doves of War (1908)

Worm's-eye Views of Flying Men

By Peter B. Kyne

Mr. Kyne, well-known to magazine readers as a teller of breezy sea tales, has written for Sunset Magazine his impressions of the midwinter aviation meet recently concluded at Los Angeles and San Francisco. In his fiction Mr. Kyne is more interested in the men who go down to the sea in ships than he is in the ships; in his facts, he finds certain of his fellow-spectators more absorbing than even these navigators of a new craft through the uncharted air.

THERE is an old, old song regarding the adventures of the bear that went over the mountain "to see what he could see." We are informed that the only thing Bruin saw was the other side of the mountain.

The editor told me to go to Los Angeles to "see what I could see" during the Aviation Meet at Dominguez Field. I was to see all that a man could of aviation, then follow the aviators to San Francisco and at Selfridge Field "see what else I could see."

And I saw—"the other side of the mountain." I realized that I was living in the greatest age of man's progress. I marveled much—for a day—for if one gazes skyward too long, the unaccustomed exercise develops a "crick" in the neck.

In common with the great mass of humanity, I thought I would like to fly—"for fun." I have changed my mind. Flying is serious business.

Now regarding what I saw: Owing to the strain on my cervical vertebrae I was forced to view the meet through other eyes than my own. For after all it is not the flying

that is wonderful, but the man who flies. And you have read all about him.

But to my story:

I dodged back under the roof of the press box at Dominguez Field. Down the stretch in front of the grandstand, droning like a giant of that species of insect (which by the way it much resembled) and which in the days of our childhood we were wont to call the "devil's darning-needle," came James Radley, the English aviator, at a speed of sixty miles an hour or some such trifle. He passed over the press box at a height of about six feet.

"Verily" I said, "that man will kill or be killed." But Radley was glancing back over his shoulder grinning. And only a minute before, the megaphone man had announced that the wind was blowing at the rate of thirty-five miles an hour.

After circling the field three or four times, however, Radley descended, and his mechanicians wheeled the Bleriot into the hangar. Mr. Radley would fly no more that day. He blamed the wind.

Presently he of the megaphone made further announcement.

"On the backstretch" he bawled,

Hubert Latham in his monoplane Antoinette fought the wind for an hour and twenty minutes

"you will observe Hubert Latham in his Antoinette. For one hour and twenty minutes he has been fighting the wind, trying to land."

Ten minutes passed and M. Latham, to the great disgust of his corps of French mechanicians, succeeded in landing unsuccessfully. He came down "regardless," landing on top of a barbed-wire fence at the foot of the mesa. The wind had won and a splintered mass of wreckage marked one man's conquest of the air. M. Latham lit the inevitable cigarette and complained of the airholes and aerial whirlpools under the brow of the hill.

Later, Eugene Ely, Glenn H. Curtiss' star performer, landed, piling his biplane up against the fence — fortunately without damage to Ely, the machine or the fence. He blamed the wind.

The shades of night were falling fast, when through his hangar tried to pass, Lincoln Beachey, Curtiss aviator and the "Tumble Tom" of the profession. In an effort to dodge a novice, who was buzzing about the field, much after the fashion of an inebriated butterfly, Mr. Beachey came to grief. He flew into

Rip Van Winkle's modern counterpart walked up to the grandstand

the earth. When the dust settled and the ambulance arrived, they found Beachey tinkering with his carbureter. He blamed the wind.

From all of which it will be seen that aviators are born and not made, and that death or injury enters not into the scheme of aviation, provided one is shrewd enough to distinguish between a typhoon and the much mooted "Swiss cheese" atmosphere.

On the afternoon of the fourth day of the meet, as I sat in the grandstand, watching Parmalee and Ely compete for a money prize in a contest for the theoretical destruction of a given spot of earth by a furious bombardment of said spot with oranges dropped from a biplane, I fell to wondering what Rip Van Winkle would have said and how he would have acted had he been awakened from his long sleep, to find himself obliged to cross an aviation field on his way home. And as I fancied old Rip's facial expression, his modern counterpart walked up into the grandstand.

He came, followed by a fife and drum corps, a brass band and half a hundred Jackies from the mosquito fleet in San Diego Bay. It was San Diego day at the Aviation Meet, and this modern Rip Van Winkle headed San Diego's delegation. I climbed over the benches to get acquainted. I wanted to see how he was going to enjoy it, this man plucked from a forgotten world, to watch the marvels of the twentieth century coquette with Death on Dominguez Field.

He told me about himself.

He is an aged Indian chief—a half-breed Iroquois—and his name is Iodine. In 1843 he broke the trail with Kit Carson and lead Fremont across the wilderness into California. He is eighty-three years old and he has seen much of life—and death. He was a man grown when the Morse code was

Three scouts at the California aviation meet: Glenn H. Curtiss, who goes scouting for speed records in the biplanes of to-day; Peter B. Kyne, who went scouting for impressions of the meet for Sunset Magazine, and Chief Iodine, half-breed Iroquois, a scout with Kit Carson in 1843

invented. He has seen incandescent lights displace the kerosene lamp, which had, in its turn, displaced the tallow-candle. He has seen the science of locomotion evolve from the prairie-schooner to the horseless carriage. But when he heard that up at Dominguez Field, outside the city of Los Angeles, men were flying in aeroplanes, turn-

Chief Iodine has ridden many a flying steed over the old Santa Fé trail. To-day he mounted into the saddle of the modern winged horse that the aerial bronco busters are risking their lives to break

Hour of the triumph. Arch Hoxsey, hero of the meet at Los Angeles, submitting his barograph to official scrutiny after breaking the world's record at an altitude of 11,474 feet

ing corners, cutting pigeon wings, pursuing and shooting wild ducks while hurtling through the air at the rate of sixty miles an hour, and, the flight ended, land on a designated spot with all the ease and grace of a gigantic buzzard, Chief Iodine, retired United States scout, soldier and Indian fighter, expressed a desire to see this crowning wonder of a wondrous age.

But it takes the stupendous sum of five dollars to purchase a round-trip ticket to Los Angeles and return, for Iodine is spending the afternoon of life in San Diego, a hundred and twenty miles distant. The sum was prohibitive. Iodine's pension is only $20 a month. He has known the gratitude of a nation, has this hero of forty years of warfare, and the luxury of extravagance is not for him.

In his humble little cabin at the foot of Third street, unknown, unnoticed, forgotten, he has lived the life of a hermit. Here, where God's smile peeps over the somber brow of old Cuyamaca, to paint with purple mists the shimmering Bay of San Diego, fading regretfully at eventide out beyond Point Loma and the distant Coronados, they told him Glenn H. Curtiss was presently to come, with his aerial staff and his man-made

birds of ash and canvas. Here, where it is summer always, he was coming to establish a camp on North Island, whence he could conduct his experiments with the army and navy. He would fly across the bay, over the city and encircle the crest of Table mountain to the south in Old Mexico. But—

Patience! Old men must wait. Yet, what if this man with his heaven chariot should not come to San Diego. Iodine is an old, old man. Soon he, too, must soar,

"Over the mountains of the moon
And down the vales of shadow—"

On the morrow it would be San Diego day at the Aviation Meet in Los Angeles. A special train would leave the La Jolla depot at eight o'clock. Perhaps in that train there would be room for an old man. He would go uptown and ask about it.

And because there are those in San Diego to whom a few dollars means little and the simple wish of an old soldier much, he came toiling up the slope that leads from the railroad track to Dominguez Field. Two bluejackets from a torpedo-destroyer had him in tow.

At the top of the bluff he paused for breath, then turned, and for a minute or two

Hazard of the game. Wreck of Hoxsey's aeroplane on the following day when the ill-fated sky explorer had dropped to his death

his faded eyes swept the country at his feet. He gazed across the valley toward Mount Wilson, then northward to where the city of Los Angeles spread across the fertile plain.

"It's changed" he said very simply, "it's changed. I don't know the country any more. I was in Los Angeles in '67. It was a village then, a stopping-place on the old Santa Fé trail. The trail's gone, too. Coming up on the train I looked out the window, but I couldn't see it. The old trail's gone."

Yes, the old trail was gone—gone with the olden golden days when guitars plunked out the strain of La Paloma and dark eyes flashed to dark eyes in the shade of the portico of the old Dominguez hacienda. Nothing—nothing left of the old days save the low rambling adobe hacienda, ancestral home of the Dominguez family. And across the broad mesa, where once a thousand "longhorns" thundered, a daredevil Englishman perched on the back of a queer June-bug contrivance was being rolled across the field by two other Englishmen, while a third Englishman held aloft the creature's tail.

As he climbed into the grandstand, Chief Iodine surveyed the apparition out in front. "Who's that chap" he asked.

"That's Radley, the English aviator. He drives a Bleriot monoplane."

There was a snort, a buzz, a stream of dust behind the Bleriot and Radley was off.

The chief watched him until he was out of sight, off toward Redondo.

"Do you think he'll come back?"

"He will—to-day" I answer. "The weather is too perfect. The day before yesterday it blew a gale, the first in months. But to-day it's glorious. Not a capful of wind, and—"

"Devil's darning-needle" exclaimed Chief Iodine. Latham was passing in his Antoinette.

I identify the aviator and explain that it's his first flight since his fall of Monday. I further advise that the Frenchman is out for endurance.

"Ughh" grunts Chief Iodine. And then I realize that the world is old always and that nothing under heaven is new any more. Ely and Willard are up in their Curtiss biplanes; Parmalee and Brookins in their Wright biplanes are dipping gracefully into Kingdom Come and out again, and the great crowd is silent under the awe-inspiring spectacle. But out in the plowed dirt of the aviation field there stands a little knot of mounted special police and it is these men that Chief Iodine is watching. One of them, a young dark-skinned Spanish-Californian, bestrides a dashing brown horse with a blazed face and four white stockings. The Spanish bit, the braided rawhide bridle and the Mexican saddle are beautifully chased with silver, the man sits his horse with the unconscious grace of that fast-disappearing race of whom it has been said that they would walk six blocks for a horse in order that they might ride a block.

Something has happened at the eastern end of the field, and suddenly the little cavalcade, led by the star-faced brown horse, sweeps furiously across the field.

Chief Iodine sighs. He is an old, old man, and youth and horseflesh, as he has known it, is all that life can hold for a man. As for the aeroplane—

"Uggh!" They are mechanical. Very wonderful, but mechanical.

The afternoon wears away. Glenn Curtiss himself comes out for a brush with Parmalee in the Baby Wright. They start from the scratch, rise together, fly up the stretch, circle and come back to the scratch, jockeying to a perfect start.

"Go!" yells the man with the megaphone, and the race is on. It was magnificent—superb airmanship, if I may coin the word. I have forgotten the record they made—something more than 58 miles an hour.

He was watching the star-faced horse and its Spanish-Californian rider

Curtiss, as in all previous and subsequent speed trials, clearly demonstrated that the Curtiss is the speediest of all biplanes.

But now the great crowd is yelling "Hoxsey! Hoxsey!"

We can see him, away off over the summit of Mount Wilson. He is just emerging from a white cloud, and the dazzling sunlight of a midwinter California day has touched his white wings with gold. Down from a height of 8,000 feet he comes in great spiral swoops, already fey with the dreadful death that is to overtake him on the morrow.

Chief Iodine glances upward and sees the tiny speck scintillating against the blue.

"I could reach him with a 30-30" he says.

Presently Hoxsey alights, and a thrill-mad crowd lifts him from his Wright biplane, while the crowd cheers and cheers.

"What has he done" asks the chief.

"That's Hoxsey. He broke the world's altitude record on Monday. Flew 11,474 feet."

"Why" said the old scout wonderingly, "that's higher than I was when me and Kit Carson came through Marshall's Pass—"

He was watching the star-faced horse out in the field.

One by one the scheduled events of the day are over with and no one is injured. Slowly the sun sinks and twilight settles on Dominguez Field. Over the broad mesa a cool breeze blows in from the Pacific, and in the grandstand the brave old relic of a forgotten world shivers in his fantastic buckskin suit. Presently he rises, gives a hitch to his belt with its nineinch bowie-knife and the Colt's 45.

"Let's go" he says, and the sailor boys, one on each aged arm, lead him to the train, waiting to whirl him back along the old Santa Fé trail to the Land of Heart's Desire — San Diego —. Never again is he to wander from beneath the shadow of old Cuyamaca. He has taken his last long journey. He has lived to see men fly.

As for what he thought of it all, I did not learn. Iodine is a great chief of the Iroquois, for is not the eagle branded on his breast? Great chiefs do not hold speech when the old legs are aweary and the heart is yearning for a silver-mounted saddle and bridle, a star-faced horse with white stockings, and the old days gone forever. For the world is old always, and nothing under heaven is new any more. We have had three years of aviation. Next! Step this way, sir. Ladies and gentlemen, it is my great pleasure this evening to introduce to you Professor Pla-Pla, who has at last solved the secret of perpetual motion.

Eugene Ely, on January 18th, flew from the military camp at Selfridge field and alighted upon a specially constructed landing on the deck of the cruiser Pennsylvania. This marked an epoch in aviation annals for it means that aeroplanes will be placed on our warships as an auxiliary for gaining information in time of war

Selfridge aviation field at San Francisco where a portion of the California aviation meet took place in

For over forty years Johnny Hyslop has been the all-seeing eye of the Merchants Exchange. From his little lookout station on Land's End, overlooking the Golden Gate, Johnny Hyslop pokes his great telescope seaward throughout the years and scans the horizon for incoming ships. Few people know it, but Johnny is the watchdog of San Francisco. Much of life passes under the lee of his telescope, and much of death. It is an old, old story to him, changing always but always the same. Clipper ship and foreign cruiser, Italian fishing-smack and Chinese junk, brigs, barks, barkentines, derelicts and life rafts all must pass in review before Johnny Hyslop. They constitute his little world. He knows them and loves them all, and as they pass in he reports them.

The world-weary and the blasé may wonder why Johnny Hyslop has endured all this for forty years; why the barking of the seals and the eternal sob of the surf have not seared his contemplative soul with the World Madness. If you asked Johnny Hyslop the reason, he would laugh at you. He knows. He has had forty years of peace ineffable.

The afternoon of January 7, 1911, however, will long remain a red-letter day in the mind of Johnny Hyslop. On that day Johnny received a shock.

It was a marvelously clear day. Before him the blue Pacific stretched in an unbroken line, save where the Farallones reared their sullen outline against the horizon. From Baker's Beach the swish of the surf came faintly to him, wafted on a five-knot breeze. It was warm and pleasant—and midwinter. And the age-old requiem of the surf, the subtle sense of peace ineffable, overcame Johnny Hyslop. Lower and lower he sank in his chair, his head nodding more and more, until presently he slept.

But only for a minute or two. Of a sudden he woke, stretched himself guiltily and from force of habit glanced out across the heads. Nearly a mile out, just circling in toward the entrance to the gate, Johnny Hyslop saw a mammoth bird flying toward him.

Johnny rubbed his eyes and spoke thus to the cat:

"I've seen a few big birds in my day, but believe me, Thomas, this here is *some* albatross. I don't recall seeing one so close in before. The albatross is really an off-shore bird—why, this one looks like a great auk. *Listen to him buzz? Great snakes*! What is it?"

January, thousands of fascinated spectators watching famous aviators experiment under the auspices of the army

He sprang to his telescope and trained it on this prehistoric aerial monster. From the business end of the telescope a mild-faced young man, smoking a cigarette in a jeweled mouthpiece, was peering in at him. He was seated in a canoe, with the propeller in front, and the sails, instead of being upright and bent to a mast, as required by all the rules of navigation as Johnny Hyslop knows it, were fastened to an outrigger and took the air horizontally.

"Shades of Jonah" muttered Johnny Hyslop, "I believe it's a man-eatin' Chinese dragon-fly and it's picked up a French-man." He rubbed his eyes, pinched himself to make sure he wasn't in bed, and looked again.

"Well, by the garboard strake of the ship of state" he said foolishly, "if it ain't an air-ship. I wonder how many of them got by while I was asleep."

And with the habit of forty odd years strong upon him he turned to his telephone and called up Jerry Daly at the Merchants Exchange.

"Say, Jerry! There's an airship passin' in right now, but I can't make out her name, and she don't appear to have a house-flag. Carries a crew of one man, and she's comin' in backward. I thought at first she was comin' bows on, but she ain't. I can see her screw in front and it's out of the water. She don't look like a double-ender either."

"I know her" replied Jerry, who holds his job because he knows all things that ever crawled or flew or sailed or swam or drifted through the Golden Gate. "Hey, Artie! Hop up to the blackboard and report the airship Antoinette, Latham master, half an hour from Selfridge Field."

The foregoing are the hitherto unpublished facts relating to the first passage of an airship through the Golden Gate, made by M. Hubert Latham, in his Antoinette mono-plane on the afternoon of January 7th, in the year of our Lord, 1911. In the depth of winter, with the hills on each side of the gate covered with green grass, while a sun storm beat down upon him, the intrepid French-man made the perilous passage, and took his place in history side by side with old What's-his-name,* who sailed in when Hector was a purp, just to see what the place looked like.

Down the bay flew Latham. Mike Fitz-gerald, sentry on the Merchants Exchange

*This is Kynese for Don Juan Manuel de Ayala, in the San Carlos, August 5th, 1775.

second outpost at Meiggs wharf, spotted him as he passed the Presidio, and made solemn report to the uptown office. Over Alcatraz Island flew Latham, along the waterfront, past man-o'-war row and away over the Potrero hills, back to Tanforan Field, or, as it is known in aviation circles, Selfridge Field.

From the time he left the field, crossing the hills to the west until he struck the seashore, when he followed the coast northward until Johnny Hyslop saw him curving in toward the Golden Gate, until he landed easily before a crowd of 200,000 persons, Latham had consumed just fifty minutes. But in that fifty minutes he had added much of historic interest to historic San Francisco Bay, and it will be long, indeed, ere his spectacular flight will be forgotten by San Franciscans.

From the standpoint of scientific interest, there was more in the meet at San Francisco, owing to the varied program, than the first meet at Los Angeles. From the standpoint of desirability as an aviation field, however, it is doubtful if even the field at Rheims is equal to the Dominguez rancho near Los Angeles, and this together with the delightful weather which obtained during the early part of January, endeared Los Angeles to the aviators.

But to one who has watched the public pulse, it is patent that the day of the big aviation meet has nearly run its course. We know, now, that men can fly, and the question of the future will be: How fast can they fly, and what can they accomplish by flying? The chief interest in the aeroplane from now on will center in the domain of practical accomplishment, and the army and navy tests will be watched eagerly by the nations of the world. As for the practicability of the aeroplane in warfare, the near future will decide that.

It is quite possible that Chief Iodine is right. One may be able to reach them with a 30-30.

In the meantime we know that at San Francisco, on January 18, 1911, Eugene Ely alighted on the deck of the cruiser *Pennsylvania*. We will read each day of the martyrs to the science of aviation, and it will dwindle to the commonplace level of a railroad accident. Verily, the world is very old and nothing under heaven is new.

In school they taught us that the earth revolves on its axis. Let us then, be patient, and await the discovery of the axis. And while waiting, let us not forget that somewhere there must be, if science is to take its course, a single-minded individual who is bending his energies toward the discovery of appropriate armor for airships.

PHOTOGRAPHS BY H. C. TIBBITTS AND GEORGE P. PITKIN

It takes at least three men to lead one of these winged horses across the field

Nearly a mile out, just circling in toward the entrance to Golden Gate, Johnny Hyslop saw a mammoth bird. It was
Hubert Latham, the Frenchman, steering his monoplane Antoinette above the course along which
Ayala guided the San Carlos cautiously nearly a century and a half ago

The Doves of War

By Lieutenant Paul W. Beck

U. S. A. Signal Corps

IN the study of geology the point which impresses itself most deeply upon the youthful mind is the vast periods of time which have elapsed in the various geological eras. The remembrance of this reminds me forcibly of the present burning subject of heavier-than-air machines, because it is so different.

Just one year ago, in Los Angeles, there was being held the first aviation meet that had occurred within the confines of the United States. To-day, aviation meets are almost as common as divorces in Reno, yet the people have just flocked by thousands to Dominguez Field at Los Angeles and to Selfridge Field at San Francisco to see the world's birdmen fly through the January skies during the California Aviation Meet recently concluded.

What was, perhaps, the most striking and important event of the whole meet, at least from the viewpoint of the army and navy, whose interest is after all the most vital, was fittingly performed by an ex-San Franciscan. Eugene Ely, on January 18th, flew from the military camp at Selfridge Aviation Field to the deck of the U. S. Cruiser *Pennsylvania*, anchored in San Francisco Bay, and a few moments later flew back to the camp.

Vast crowds acquired the aeroplane neck at Selfridge field, San Francisco, gazing skyward at the man-birds

This marks an epoch in aviation annals and beyond the shadow of a doubt it will place the aeroplane on our warships as an auxiliary for gaining information.

For this experiment there was a specially constructed landing stage, one hundred and thirty feet long by thirty-two feet wide, built from the stern of the *Pennsylvania* to the after-gun turret, on a five per cent pitch. This special feature will not again be necessary, for the results were so satisfactory as to warrant the next test being held at sea on the unmodified deck of the ship itself.

To act as a brake for stopping the aeroplane quickly, Glenn H. Curtiss had devised a scheme which utilized sandbags connected in groups of two, to ropes running at right angles to the main axis of the vessel. Grappling-hooks attached to the bottom of the lower plane of Ely's airship caught these ropes and, dragging the sandbags along the deck, brought the machine to a quick and easy stop.

Just one year ago the writer predicted in SUNSET MAGAZINE that this event was feasible and the resulting success which attended Mr. Ely's flight is a source of great gratification in bearing out this prediction. Conditions under which Mr. Ely operated were as difficult as they could have been made. The wind was blowing from the starboard quarter at about fifteen knots an hour and the fact that the ship itself was at anchor multiplied the dangers. It is hoped that the next experiment will be held at San Diego in the near future. When this is done, it will be on the deck of a warship at sea under service conditions in normal weather. Captain Charles F. Pond, commanding the Cruiser *Pennsylvania*, is enthusiastic and predicts that, within a very short time at least one ship of each fleet will be equipped with aeroplanes for the gaining of information.

I started this article by moralizing on the lapse of time, and Ely's great performance drove all thought of it from my mind. To return to my thesis:

In an article which the writer prepared for this magazine last year and to which reference has been made, great stress was laid upon the fact that M. Louis Paulhan had attained the magnificent altitude of almost 4,700 feet. The shades of Johnstone and Hoxsey must look down to laugh! Since Paulhan's flight the record has gone up by leaps and bounds until it now stands,

unofficially, at 11,474 feet, where it was placed by Arch Hoxsey, who, two days after, lost his life through an unexplained accident.

The speed records of a year ago, when Glenn Curtiss in his tiny racer was monarch of the air at sixty miles an hour, have been so badly shattered that if the pieces were steel and the whole earth a magnet, there would not be a fragment nearer than the sun in the next ten thousand years. James Radley is now the official speed artist at 79.97 miles an hour, and Walter Brookins, in his Wright Baby racer, was traveling one hundred and fifteen miles an hour when his gasoline failed and the resulting contact with a telephone pole relegated the Baby Racer to the scrap heap. The former of these events occurred at Lanark, Scotland, last summer, while the latter occurred at Belmont during the International Meet last October.

A Farman machine in France has carried five passengers, and Henri Farman himself has remained in the air for eight hours and twenty-three minutes and has traveled a distance of three hundred and forty-four miles without coming to earth. From all of which it is very easily to be seen that the science of heavier-than-air flight is most decidedly still in its swaddling-clothes. As a general rule, aviation meets have not been financial successes. This is due to lack of knowledge as to the best methods of conducting such meets, to the newness of conditions surrounding them, and to the fact that it is practically impossible to obtain locations which necessitate entering the gate to the enclosure to enable one to obtain a view of the proceedings. In fact, during the Belmont Meet it was reported by the newspapers that for one paid admission there were at least ten unpaid admissions. Our San Francisco record shows three paid admissions to one unpaid. Of course from a military standpoint this is entirely beside the mark; yet to obtain congressional recognition in the shape of appropriations the public must have its interest aroused and kept alive, and in order that this may occur these meets must be held. Therefore we of the army are praying for the discovery of the loss-less meet.

It would seem to the casual observer that the financial instability of aviation meets must speedily kill the sport. In fact, many already argue from it that the general public is even now becoming satiated with the phenomena of heavier-than-air flight and is looking for those thrills which come only with imminent danger. This might be true were it not for the fact that there are so many lines of investigation open to the scientific mind that it will be many years before the ultimate of heavier-than-air machines is achieved. To begin with, the aeroplane itself is far from being developed to its fullest capacity. Improvements must be along the line of stability, weight-carrying, and speed. We omit discussion of helicopters, ornithopters and feathering paddlers.

Included in stability we have, naturally, safety. Professor J. J. Montgomery of Santa Clara, Cal., very recently gave an apt illustration of the probable progression of aeroplanes as to stability. He likened the existing successful machines to the bicycle, which is inherently an unstable machine, depending for its equilibrium on the balance and skill of the rider. The successful aeroplane of the future, Professor Montgomery contends, will be likened to the automobile, which is inherently stable and which will remain upright unless its stability is abused by gross carelessness or ignorance on the part of the driver. It is toward this stability that the greatest progress must be made.

As to weight-carrying, we must admit that the size of aeroplanes is limited by natural laws which cannot be overcome. Progress toward greater weight-carrying ability must depend upon the manufacture of relatively lighter engines per horsepower produced. There has been but little advance during the past year along these lines, the Gnome engine still being far in advance of anything since produced. This weighs approximately two and one-half pounds per horsepower.

The question of speed involves the inter-consideration of all other vital points, principal thought being given to the minimizing of wing spreads under a maximum of power. This was accomplished in the Baby Wright racer, which was destroyed at Belmont, and it is probable that the twin propeller system of the Wrights affords the most logical existing speed medium. When machines having but a single propeller attempt great bursts of speed, they fail of their object for the reason that when the wing spread is reduced sufficiently to admit of rapid propulsion, the torque from a single propeller is apt to cause lateral instability, which has, in at least one instance, resulted in the revolution of the planes while the propellers remained stationary.

Last year it occurred to the writer that the aeroplane was a feasible vehicle for aggressive use in war. This has since been affirmed and denied by many prominent men on many different occasions. Personally, the prominence of the men has never appealed to me as giving weight to their utterances on this particular subject. Aviation is so new and its principles so little generally known that one is as apt to find sound reason behind the opinions of a sixteen-year-old boy as he is behind those of an ex-president. It is perfectly obvious to me that the aeroplane will be of aggressive use in war. From this it must not be concluded that the claim is made that an airship is analogous to a warship, or that any of the present known aggressive engines will be railroaded to oblivion because of the arrival of this new auxiliary. At best the aggressive use of aeroplanes will be merely supplemental to that of a known and established engine of destruction.

One year ago the writer brought forth the claim that certain tables could be worked out, certain projectiles could be manufactured and a degree of accuracy of drop acquired which would result in the universal acknowledgment that the aeroplane can be successfully used aggressively. These tables have been constructed; these projectiles have been made, dropped, and have struck the target.

The problem has not been solved in its entirety for the reason that the altitudes attained have been insufficient. This is not of itself an argument either for or against the aggressive use of the aeroplane. It is simply the result of conditions under which these experiments have been conducted. In the first place, the Aviation Meet at San Francisco was a spectacle for the amusement of the general public. There is little of the spectacular in the conduct of any serious progressive experimental work along any line whatsoever. That holds true in this case as well as in other cases. Add to this the necessity for keeping up the public interest in an aeroplane meet, the even greater necessity for insuring the safety of the crowds attending the meet, and we have in a nutshell the reason why these experiments were not conducted at altitudes of three thousand feet and above. This height of three thousand feet is taken arbitrarily and may or may not be the dividing-line between imminent danger from hostile rifle and machine-gun fire and comparative safety of the aviator. Personally, the writer is of the opinion that if an aeroplane attains an altitude of three thousand feet or more and travels at a speed of forty-five miles an hour or more it should be much safer for the aviator and his companion or companions than these same men would be were they part of the fighting line in a land engagement.

As a result of the bomb-dropping experiments recently conducted in San Francisco, we have valuable data on which future experiments can be based, and it is hoped that the Government of the United States, through Congress assembled, will see fit to appropriate during the present session a sufficient sum of money to enable the Signal Corps to purchase the necessary aeroplanes to complete these investigations. It is not reasonable to expect that the aviators or manufacturers of flying-machines should interest themselves in the conducting of purely military investigations. Their work consists in manipulating and manufacturing the machines themselves. In order to prop-

A group of distinguished aviators. Upper portrait, Eugene B. Ely. In the center (from left to right), Hubert Latham, Walter Brookins, and Philip Parmalee, who at San Francisco broke America's endurance record. Lower portrait, James Radley

erly try out these military questions, it is imperative that the government should itself own these machines and that certain officers and men should be permanently detailed from the War Department to work out the solution of the problems. If this be done, it will undoubtedly give great impetus to the art of flying, for Mother Necessity will immediately give birth to many new inventions as a result of such investigations.

From the standpoint of information it is entirely necessary that the army should own and equip its own aeroplanes. The gaining of information without the power of transmitting it to a distance is useless in warfare. The only feasible method for transmitting this information is by wireless, either the telephone or the telegraph. In order to properly utilize the wireless, special sending and receiving devices must be invented and installed on the aeroplanes and particularly on the sending apparatus there must be great economy of weight. The sending side of the wireless telegraph set devised for use at Selfridge Field, weighed about one hundred and twenty pounds. This can be reduced to less than forty pounds,

Explosion of a bomb dropped at a target from a flying aeroplane. From a photograph taken by Lieutenant Beck

provided the wireless experimenter and the aviator can work together for an extended period of time. There are many compromises to be made and many difficulties to be overcome. Of course, the weight of one hundred and twenty pounds is not prohibitive, yet when every pound is precious, as is the case in heavier-than-air flight, weight should be reduced to a minimum.

The difficulty of receiving wireless on an aeroplane is mainly one of audibility. Engines make such an infernal racket that the faint impulses as reproduced in the telephone receiver are insufficient to be heard. Engines must be muffled. Specially designed ear pads must be devised. Louder receivers must be invented.

All these things will be done, but not until the Signal Corps of the United States Army is provided with the ways and means for doing them.

After all, having considered both the aggressive and information uses of the aeroplane, we arrive again at the beginning, which is: what will The Hague say as to the humanitarian view of these aerial monsters hurling their destroying missiles on a helpless army or dropping burning

Bird's-eye view of South San Francisco, looking east, taken at a height of about 1,200 feet, by Lieut. G. E. M. Kelly, U. S. A., in a Wright biplane, Walter Brookins, aviator

projectiles on a defenseless city? It may be that by preparing for war, even along this latest line of attack, we will most effectually bring about that longed-for epoch of universal brotherhood and peace.

4.
Learning to Fly
(1911)

THE
OUTING
MAGAZINE

FOUNDED 1882

MAY, 1911

LEARNING TO FLY

BY AUGUSTUS POST

Illustrated with Photographs

FLYING is a fascinating sport; it calls for the greatest exercise of self-control and requires, as essential elements for success, bravery, daring, to a slight degree, courage, confidence in yourself, your men, and your machine, good judgment, clear sight, intuitive knowledge, quickness of thought, positiveness of action, all combined with a most delicate sense of feeling and acute powers of perception. Good health is both a result and a prerequisite of good flying, and your mind must be clear and free. When flying in ordinary calm weather and under perfect conditions, when your movements are automatic, the mind may wander to the beauties of the landscape below; Mr. Orville Wright once remarked, that he nearly went to sleep while flying round and round over the same place for a long time.

In addition to these qualities, which apply primarily to what is done in the air, there is another side to the business of flying which must by no means be overlooked. The aviator should have a good knowledge of mechanics and should understand something about materials and construction with metal and wood; it is not enough merely to order this or that part built; you should also know how it is to be done and what materials to use. You must have a sense of relative values and proportions and know the comparative weights and strengths of the various articles used.

The aeroplane with its light wires and thin framework is quite as strong and heavy, when compared with the air in which it moves, as a boat is when compared with the water in which it floats, which is eight hundred times denser than air, or the structure of an automobile when compared with the ground over which it runs. What looks to be a flimsy structure of wood and wire is as proportionately strong when compared with the medium in which it flies as is any vehicle for land or water. Bolts should be of just the right size to stand the strain and to perform the structural

Photograph by Pictorial News Co., N. Y.

READY FOR THE START.

function for which they are used without unnecessary weight or size, and so it must be with all the other parts, whether of wire, metal, or wood.

It must be borne in mind, however, that the entire proportions of the design must be adjusted to an element eight hundred times less dense than water, and harmony in weight and strength must exist through all elements of the structure. It is easy to see the fundamental difference between an aerial motor and one of marine or automobile type. The same difference is evident in a well-built frame and chassis.

Another element enters into the construction of an aerial motor, which is the comparatively constant speed at which it is required to run; there are no shocks or jars caused by changing gears or reversing the direction of the thrust, so much lighter construction can be used. The main structure of the aeroplane itself is lighter than the framework of water and land vehicles, in regard to weight and strength, as the aeroplane is comparatively free from great irregularities in its path such as waves on the water and rough roads on the land.

There is no cushion so soft as the air although special construction is required for maintaining equilibrium and absorbing the shock of landing, but it must be admitted that the strain of making spectacular dips and spiral circles is almost as severe as even a sailboat may have when you suddenly jibe its sail. The wings and braces creak and give under the increased pressure until it seems as if they must break. This is what has happened in several accidents, notably the one in which C. S. Rolls was killed in England last summer during an accurate landing competition. He miscalculated the distance and was forced to make an abrupt descent in order to land within the prescribed limits; one of the rudders gave way and the machine fell to the ground.

In the accident to Johnstone's machine in Denver something seemed to be wrong with the warping device and the machine became uncontrollable, but whether this was due to excessive strain or to a defective repair is not quite clear. This accident seems to emphasize the fact that the mechanical knowledge referred to as an essential element in a flier, although it need not be of such a degree as is necessary to invent a machine, should be enough to enable the aviator to repair his machine when it is broken or to direct the manner in which

Photograph by Pictorial News Co., N. Y.

UNDER WAY JUST BEFORE RISING.

the repairs should be made, and to know also, when they are completed, whether the work was properly done.

With the same regularity that a track walker goes over the roadbed of a railway, must the mechanic examine the fastenings of an aeroplane to look for weak places; failures cannot be remedied in the air and a human life depends upon the absolute reliability of every detail. Safety devices of all kinds are used and important wires and braces are made double; cable is largely used in places of single strand wire; struts, wires, and braces that might break and fall into the propeller are tied so that this cannot happen; rudders and ailerons are fastened by safety wires to prevent their becoming free, if their hinges should break, just as chains are used to hold railway cars together in case the couplings break.

Wires from the magneto are fastened in their place so that they cannot come loose or the connections be broken; valves from the gasoline tank are fastened open so there is no possibility that they will become closed by the vibration. The same degree of care that is used in railroad operation is necessary in the practice of aviation.

There is still another side to flying that affects the aviator of the present time which is of no less importance than the possession of the necessary qualities and mechanical knowledge. I refer to the study of the air itself and the familiarity that must be gained with its conditions, actions, and effects. The study of the subject of meteorology bears the same relation to flying that navigation and hydrography bear to sailing and geography and touring to automobiling.

Lists are already prepared which give the prevailing weather conditions in different parts of this country and indicate the best times of the year for flying, the prevailing direction and velocity of the wind, and other matters of general information.

A great deal has been said in the newspapers about "holes in the air," but there is no such thing; holes do not exist in the atmosphere. It is a fact, however, that you encounter rising and falling currents about as often as those which blow in a horizontal plane.

When the aeroplane enters one of these descending currents, the wings are blown down precipitately, on account of their large surface, giving the sensation of falling in a vacuum. The machine descends so rapidly that it is necessary to strap the aviator in his seat, as the machine would otherwise leave him sitting on nothing and he would have no solid purchase to enable him to operate his controls, for you do not seem to start to fall, when this occurs, as quickly as the machine is blown down by the wind.

A thorough inspection of the field is the very first thing to be done before flying is attempted, and the aviator should take great pains to walk very carefully over every foot of the ground over which he intends to fly. He should observe every detail and examine every obstacle, making a clear mental map of its location. The actions of the air currents should be studied and every minute thing that could in any possible way affect the flying of the machine should be most accurately observed and distinctly remembered. He should not confine his investigations merely to the field over which the flights are intended to be made, but all the open country in the vicinity should be examined also, and the direction and extent of their available smooth ground for landing should be thoroughly mapped in the aviator's mind. Once when Mr. Ely was flying at Poughkeepsie, N. Y., a rudder wire broke on the machine so that he could not change the direction of his aeroplane and he was forced to fly in a straight line until an open field appeared which offered him a safe landing place.

Besides the chance of accident, the wind may blow the machine far away from its starting place and it may not be possible to get back; Ralph Johnstone was blown in this way nearly sixty miles away from Belmont Park during a severe gale.

Beware Even the Gentle Breeze

The novice must attempt practice flights only when the conditions are perfect and the air is dead calm (and this means *dead calm*—when not a breath of air is stirring the leaves of the trees). There is plenty for the aviator who is making his first flights to do to manage the machine itself without being required to look out for gusts of wind and unknown and unforeseen dangers. A beginner should no more think of attempting a flight in high wind than should one learning to drive an automobile take his first lesson on Fifth Avenue during the crowded part of the day. The quickness of thought required to make the decisions necessary for passing through the maze of traffic safely leaves no time, energy, nor attention for thinking which lever must be used, and you must perform the mechanical movements which are necessary in such a place as you use your feet in walking—with absolute unconsciousness, and without the least demand upon the attention.

The accident to Moisant was described to me by a person who was as close as anyone to him, and it seems a good illustration of just this point. Moisant went up in a machine which had been used by his friend, Barrios, because it had a much larger gasoline tank than his own, and extra fuel was necessary as he intended to attempt to win the Michelin Cup and to beat the world's long-distance record of 365 miles recently made by Maurice Tabuteau in France. The machines were the same in every way except that the spark and throttle levers controlling the engine of this machine differed slightly from those on his own machine.

Moisant flew from the City Park race track in New Orleans to a field at Harahan, about twelve miles away, where preparations had already been made for making the record flight. The prepared landing place was not very large and after twice circling the field, as Moisant was about to land to fill his fuel tanks for the long flight, he was seen to shut his motor down and immediately afterwards, it is said, he seemed to straighten up his machine as if to make another circle of the field, probably to stop earlier in order to have more clear ground for his machine to run over after landing.

The motor apparently failed to respond immediately and it became necessary to descend very abruptly, as he was nearing the end of the ground suitable for landing. The machine pitched down at such a steep angle that Moisant fell out and was killed. The levers, I understand, indicated that the motor had been stopped. This seems to show that there was a moment of indecision or a sudden change of intention on the part of the

WELL AWAY FOR A FLIGHT. AN ACCIDENT AT THIS HEIGHT IS MORE DANGEROUS THAN IT LOOKS, BECAUSE THE AVIATOR HAS SCANT ROOM IN WHICH TO MANEUVER.

Photograph by Pictorial News Co., N. Y.

AN IDEAL LANDING, ONE OF THE FIRST THINGS THE AVIATOR MUST LEARN IS TO COME DOWN EASILY IN THE
RIGHT PLACE.

aviator which was fatal. This may have been caused by his pulling the wrong lever when he wanted to accelerate the motor, and finding that it did not respond, he turned down at once, taking a chance that it could be accomplished in safety.

At a later stage in the course of instruction, when the aviator has gained confidence and after all the movements necessary to operate the machine have become purely automatic, so as not to require the least thought on his part, the aviator's attention may then be devoted to overcoming the problems presented by the wind. Gusts are felt without warning; swirls of air are encountered when passing over or near buildings, and puffs come without regularity and without warning. When sailing a boat they cause ruffles on the water and thus give the helmsman warning in time to prepare for them. It is not so when flying in an aeroplane.

Gusts of wind are only evident when they are perceived through the delicate and highly acute sense of feeling of the aviator, who must immediately adjust his balancing devices and rudders to meet the situation and to counteract the effect. When you become exceedingly skillful you can tell just how much to do and how much not to do, allowing the machine to follow its own inclination to a slight degree, to go with the undulations of the air or be turned out of its path by the air currents, allowing it to drift back again slowly of its own accord, when it will resume its proper direction with a gentle and easy return and with much more saving of friction than an excessive or impulsive movement of the controls would occasion.

This ability to let the air have its way, like letting a horse "have its head," is equally important and perhaps more apparent in the handling of a balloon, for the aeronaut soon gets the touch or the "feel of the air" and quickly learns just how much ballast to use to check the balloon when it starts down. The same "feel of the air" can be learned in a flying machine.

A usual fault with all beginners in anything, and sometimes with old hands when they lose their flexibility, is that they are inclined to be too abrupt and to steer too close to a line. We all remember our first experience on a bicycle when we wabbled all over the road and turned the front wheel much too great a distance in the opposite direction in order to correct a slight tendency to turn in the other. This overcorrection itself requires to be righted and is apt to cause complications in other directions, especially if there are many obstacles.

There seems to be also a lesson to be drawn from the accident to Archie Hoxsey, who was killed at Los Angeles while flying in a high wind and attempting to surpass his own record for altitude. After three days of marvelously successful flights, during which he exceeded the world's altitude record and set it far above all others, Hoxsey ascended when the wind was too high for some of the other aviators to fly and after they had tried out the conditions in their own machines. There can be no conception of the terrific strain that he was under as a result of his previous success; this feeling, amounting almost to overconfidence, that nerved him up may have been responsible for the momentary loss of control or attack of air sickness, caused by his aeroplane coming down at too great an angle of descent and at such a frightful speed that the wind was seen to turn it completely over in the air, after which it dashed to the ground before it could be righted, instantly killing the daring pilot.

Not Always the Machine's Fault

Whether it was the prolonged strain or the violence of the wind that caused this accident it is hard to tell, but it seems to show that the machine itself is not always to blame. A mistake in judgment, air sickness, which may be caused by too quick a descent, or momentary lack of attention at a critical moment, are equally to be guarded against. Cecil Grace was seen to take a wrong direction and head for the North Sea instead of the shore of England, and finally become engulfed in a dense fog while returning after a successful flight over the English Channel. The mere thought of being lost in a fog is bad enough, but to be compelled by necessity to continue on flying until overtaken by exhaustion is enough to send the cold shudders down one's back.

It must be realized that the aviator practically steers in three directions at once, up and down and to right or left, and he must also maintain his balance. All these functions must be kept in his mind at the same time; and this is only a small part of the problem presented to him in flight. It is like steering an automobile upon a moving sidewalk, or an even more realistic simile would be steering an automobile upon a great moving escalator mounted upon a moving sidewalk; thus, motion in three planes may be visualized, for the path of the aeroplane would be the resultant of the movements of all three machines.

Imagine that you are endeavoring to avoid an obstacle upon which your mind is fixed, as, let us say, a tree in the center of a large field; some subtle force seems to be always drawing us toward the very obstacle from which we desire to escape; it seems to fascinate us and we are almost sure to collide with it as long as it is a dominant idea in our mind. But when we forget about it, or pay no special attention to the thought, its terror vanishes. When Captain Baldwin was making practice flights at Hammondsport, N. Y., there was a lone tree in the flying field which had plenty of clear space all around it, but he succeeded in hitting it, for no other apparent reason than that he was trying so hard to avoid it.

My own machine, a Curtiss biplane, fell while I was flying in New Orleans last December, but this accident was caused by a combination of circumstances which illustrates other problems of the air which the aviator must overcome. We were flying at the City Park race track, just outside the city. Only a little more than half of the infield of this mile track was available, because of a large pond or lake which occupied one end of it; on the far side of the grounds, opposite the grand stand, there were tall oak trees which grew in the City Park; this made it necessary to attain a comparatively high altitude very quickly after starting from the ground, as a sharp turn had to be made at the western end of the track.

To make a quick turn with a low-powered machine, such as I was flying, it is necessary to fly at a sufficient height to enable you to pitch down at a steep angle on the turn in order to gain additional speed to compensate for the loss of headway caused by the resistance offered to the air by the rudders and controls when they are turned in steering. In maintaining the proper banking angle for the turn it was also necessary to compensate for the loss in support gained from the air because of the machine's slewing sideways while turning and moving obliquely forward instead of presenting its wings squarely in the direction of flight; in addition to these considerations, which are always present, even when the air is still, the air was somewhat puffy, and although the start was made against the wind, on the turn and upon flying with it, speed, relative to the wind, was also lost, causing the machine to sag and sink lower and lower toward the tree tops along the back stretch.

One tree stood out a little distance in front of the others, and while endeavoring to steer clear of it, the left wing of the aeroplane caught one of the top branches, a big limb of the tree was broken off, and the aeroplane spun around as if on a pivot, and then it turned completely over, looping the loop in air as it fell. The front control, the sides, and the tail were uninjured, but the wheels of the running gear were forced up through the lower plane and the engine was broken loose by the jar of the shock.

Effect of a Fall

They told me afterwards that I crawled out of the wreckage and said I was not hurt and begged McCurdy, who insisted on taking me back to the hotel, to remain and finish the flights. Later in the evening I woke up in my bed in my room without even the faintest recollection of what had happened. The last impressions that I remembered were of going out to the grounds in a taxicab with the other fellows. But by delicate questions on my part and from the an-

BANKING AT THE TURNS LOOKS EASY TO THE SPECTATORS, BUT IT IS ONE
OF THE MOST DANGEROUS PARTS OF THE GAME.

swers that I received the whole story was made clear to me. A day or two later I began to feel a stiffness in the cords of my neck, due probably to the great concentration of mind during the rapid course of events which were too speedy for my senses to follow, and partly due to a possible shock. All these effects finally passed entirely away, but this experience serves to show the serious results that may follow even a slight miscalculation among many which the complicated conditions demand.

The aviator is confronted with another curious feature of the aeroplane which can hardly exist in the mind of a person who has not had the actual experience of these conditions in the air. It is almost impossible for an observer on the ground to conceive of the results which follow the tipping or the tilting of the aeroplane while banking on a curve, or making a "spiral dip," such as was made so famous by Johnstone and

Hoxsey, who turned their machines up sideways until they were flying at an angle of nearly ninety degrees to the horizontal, or at almost a right angle to the normal position of the aeroplane in flight. Let us see what happens to the rudders and control planes when they are revolved about a fore-and-aft axis until they are at right angles to their normal position. The horizontal front control ordinarily used for ascending and descending is completely turned from the horizontal plane to the vertical and becomes a rudder which steers the aeroplane to the right or to the left; the vertical rudder in the rear, on the other hand, assumes a horizontal position and by its operation tends to make the machine ascend or descend like a rear control.

Hence, in making a spiral dip, the steering must be accomplished by means of the elevating plane, and as you draw the control lever toward you the ma-

WHEN AN AVIATOR CAN TAKE HIS WIFE UP FOR A PLEASANT LITTLE SPIN
IT'S A GOOD SIGN THAT HE HAS MASTERED HIS ART.

chine comes around like a bicycle on a "saucer track," while the steering rudders must be carefully adjusted to control the descent. When the aeroplane is flying at an angle of forty-five degrees to the horizontal, the front control and the rudder should, theoretically, be equally able to perform the functions of the other.

Careful adjustment must be made between the movements which control these functions, and after long practice they become instinctive. It is in just such fine points as these that the personal equation and the characteristics of the individual aviator reveal themselves most clearly.

The art of preserving the lateral equilibrium or balance must be studied carefully, for the tendency of the aeroplane to slip sideways or skid through the air on the turn causes it to lose the support of the air which is gained by its forward motion and makes it necessary to bank the planes on the turns; if they bank too much, on the other hand, the whole machine will slip down through the air on the inside of the circle and may easily come to grief by striking one wing on the ground. Fortunately, the machine tends to take its natural inclination, for in turning the outside wing proceeds faster than the other, giving it a slightly greater lifting effect and canting the machine on that side, as has already been mentioned.

The aviator must be very delicate in his movements, keenly sensitive to the least suggestion of what may be required, and quick and sure to act, but not in an arbitrary manner, for the "feel of the air" is one of the most fascinating and subtly artistic touches that can be learned. Like confidence in swimming or riding a bicycle, if once secured, it never leaves you.

There is often discussion among aviators as to whether you should "bank" before using the rudder in turning, or use the rudder to turn and have the banking take place automatically, because of the fact that one wing travels faster than the other, giving it greater lifting power. Mr. Curtiss has often criticised his pupils for not banking enough when making a turn, for it is extremely necessary to get just the right angle to prevent a serious accident.

In the construction of a flying machine the movements that the aviator must make with the controlling levers should be as instinctive as possible. There should also be some natural relation between the movements of these levers and the effect which it is desired to produce.

The Blériot monoplane has a standard with a small hand wheel on its top, placed just between the knees of the aviator (very much like the steering post of an automobile, but much smaller). This hand wheel is pulled backward toward the operator if you wish to rise, and this seems quite a natural movement to make. If it is desired to descend, this hand wheel is pushed forward, also a perfectly natural movement to make with the body. If the machine tips up on the right side, the standard is moved to the right to counteract it. If it tips to the left, it is moved to the left.

Combined movements, or movements diagonal to these cardinal movements, can also be made when it is necessary to balance and ascend or descend at the same time, for the standard is mounted on a universal joint, so that it can be readily moved in any direction. Steering is done by the feet, which rest on a bar pivoted in the center and connected by wires to the rudder in the rear, like the steering arrangement in a single-oared shell.

The Farman biplane is controlled in much the same manner, but a lever at the right hand of the aviator takes the place of the small hand wheel control post of the Blériot; the motions are the same, however, but the left hand of the aviator is free to control the motor or hold on to one of the vertical posts.

Steering is done by the operator's feet, which rest on a pivoted cross-bar attached to the foot rest, as in the Blériot.

The beautiful Antoinette monoplane is controlled in quite a different manner, however, from any of the other flying machines, although the principle, of course, is the same. This aeroplane has two hand wheels, one placed on each side of the aviator, which rotate in the fore and aft plane. The right-hand wheel controls elevating and descending, and the left-hand wheel warps the wings. Steering is done by the feet, as is the universal custom in all of the foreign machines.

At this point it is interesting to consider whether it is a good practice to confide to the feet such an important function as steering, and also whether the shoulders and body of the operator are sensitive and quick enough to accomplish the movements necessary in delicate balancing, or whether the hands of the pilot should not be used to perform these delicate functions. The most popular types of French machines are all steered by the feet of the aviator and balanced by the hands, but the American type of machine is steered in almost every instance by the hand of the aviator and the balance is very generally accomplished by the movements of his shoulders or body.

Where American Machines Are Different

Why the American aeroplanes differ radically from the foreign machines in this point is hard to tell. The Curtiss, a typically American machine, and one copied more than any other by other builders, uses the shoulder yoke and the instinctive movements of the body for preserving the lateral stability or to balance the machine.

This lateral stability has always been the "bugbear" of flying-machine inventors, but Mr. Curtiss says it is as easy to become accustomed to guarding against falling over sideways as it is to prevent falling over forward or backward; you unconsciously do it when walking, or riding a bicycle, and it does not cause any great trouble there. Why can you not learn the same thing in the operation of an aeroplane?

The Wright biplane is controlled by two levers, one at the left hand of the aviator is moved forward or backward to operate the rear horizontal control, for in their new type machine they have moved the original front control to the rear, where it acts in the same manner as the rear horizontal control of a monoplane for elevating and descending. At the left hand of the operator there is another lever which is practically a double lever, as its main portion is moved forward and backward to warp the wings, while the handle of this lever may be moved transversely to operate the vertical rudder planes in the rear.

A delicate combination of movements, both in the fore and aft and in the transverse planes, must be made by both the arm and the wrist to operate this lever, for in this machine, when the wings are warped, the theoretically increased resistance caused by the greater curvature given to the surface on one side over the theoretically decreased resistance on the other wing caused by flattening it out, may give a turning tendency to the whole machine which can be offset by turning the rear vertical surfaces in order to interpose an equal amount of resistance, which tends to keep the aeroplane on a straight course through the air.

On a two-passenger machine an extra seat is placed on the right of the aviator's seat, and a duplicate elevating and descending lever connected to the main lever is placed at the extreme right of the passenger seat. This enables each to operate the machine, except that the operations of the right and left hands are reversed.

No doubt two aviators will ascend and take "tricks at the wheel," as the pilot and aide in a long balloon journey are accustomed to do, eating and sleeping by turns. One of the foreign aviators has already made arrangements so that he can eat in his aeroplane, and on one occasion he has taken two meals while in the air. Mr. Henry Farman built a cabin on his machine to protect himself from the severity of the weather during his great flight for the Michelin Trophy, when he made a new world's record by flying continuously for more than eight hours.

The Curtiss biplane is possibly the most natural of all the types to operate, for the movements of its controls are perfectly instinctive and so natural that the aviator, in a time of excitement, when he might possibly forget for a moment, is inclined to do the right thing and to operate the control levers in the correct way. A vertical hand wheel is placed directly in front of you as you sit on the seat of the machine. This wheel is grasped by both hands and is pulled back to cause the aeroplane to ascend and pushed forward if you wish to descend. If you turn the hand wheel around on its axis to the right, it turns the machine to the right. Turning it to the left turns the machine to the left, under normal conditions.

A "shoulder yoke," which is simply a swaying back with high arms, is hinged to the seat in such a manner that it can be moved by the aviator's shoulders toward the right or the left side. Wires extend from this shoulder yoke to the balancing planes hinged on each side of the aeroplane. When the machine tips up on the right side, the most natural movement for the aviator to make is to lean toward the high side, and this is the movement which must be made to bring the machine back to an even keel. The movement is reversed to counteract a tilt in the other direction; a pedal operated by the right foot stops the motor, and one operated by the left foot opens the throttle, accelerating its speed.

After examining all the various machines, and having chosen the one that you think is the best, go to a good aviation school or follow a good aviator and stick to him, remembering that "the only way to fly is to fly." "Drive a peg and then pull to it," is a favorite saying of Captain Baldwin, the father of American aeronauts and aviators.

The most important moment in the history of its development will come when a human life is saved by the aeroplane. It will then be hailed as the greatest blessing to mankind, and just as the wireless was taken to our hearts, so will the aeroplane and the aeronaut be honored and rewarded.

5.
A Modern Aeronaut
(1901)

M. SANTOS-DUMONT'S AIR-SHIP READY FOR THE ASCENSION.

THE MODERN AËRONAUT.

BY JACQUES BOYER.

ON the 21st of November, 1783, the Marquis d'Arlandes and Pilatre de Rozier, after many ascensions in captive Montgolfiers, allowed themselves for the first time to be carried up into the air in a free balloon. Starting from the Château de la Muette, where the Dauphin then resided, they passed above the towers of Notre Dame de Paris, and alighted safely near the Gobelin manufactory. Their flight lasted only twenty minutes. It is a far cry from these modest beginnings to the aërial voyage of thirty-six hours made in 1900 by the Count de la Vaulx.

However, the experience of the French aëronauts of the eighteenth century created

INFLATING IN THE BALLOON PARK AT VINCENNES.

69

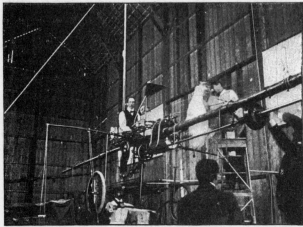

M. SANTOS-DUMONT MAKING PRELIMINARY TRIALS OF HIS MOTOR.

the least distance from a fixed point. In the beginning the wind drove the aëronauts toward the ocean and forced them to descend to earth earlier than they would otherwise have done. Some of the contestants, indeed, came very near perishing tragically. Thus the Count de la Vaulx, after having sighted the Minquiers Isles, alighted on August 27th near Guingamp, Côtes-du-Nord. The accompanying photographs, which show his balloon all torn to pieces, indicate how dangerous was his landing. Monsieur Juchmès, the winner on this day, also had an exciting journey. Carried by the atmospheric currents toward the Cotentin peninsula, he was able, thanks to a sudden change in the wind, to stop himself just on the banks of the Loire. For the later races the weather was more clement. Monsieur Balsan remained in the air for thirty-five hours on September 16th; a fortnight later, the Count de la Vaulx, passing over Germany, came to earth again quite near Warsaw.

the greatest enthusiasm in both hemispheres—for Rittenhouse, of Philadelphia, made ascensions in America in that same year of 1783. All humanity saw itself, in the near future, mistress of the ethereal ocean; but, although more than a century has passed, we have not yet seen the realization of this dream. However, while awaiting a solution of the problem, many Parisian sportsmen have devoted themselves enthusiastically to the pleasures of the aëronaut, which have become in our day a sport quite devoid of danger.

The great development of the new sport in France dates only from the foundation, on the 28th of January, 1899, of the Aëro Club, a society the membership of which now numbers more than three hundred experts. Two of its members—Count Castillon de Saint-Victor and M. Maurice Mallet—not long ago achieved a remarkable journey from Paris to Sweden, which, however, was eclipsed soon after by some of the notable competitions at the Universal Exposition. Organized most carefully by MM. E. Godard, W. de Fonville, Colonel Renard and some others, these competitions comprised four kinds of contests: trials of endurance, of altitude, of horizontal distance, and of alighting at

On October 9, 1900, the day fixed for a most important contest of endurance and of distance at the same time, the aërodrome of Vincennes presented an unusual aspect, owing to the large number of spectators present. Shortly before half-past four

DEFLATING THE "TOURING-CLUB" AFTER A RACE.

Photographed by M. Simons from an altitude of two hundred and fifty meters.

THE BALLOON PARK AT VINCENNES BEFORE THE START.

M. GODARD.

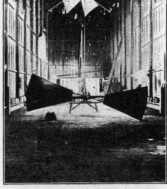

THE PROPELLER OF THE SANTOS-
DUMONT AIR-SHIP.

o'clock in the afternoon all the balloons were inflated and ready for the trial. By five o'clock the aërial flotilla commenced to move. The "Aëro-Club," directed by M. Jacques Faure, opened the ball; and then it was the turn of the "St. Louis," which carried off Messieurs Balsan and Godard. Finally, at twenty minutes past five, the "Centaur," bearing the Count de la Vaulx and M. Castillon de Saint-Victor, gently soared away into the distance, its huge bulk gleaming gold in the rays of the setting sun.

The "Centaur" traversed successively Fontenay-sous-Bois, Rosny and Sevran. Then, after having thrown out a few handfuls of sand, their basket-car balanced itself at an altitude of one thousand five hundred meters. A few rare sounds alone reached their ears. Finally the fog disappeared little by little. The plains of Champagne—Reims, whose cathedral under the pale light of the moon seems to be a marvelous triumph of stage scenery—and the valley of the Suippe passed in turn under their eyes.

M. JUCHMÈS.

At midnight the shadow of the balloon glided over the waters of the Ardennes canal. Then the French frontier was reached, but—happy mortals!—they passed it without any of the unpleasant formalities of the custom house. At half-past four the dawn appeared—a smudge of blood on the horizon—and a little later, under the action of the cooling atmosphere, the balloon descended to five hundred meters. The aëronauts then made a vain effort to discover where they were. When the fog disappeared they saw Silesia, where soon the "St. Louis" rejoined them. The struggle between the two balloons became intense. They passed together over Breslau, and at thirty-five minutes past three they reascended to four thousand meters. The "Centaur" definitely lost sight of the "St. Louis." A temperature of twelve degrees below zero chilled them, and in order to continue their way they had to take alternately mouthfuls of cogniac and breaths of oxygen. They were over Russia at sunset, and nature provided them with a concert which they would willingly have dispensed with: black clouds gathered in the northwest, and in the distance they heard the heavy rumble of thunder. Their aërial ship was terribly buffeted.

Shortly after this, piercing cries of water-fowl and the lugubrious croaking of frogs in the immense marshes of Pinks disturbed the silence. With the first flush of dawn they saw under their basket broad plains sown here and there with tiny villages. At intervals churches with gilded domes and Byzantine belfries glistened superbly in the rising sun.

Their provision of sand and of oxygen being about exhausted, they loosed their guide-rope over the roofs of Korostichef in the province of Kiev. Then the anchor

M. BALSAN.

M. SIMONS.

M. FAURE MAKING AN ASCENT IN THE "AËRO-CLUB."

was thrown out into the fork of a tree, while the Count de Castillon pulled the valve open. Immediately men and women appeared from all sides to stare at the spectacle, and finally conducted the aëronauts to the police bureau. The Commissioner received them well, and the necessary authority to return to France was obtained.

Their return was a veritable triumph. They were fêted and feasted on the journey by both Russians and Poles. It took them four nights and three days to return by railway, while thirty-five hours and forty-five minutes had sufficed the ''Centaur.''

A CAR EQUIPPED FOR THE TRANS-MEDITERRANEAN TRIP.

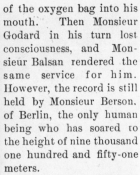

of the oxygen bag into his mouth. Then Monsieur Godard in his turn lost consciousness, and Monsieur Balsan rendered the same service for him. However, the record is still held by Monsieur Berson, of Berlin, the only human being who has soared to the height of nine thousand one hundred and fifty-one meters.

On the other hand, the races of the least distance to a point designated in advance were very interesting, for all the sportsmen who took part in them evinced admirable skill in their manœuvers. Thus in the contest of July 22d seven balloonists out of twelve alighted at the commune of Mornant, the prearranged point of descent. We should not forget, either, the contest of August 19th, which was highly original. According to the set program, the contestants were to rendezvous at a designated place, ascend into the air again and finally repair to the appointed destination. The results were eminently satisfactory, since

The "St. Louis" had carried Messieurs Balsan and Godard to Russia also—to Opatchke, in the province of Pskov. These gentlemen had covered one thousand three hundred and sixty-one kilometers in twenty-seven hours and fifteen minutes. As to Monsieur Faure, he landed the "Aëro-Club" at Schnitz in Moravia. Monsieur Maison, who, with his wife, had ascended in "La Loraine," stopped at Weimar in Saxony. Monsieur Juchmès, in the "Touring-Club," reached Brückenau in Bavaria. Finally, the "Nimbus" carried Monsieur Hervieu to Beringen in Switzerland. All the contestants thus acquitted themselves most creditably in this aërial race.

The competitions for altitude at the Universal Exposition offer less of interest, and the only one which is worthy of our attention is that of September 23, 1900, in which MM. Jacques Balsan and Louis Godard ascended to an altitude of eight thousand four hundred and seventeen meters. The ascension almost ended tragically. At one moment Monsieur Balsan fainted, and his companion was compelled to force the end

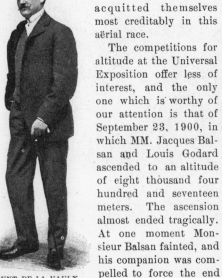

COUNT DE LA VAULX.

M. RAMBAUD ABOUT TO MAKE AN ASCENSION.

in one of the ensuing races each captain himself appointed the end of his journey, and the Count de la Vaulx came down in the very village he had designated.

Finally, to the Count de la Vaulx fell the "grand prix" of aërostation, which was decided on the entire program of contests at the Universal Exposition, while Monsieur Balsan took second place. Next came M. Jacques Faure, who, with his wife, ascended on November 26th last on board the "Microbe," a little balloon of five hundred and eighty cubic meters' capacity. This sentimental journey in the air was completed in the happiest manner imaginable. Monsieur Simons won the competition for the best aëronautic photographs, and it is to his courtesy that

M. SANTOS-DUMONT'S AIR-SHIP IN FULL FLIGHT.

I am indebted for some of the photographs illustrating this article.

French manufacturers also favor the new sport by all means in their power. M. Henry Deutsch has put at the disposal of the Aëro Club the sum of one hundred

Photographed by M. Simons from an altitude of four hundred and fifty meters.
LAKE DAUMESNIL AT VINCENNES.

START OF THE FIRST BALLOON RACE, JUNE 17, 1900.

M. RAMBAUD IN A FREE BALLOON.

thousand francs for the experimenter who, starting from the Longchamps race-course, shall sail around the Eiffel Tower and return to the point of starting within half an hour. He has also offered four thousand francs a year annually since 1900 for the encouragement of the most meritorious aëronaut. Monsieur Santos-Dumont has just won the smaller sums, which he has generously relinquished in order to found another prize.

Abandoning ordinary balloons, Monsieur Santos-Dumont applied a petroleum motor to an air-ship of his own invention. The apparatus consisted of a cylinder ending in two cones, twenty-five meters long and three and one half meters in diameter and containing one hundred and eighty cubic meters. Its varnished silk cover weighed only thirty kilograms. The start was made by pedaling.

Two bags of sand, attached to the basket, or car, by means of cords, made it possible to change the center of gravity of the system, making the axis incline according as the pilot wished to ascend or descend. On September 20, 1898, his flying-machine performed various evolutions under the combined action of the propeller and the rudder amid the acclamations of an assemblage of enthusiasts.

During the following years this resourceful mechanician continued his attempts with still larger balloons.

MM. DE FONVILLE AND GODARD ON A BALLOON RACING-DAY AT VINCENNES.

MR. LAMSON'S KITE READY TO RISE.

The most notable of Monsieur Santos-Dumont's ascents took place on September 19, 1900, in the presence of the members of the Aëronautic Congress. On that occasion he succeeded in making headway against the wind. Encouraged by this success, the inventor set to work again with renewed enthusiasm, and the "Santos-Dumont No. 5," the details of which are shown in the accompanying photographs, was soon constructed. The whole construction—sixteen-horse-power motor, oil reservoir and all—weighs only two hundred and fifty kilograms. His subsequent aërial journeys have been made with machines differing but little from that shown in the photograph.

The most daring of French aëronauts, the Count de la Vaulx, is pre-paring to cross the Mediterranean in a balloon. The laurels of Lhote, who, after many attempts, crossed the British Channel in this way, keep him from sleeping. A French daily, "L'Echo de Paris," has opened a subscription to cover the expenses of the enterprise, which is under the patronage of the Minister of the Navy, M. de

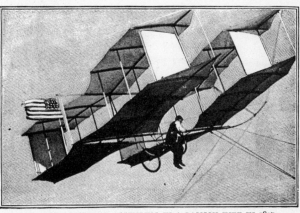

MR. FRED BICKFORD ASCENDING IN A LAMSON KITE IN 1897.

A METEOROLOGICAL KITE FLYING UNDER THE
CLOUDS.

Lanessan. The project is not so dangerous as at first blush it would seem.

Near the waves the temperature changes only gradually, and a balloon when over the sea possesses great stability, the difficulties that beset the aëronaut in a journey over land disappearing in a measure. A sheet of water presents, therefore, in spite of the general opinion to the contrary, a remarkably attractive field for journeys of this kind. More-

MR. C. R. LAMSON.

over, the addition of certain appliances that cannot be used on land still further increases this stability. There are, in the first place, guide-ropes, immense hempen cables attached to the ring of the balloon, and the equilibrators, enormous strands of rope wrapped in cloths which are very heavy. When, in consequence of a sudden cooling of the atmosphere, the weighted balloon begins to descend, these devices, resting on the ground, progressively lighten the balloon. On the other hand, if the solar action increases the upward movement of the balloon, the lifting of a certain weight of guide-rope acts as a drag on the ascent. But this means of preserving equilibrium is impracticable over fields, forests and cities, for the ropes would catch on houses, trees and other objects that might lie in their path. Sometimes, even after being dragged for many hours, the guide-ropes become unraveled, catch in some object and stop the balloon. Then, in calm weather, the captain's only resource is to cut the cable which holds him. But in this case it is impossible to

continue the journey for long. When the wind is high, the sudden stop dashes the frail bark to the ground, where the silken envelope of the balloon is torn—to say nothing of the danger to life and limb to which the passengers are subjected.

Moreover, the sea constitutes a marvelous ballast which the steersman may take on or throw out at will.

As a starting-point the Count de la Vaulx's choice has fallen on Toulon, in which city he will find almost all he needs for his journey. The government's marine aërostation depot will furnish him hydrogen for inflating his balloon.

Although it is still in its infancy, they have already baptized the balloon which is to carry them the "National." It is spherical in form, with a capacity of three thousand cubic meters. It will be provided with a compensating balloon, in order to prevent the possibility of its collapsing, operated by means of a valve in the car. A large valve in the upper part will serve for the final descent to land, another and smaller valve being provided by which the balloon may be manœuvered,

MM. JUCHMÈS AND DARD AND CAPTAIN RADISSOY
ON A TRIP FROM PARIS TO WARBURG.

THE WRECK OF COUNT DE LA VAULX'S BALLOON AFTER HIS LANDING AT GUINGAMP.

and, thanks to a number of inflated buoys, the basket would, in case of necessity, be able to keep afloat for a long time. Finally, a series of deviators makes it possible to steer the balloon in a direction different from that of the wind in order to avoid obstacles.

The "National" will carry wireless telegraphic instruments and carrier-pigeons by which communication with land may be kept up. Swift launches will follow the balloon to be on hand in case of accident. Count de la Vaulx will have four companions with him.

Recent American efforts toward the solution of the problem of aërial navigation have been directed along different lines. The balloon has been discarded and experiments have been made with large kites fitted with aëroplanes. The aëronaut regulates the angle at which these planes are inclined according as he wishes to soar upward or downward.

THE PLATE AWARDED TO WINNERS IN THE 1900 RACES—OBVERSE.

Mr. Lamson, of Portland, Maine, whose air-ship is seen in the accompanying illustrations, believes that he has solved the problem of aërial navigation so far as pleasure alone is concerned. He can rise, maintain himself at a height in the air and, like the vulture, glide downward. But, unlike the vulture, he cannot catch the wind again and soar upward. When this can be done with safety, the problem will be solved.

THE PLATE AWARDED TO WINNERS IN THE 1900 RACES—REVERSE.

THE "CENTAUR" AT VINCENNES BEFORE ITS DEPARTURE FOR RUSSIA.

The Lamson air-ship is believed to be the biggest kite or air-vessel ever flown in the world. It maintained at an altitude of over six hundred feet the heaviest weight ever attached to a kite. Before Mr. Lamson trusted himself to a flight in his latest air-ship, a one-hundred-and-fifty-pound dummy was placed upon the car and the ship was allowed to rise six hundred feet into the air. The wind, however, proved too strong and the rope snapped. The work of months, representing the study of years, seemed likely to be destroyed, but instead the accident proved to be a fortunate one, for after a brief trip heavenward, during which its meanderings were breathlessly watched by Mr. Lamson and his at-tendants, it descended to earth uninjured.

At the present time French inventors are more active than American ones, and it will be interesting to see which nation will contribute the perfect air-ship.

The French plans for next year are on a larger scale than those of any previous year, and notable progress is certain when so many brains are devoted to solving the problem.

The activity of modern aëronauts bodes well for the future of aërial travel. While they have for the most part given it attention merely as a sport, there is no doubt that its commercial possibilities are great, and it seems likely that transportation of freight and passengers through the air will be a question of a comparatively short time.

6.
The Perils and Pleasures of Ballooning (1906)

DR. THOMAS'S BALLOON, THE *NIRVANA*, HALF A MILE ABOVE NEW YORK CITY

The Perils and Pleasures of Ballooning

AN INTERESTING ACCOUNT OF THE EXPERIENCES OF A NOTED
AERONAUT WHO HAS MADE MANY DARING ASCENTS BY NIGHT
AS WELL AS BY DAY AND HAD NARROW ESCAPES FROM DEATH

By Dr. Julian P. Thomas

WHEN I was a small boy it was a favorite pastime of my companions and myself to climb high up in trees and swing from branch to branch. The tender pines which grew about my Georgia home would sway as we jumped, and I could make leaps of from twenty to thirty feet. I excelled at the sport and none of my companions could catch me. I believe that in that squirrel-like amusement were born the wishes and ambitions that have led me to go up some twelve thousand feet in the air, sailing through the clouds, seeing the glories of the sunset, high above the land, and spending fourteen hours in the midst of a terrific storm with the lightnings playing above and below me; and to do all this suspended in a frail basket under the gas-bag of a balloon.

I must refer again to my youth in telling of my balloon experiences. I suffered at one time from a severe attack of malarial fever, and after that I was unable to climb trees and jump from one to another. For the first time I experienced fear while doing so, and my confidence was never regained. Later I learned that I could not look from a great height without wishing to jump off, and this feeling has bothered me all my life. I wished to overcome it and was always extremely anxious to know if the same sensation would be with me when up in a balloon. On the day I made my first ascension I climbed to the top of the gas-tank from which the balloon was being filled, and as I mounted the frail stairs the sensation was experienced again. However, I was determined to make the ascent and was delighted to find that as I rose from the ground there was neither fear nor the wish to jump, to disturb the enormous pleasure that awaited me.

I have since decided that the natural vibrations of the body, which one becomes conscious of when on a great height, cause the fear of falling and the wish to get over the suspense by actually making the leap.

One is resisting the wind when over a precipice. This adds to the swaying of the body and exaggerates the sensation. But in a balloon there is no wind; all is quiet and calm. The first great sensation is that of losing that which is disturbing as the world, with all its turmoil and strife, recedes from the man in the balloon.

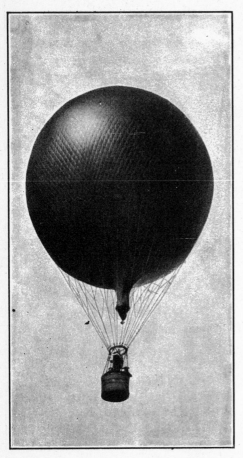

A TYPICAL PLEASURE BALLOON — THE RICH MAN'S NEWEST HOBBY

The discordant noises, the shrieking of whistles, the harsh cheers of the crowd, all of which generally attend an ascension, die down and, becoming fainter and fainter, finally end in a noiseless peace which those who have always stayed on the earth cannot appreciate.

I had been through the list of sports which have in them the element of excitement. I had broken bronchos on the plains, and raced automobiles at terrific rates of speed. There seemed nothing for me to do that would satisfy my desire for excitement until one day I saw Knabenshue sail over New York in his air-ship. In that hour I made up my mind that I would navigate the air, and I have faithfully kept my resolve. Not in a haphazard way nor looking merely for the excitement of the ascents, but in the laboratory, by study and numberless experiments and by learning the conditions that are to be met in the air, I have tried to solve the problem that is probably the greatest one confronting the intellectual world to-day.

I began by experimenting with the hot-air balloon, and sent up numbers of them in order to become familiar with the currents of the air as well as to decide on the best shape. After using every conceivable form of balloon, I reached the conclusion that the spherical one has advantages over all others. At the same time I planned a series of experiments in the manufacture of hydrogen-gas, which is still being carried on.

It was of course necessary for me to make ascents to carry out the ideas I had, actually to test the various devices I was making, and to give me a chance to experiment at all altitudes. Accordingly, last summer, I bought from Mallet, of Paris, my new balloon, *Nirvana*, the largest one in the country, which has a gas-bag with a capacity of sixty thousand cubic feet, is forty-seven feet in diameter when inflated, and stands sixty feet high when ready for an ascent. In this balloon I have made some dozen ascents, on two occasions taking my wife with me, which fact will give some idea of the degree of safety with which I believe ballooning can be done.

There is something about the start of a balloon ascension which gives a thrill that cannot be experienced on any other occasion. This is especially true to the one who is to be the navigator. He cannot delegate to others, entirely, the responsibility of seeing that the balloon is in perfect condition before he trusts his life to it. The valves must work properly; the cords must be strong; the bag itself must not leak; the net must be on correctly; the basket must be properly attached and stored with instruments, water, and food. It would take but a moment in the air to find out a mistake that would cost the navigator and his passengers their lives. I believe that a

THERE IS NO FEAR AS ONE SEES THE EARTH RECEDING FROM UNDER THE BALLOON

A WINTER ASCENSION AT WEST POINT, NEW YORK

broken cord had much to do with causing the death of Paul Nocquet. Wausher forgot his knife when he made an ascension last spring, and when he landed in the marshes the bag collapsed over him and he could not free himself from the rigging. Only the speed of our boat saved him from death, for he was unconscious from the escaping gas when I reached him. It was a defective wire holding the bamboo stays of the aeroplane in place which, giving way in mid-air, caused the frame to snap and dropped Israel Ludlow a thousand feet to the ground at Ormond Beach last winter and broke his back.

It takes hours to inflate the balloon, but there is plenty of work to do as the gas slowly lifts the limp bag and spreads it out into a firm sphere. When it is tense and tugs at the numerous sand-bags the car is made ready, slipped under, and attached. All is tested again and the navigator steps in, the bags are let loose, one by one, the assistants hang on for a minute, then let go, and soon the earth is far behind.

There is no fear as one sees the earth receding from under the balloon—at least there was none with me. At the height of a few hundred feet a sense of tranquillity comes over one, and actual happiness, which increases with the distance from the earth,

begins to be felt. The atmospheric pressure which the man on the earth is all the time enduring diminishes as the balloon rises in the air. Physical and mental exhilaration follows. The muscles seem harder, the heart beats with more ease, and there is a sense of lightness and freedom that cannot be easily described. At the same time there is an awakening of the mentality. The senses are keener. Perception is increased; one thinks more quickly, and the thoughts are more exalted. The amount of nervous energy which one expends while in the air is enormous. It is not appreciated, of course, until the earth is reached again. But then the effects are severe and often lasting.

The wonderful sensations experienced in the air are, to a great extent, compensated for by the depression which follows the descent. The sensation is similar to that of coming out of a caisson where one has been under the pressure of many atmospheres. As is generally known, it is dangerous to come suddenly from under a heavy air-pressure out into a normal atmosphere. In a rapid descent in a balloon something like the same sensations are experienced. In a trip I made in August I dropped to the ground with terrific rapidity from an altitude of ten thousand feet. I had gone up early in the morning, with my brother, after having been out for several hours with the balloon the night before. Leakage overnight, while the balloon had been tied to a tree, had considerably deflated it, but I counted upon the sun expanding the gas, as it always does, and the bag being therefore well filled again.

We had reached the high altitude above mentioned and were sailing along rather aimlessly when we suddenly struck a cold current of air and immediately began to fall. We dropped through clouds which chilled and contracted the gas still more, and shot down as fast as a partially inflated balloon can fall. We were tearing down faster than sand could fall, for when we threw a little out, it seemed to shoot up-ward, and pieces of paper that we let go were apparently whirled above us. To make things worse we were landing over a forest, which also had a cooling effect. When but a short distance from the ground I let go what ballast we had, which of course affected the speed of the descent, but nevertheless we crashed through the tops of the trees, tearing the limbs off as we went, and landed with considerable force on the ground.

It was necessary for my brother to get out and for me to dispose of everything I could before the balloon would rise again high enough to be brought down in a place where it could be safely deflated.

One of the strangest sensations that the balloonist experiences is that of being lost

DR. THOMAS, MRS. THOMAS, AND THEIR SON READY FOR AN AERIAL EXCURSION

A BALLOON RACE AT MADRID STARTING FROM THE AERO CLUB'S GROUNDS

AN ENGLISH WAR-BALLOON ASCENDING FROM THE PARADE-GROUNDS AT ALDERSHOT

in a fog. The absolute separation which one feels at that time cannot be duplicated in any other human experience. At such a time there is no calculating of position. The statoscope tells whether the balloon is rising or falling, but beyond that there is no way of knowing east or west, north or south. When one can see, the drag rope, extending three hundred feet below the car, will tell by its swaying which way the balloon is proceeding. But in a fog this, of course, cannot be seen. The knowledge of the direction in which a balloon is drifting is of extreme importance to those who are in it.

The sea is the great danger of the aeronaut. It is the one dread thing that is always before him. The peril of being blown out over the ocean or other large body of water is ever in his mind, and he is constantly calculating his position with this thought in view. To be lost in a fog, then, exposes him to his greatest enemy. The balloon has a tendency to revolve, and one cannot long keep any sense of direction in his head. The compass is likewise useless, placing the aerial navigator at the mercy of the unfelt wind. In this situation there are sounds which resemble those of the sea, and occasionally the fog seems to part and open up the awful deep. It is strange how a man can face such moments with merely a fleeting sense of fear. What it would be to find oneself over the ocean can be easily imagined. Yet even when the terrible conviction comes, that below the fog is water, it is accepted, in the exalted state a man's mind is in when high in the air, without disturbance, and the result is watched for with perfect tranquillity. It is something like a man eating just before he is hung; or the calmness with which a person can look down the barrel of a revolver in the hand of his enemy.

I remember we were lost in a fog on the long trip we took a few months ago when we landed near the coast of the Atlantic Ocean in Massachusetts. It lasted for hours. At times we could hear water under us, but did not know whether it was a river that would be able to do us little harm if we landed in it or the unfathomable ocean that would mean death if we ever touched it. There is nothing for the balloonist to do in such a situation. If he fears that he is over the sea, he must stay up as long as he can or until the fog breaks and possibly relieves

THE SHADOW CAST BY DR. THOMAS'S BALLOON ON A LONG ISLAND FARM—THIS PHOTOGRAPH WAS MADE BY DR. THOMAS FROM THE CAR OF THE *NIRVANA*

ISRAEL LUDLOW SAILING SKYWARD IN HIS AERO-
PLANE OVER THE HUDSON RIVER

THE *NIRVANA* IN FULL FLIGHT OVER
LONG ISLAND

his suspense. Several times when I have been in such a position the fog has cleared underneath me in such a way as to make me believe that I was over the great wide ocean with all of its terrible possibilities.

But far more wonderful than the fog or the loveliness of the cloudland which looks like great white mountains floating around in space, and more impressive even than the broad expanse of land on a clear and sunny day, is the storm. To be in the lightning, to have it above and below, to hear the thunder crash about me, to see the clouds condense and the moisture gather on

Copyright, 1906, by H. C. White Co.

AN ASCENSION AT THE PORTLAND EXPOSITION

the bag of the balloon and fall down the sides until it was a perfect spout, pouring down on my head—this was an experience I once had that lasted for fourteen and a half hours. The storm was so grand that in its horror it failed to terrorize. The lightning was not forked nor in streaks; there would simply be an opening up of blue flame which extended on all sides and cannot be described by anything except the old-fashioned idea of hell. The electricity was so prevalent that the ropes snapped as I touched them. Yet the very fact that I was immediately in the storm with the lightning completely surrounding me, prevented the gas-bag from exploding, as it would have done had a match been touched to it.

But it is neither in the storm nor in the unusual manifestations of the forces of the air that the real pleasure of a balloon trip is found. It is, rather, in the sailing over the earth where the city and the country can be seen as a bird sees them, watching the rivers that look like threads and the mountains that are mere playthings below, and being in a way a master of space as man in all the ages has not been. And this is the exquisite joy

AN ASCENSION FROM THE BRONX GAS-WORKS, NEW YORK—DR. THOMAS AND CHARLES LEVEE IN THE CAR

of the balloonist, that he can claim to have found a sport with which none other can compare.

Interest in ballooning has been much stimulated by the very successful long-distance race held last September under the auspices of the Aero Club of Paris. Sixteen contestants started, and there were no mishaps. The winner was Lieut. Frank P. Lahm, of the Sixth U. S. Cavalry. In his balloon, the *United States*, he covered the distance of four hundred and fifteen miles between Paris and Fylingdale, Yorkshire, England, in twenty-six hours and fifteen minutes.

A CAPTIVE BALLOON WITH A CARGO OF SOCIETY FOLK—THE MOST MODERN FORM OF SOCIAL AMUSEMENT

7.
Bird Flight and Air-Navigation (1910)

BIRD-FLIGHT AND AIR-NAVIGATION

BY T. R. MacMECHEN AND CARL DIENSTBACH

Authors of "The Aërial Battleship," "Fighting in the Air," "The Dirigible of To-day"

AIR-NAVIGATION has made its greatest advance toward actual mastery of the elements through a discovery by Professor Ernest Huebner, the German naturalist, that migrating birds never cross the seas and oceans except on storm-currents and sometimes on the storms themselves. His investigations also show that the bird determines from the wind's direction when to start on its single flight over-water. Storm-paths and ballooning experience have both shown that these currents have tremendous velocity, and a sustained directness that guides the bird to its destination. Huebner found that bird-flight is not affected by temperature, sunshine, rain, snow, or ice; nothing but a sudden blizzard from an adverse quarter, or a fog, compels the bird to seek refuge on islands or the nearest mainland. In Germany, these facts have given the key to air-navigation, and there it is believed that air craft will soon navigate with the aid of the storm's force, which before had been thought necessarily to interfere with air-travel.

The tiny German redbreast, a typical bird of passage, which migrates across the Baltic in October, was the subject of Professor Huebner's investigations, which were carried on at Stralsund, in Germany, on the Baltic, where many parks, ponds, and gardens enabled observers to check closely the bird's movements. From 1899 to 1901, the stations were on Rügen Island. In October of 1902, five stations covered forty-three miles east and west of Stralsund, and one on the promontory of Thiessow, where redbreasts arrived from over the sea. Other stations were on Rügen Island, and in the forests of Elmenhorst, Abshagen, and Schillemmin, all west of the city. In 1903, more comprehensive observations were conducted with Stralsund as the center of a cross, the north and south arms of which had twelve, while the east and west arms had eight stations.

It was found, by a rigid comparison of the birds' movements with the weather-map that their flights were invariably started by winds emanating from two kinds of air-wheels, which meteorology distinguishes as cyclones and anti-cyclones, working together. Cyclone is simply the scientific name for the atmospheric disturbance commonly called a storm; while the anti-cyclone, or mass of high air-pressure, may also be described as an aërial merry-go-round, cooling and clearing the atmosphere by scattering whirling winds that drive clouds, moisture, birds, and balloons from its vicinity. In another region, a low pressure will start an eddy that becomes a widening whirlpool, and drains the atmosphere within an area of hundreds of miles. Ballooning experience has recently established the fact that air flows with increasing speed from a high toward a low pressure, wherever these foul-weather or fair-weather storms are carried from west to east by the prevailing planetary drift in the Northern Hemisphere.

BIRDS NAVIGATE THE CYCLONES

DURING the whole period of observation, the redbreasts never came from over the

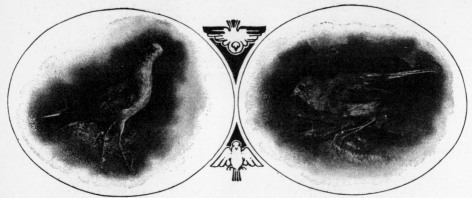

From specimens in the American Museum of Natural History

AMERICAN GOLDEN PLOVER
This bird flies in storm-currents from Nova Scotia to South America.

GERMAN REDBREAST
Though no larger than a canary, it crosses the Baltic in a cyclonic current.

Baltic except with the storms themselves, or on high winds blowing from anti-cyclones in Scandinavia toward storm-centers in southern Germany or France. In the second instance, the bird virtually coasts with increasing speed from a high to a low air-pressure. But as surely as that great autumn storm, the "Fall Low," set across the Baltic, countless thousands of redbreasts arrived almost simultaneously with the storm. It was obvious that the winds had carried the birds over the water at high speed. Though as small as a canary, the redbreasts at no time seemed fatigued by the distance of this single flight, for if the storm-current ceased immediately after their arrival, the birds continued to fly about in the ordinary winds; but if, on landing, the storm-current continued in their vicinity, they at once stopped flying and sought shelter. To the air-navigator this proved that the birds do not employ the strongest winds except for the purpose of traveling long distances.

What is true of weak birds like the redbreasts is equally true of strong birds, as shown by Professor C. C. Trowbridge of Columbia University, who for fifteen years has noticed that hawks in autumn migrate on winds from a northwest quarter. It is well known that north and northwest winds are directly due to storm-centers to the eastward. With these winds, the hawks drift southeastward to the coastline of Connecticut, and continue their flight along the shore. The birds pass westward flying against the wind to New York and New Jersey, where they can

again fly southward, with the aid of the favorable wind. Fifty years ago, Professor John Wise, the balloonist, sailed out over the ocean on the upper current, and returned to land on the lower current. In January, 1910, the French aviator Paulhan, in an aëroplane, used these currents between Santa Catalina Island and the California coast. Professor Trowbridge noticed that the southward flight of hawks stopped suddenly when the storm-current ceased. After a week of southerly winds or a calm, a second wind from the northwest always brought a second flight of many hawks. A wind from the same quarter for three days rarely produced a flight on the third day. It was found that the wind not only changed the line of the hawks' flight, but was the immediate cause of their travel. The birds migrated only on days when the wind was favorable. When the wind blew more or less across the line of travel, the hawks made decided deviations in the course of their southward journey, which usually began after September 5, and lasted from fifteen days to a month.

That winds control flight has been shown by the fact that birds that do not usually fly over water are sometimes carried far seaward. October 11, 1900, five hawks came aboard the steamer *Curitiba* five hundred miles northeast of Florida. The following day two more hawks arrived. October 10, at 8 A.M., the weather bureau at Cape Hatteras gave the wind as north, 28 miles an hour; and October 11, north, 11 miles an hour. Records at

Cay Lobos Lighthouse, Bahama Islands, show that from August, 1900, to May, 1901, specimens of migrating birds were caught on every night that the wind was favorable to the direction of bird-travel at that season. On the nights of October 20 and November 20 the wind was from the northeast. March 15 and 21, and April 15 and May 13, during the north-bound spring travel, the greatest variety of birds passed the light. On three of these dates the wind was from the south-east.

AIR-SHIPS WILL TRAVEL WITH CYCLONES

CYCLONIC currents being navigable, human intelligence, with its superior equipment, eventually should far surpass the bird's capabilities. Even at present, German air-ships fly with increasing speed from the vicinity of a high to that of a low pressure. The air-pilot understands that his ship, when meeting a storm, can travel with tremendous speed on the side of the cyclone that is moving directly toward the air-ship's destination; for since German air-ships now receive wireless weather-bulletins that fix their positions in reference to the movements of the air, they should at least equal the ocean ship, whose navigator "rides the cyclone," as using its storm-currents for fast sailing is sometimes called in maritime navigation. The air-ship has the advantage of being immersed in the element that it is navigating; therefore its wireless equipment, which furnishes news of the winds, should be more serviceable at times than even its own high-powered motors. That the redbreast arrives at its destination on the cyclone shows that such a frail creature's motive energy enables it to avoid being spun around in the center of the storm's eddies. A balloon, without engine or rudder, cannot be prevented from traveling in a circle or a semi-circle, and coming back on its course, unless directed by a master pilot. Yet the air-navigator's near mastery of the cyclone is foreshadowed by the fact that a few balloon pilots already understand the meteorological laws of the air.

In the international race for the Bennett Cup in 1907, Major Henry B. Hersey, Inspector of the United States Weather Service, in deliberately navigating cyclonic currents, steered his balloon for 756 miles in a course, which he said, before starting, he would follow, and did not deviate from calculations intended for a 1400-mile flight across Lake Michigan and down the St. Lawrence valley, ending at the ocean. From St. Louis he coasted north on a lower current flowing from high pressures in the south and east toward a storm-center then starting from British Columbia across southern Canada. As the balloon slowly rose, the approaching influence of the high eastward drift caused it to describe a curve to the northeast. In Illinois, when on a line with Chicago, this bird-like pilot required no wireless bulletins to notify him that the storm-center had traveled east, and was then nearly north of his position. To keep abreast of it until well north of the lakes, he suddenly changed the course to east by

From a photograph by Herbert K. Job

A HERRING-GULL

Aëronauts have studied the poise and flight of this bird in arriving at the principles of air-navigation.

quickly ascending into the east drift, where he flew at a speed of forty-three miles an hour over Chicago, Lake Michigan, Lake St. Clair, passing between lakes Huron and Erie and out over Lake Erie. The sun was sinking, a time of day when sea and lake breezes blow strongly inland, and

A GERMAN MARINE GUN WHICH CAN BE USED AGAINST AIR-SHIPS
The position of the gun shows the extreme elevation at which guns on men-of-war can be fired into the air.

Major Hersey dropped into this breeze, and was blown back to land; but at the western end of Lake Ontario, lack of ballast forbade further flight over water.

In the same race it was proved that while cyclones were controlling the lower air-currents, direct travel in the upper levels was not interrupted. Oscar Erbsloh of Germany and H. H. Clayton, the American meteorologist, steered a calcu-

lated course toward New England by remaining in the currents just under a mile, but lost their direction while crossing the Alleghanies, and landed on the New Jersey coast. Their rivals, Alfred Leblanc, the French pilot, and Edgar W. Mix, who accompanied Leblanc, drifted almost directly east in the currents above a mile, and landed on the ocean's brink, only six miles from the German victors.

FLYING FROM NOVA SCOTIA TO SOUTH AMERICA

THE distance traversed by the redbreast, though great for the bird's size, is trifling when compared with the thousands of miles covered in a single flight by birds hardly larger. The exhibit that attracted the greatest attention at the Aëronautical Exposition at Frankfort, Germany, in the summer of 1909, was the large map of the Northern Hemisphere, showing a broad, red ribbon down the middle of the Atlantic Ocean from Nova Scotia to South America. That ribbon marked the 2500-mile migratory flight annually made by the American golden plover. Air-navigators from all over the world gazed with wonder at this map, because it indicated that the bird flies all that distance directly across the mighty west-to-east drift of the air. This was regarded as an "eye-opener" as to what air-ships may soon accomplish. The plover's movements have been closely traced by field naturalists of the United States Biological Survey from their Northern haunts to Guatemala, assisted by hundreds of ornithologists all over the country. Every spring and autumn their reports give records of when the birds are first seen and when they disappear from each locality. Also, lighthouse-keepers provide records of the birds while they are flying along the coasts and over the water. Wells W. Cooke of the Biological Survey, in the official report of 1905, states that plovers start from Nova Scotia, and take a course over the Atlantic for the eastern-most islands of the West Indies, 1800 miles away, and 600 miles more to the eastern coast of South America. The Bermudas, 800 miles from Nova Scotia, are the only land along the route. When the winds continue to be favorable, they fly past the Bermudas, and, indeed, are often seen by vessels 400 miles or more east of those islands. On sighting their first land

From a German photograph

A CAPTIVE TARGET BALLOON HIT BY A SHELL

The trail of smoke left by the shell is produced to indicate its trajectory, so that the aim of the gun may be corrected, if necessary, at the next fire. This device is expected to facilitate accurate fire in a fight between air-ships.

in the Antilles, the flocks often do not pause, but keep on to the larger islands farther south, and sometimes to South America. There the flocks again disappear, and later their arrival is reported in Brazil and in the whole prairie region of the Argentine Republic almost down to Patagonia, where they remain from September until March. Returning, they cross the Gulf of Mexico to Texas, and thence overland at a more leisurely pace to their breeding-grounds at the arctic circle.

The aëronautical staff of the University of Göttingen has recently adopted the observations of F. W. Lanchester, the English engineer, an accepted authority on aërodynamics, that plovers, turnstones, or curlews, and more especially redbreasts, cannot fly thousands of miles by their own exertions. Though their power to rise is greater than that of larger birds, they meet with much greater resistance in flying fast, even folding their wings to become smaller; and flying in leaps and bounds, as

A GERMAN FIELD-PIECE FOR FIRING AT AIR-SHIPS

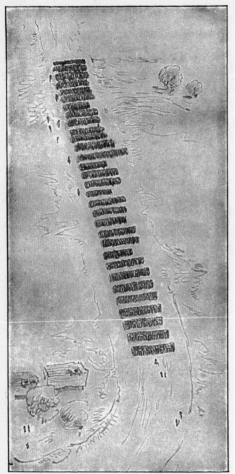

Redrawn from a book issued by the Aëro clubs of Germany

A REGIMENT OF MARCHING SOLDIERS AS
PHOTOGRAPHED FROM AN AIR-SHIP

This picture shows that soldiers in formation will prove
an easy mark to air-ship artillery.

by the sighting of pilot balloons and kites, have established beyond dispute that while at the ground the wind usually blows fifteen miles an hour, it increases at the rate of three fifths of a mile for every 330 feet above the earth. C. Dixon, the English authority on bird-flight, says that, since the dotterel, which breeds in arctic Euro-Asia and winters in Africa, is scarcely ever seen during its spring travel, ornithologists believe that this flight of 2000 miles is performed without rest between sunset and sunrise. "If the dotterel starts from its African haunts, say, at 7 P.M., it would reach the arctic moors, by flying 200 miles an hour, at about five the following morning." Herr G. Gaetke, the German naturalist at Helgoland, has recorded that plovers and curlews travel 22,000 feet, or four miles, in one minute.

It is a matter of common knowledge that the winds at great heights have carried balloons with tremendous speed. In 1857, John Wise, in his balloon Atlantic, traveled seventy miles an hour. During the siege of Paris, a balloon drifted from Paris to Norway in one night. That the instinct of birds enables them to base their migrating flights on the highest winds also gives promise of remarkable speed for air-ships driven by motors, and steered by pilots advised by wireless, and having a perfect understanding of the wind situation. "Yea, the stork in the heaven knoweth her appointed times; and the turtle and the crane and the swallow observe the time of their coming."[1] On Helgoland, that "semaphore-station" of bird-travel, there is a saying, "Time gone by, birds gone by," which means that if certain birds are not seen at their usual time, they have passed unnoticed, and will not be seen that season. Still, it has been noticed that when the barometer was falling there was a rush of birds; hence in many countries it has been possible to foretell the weather by watching the birds.

THE BIRD AS A METEOROLOGIST — HE
PICKS WINDS TO GUIDE HIS FLIGHT

On their voyages over the open sea, there is nothing but the winds to guide the birds. How this may be done, has been shown by N. E. de Cyon, a French scientist, in a careful experiment disproving that a mysterious sixth sense of locality resides in the

seen in the wavering flight. Lanchester says that no bird can fly more than fifty miles an hour by its own energy, and therefore that tremendous migrating speed is made only on the swiftest winds. Apparently the plover is not on the wing much longer than twenty-four hours, and is compelled to make the highest speed over the ocean. Above a mile, even at the wind's normal speed of thirty-six miles an hour, the plover, which is built like a race-horse, can fly at least seventy-six miles an hour between Nova Scotia and South America, and much faster in storm-currents.

Measurements of moving clouds, and

[1] Jeremiah viii, 7.

From "Aëronautics"

THE ZEPPELIN III SWOOPING AT FRANKFORT-ON-THE-MAIN

This manœuver, photographed during the Frankfort Aëronautical Exposition, in 1909, foreshadows
the tactics of an air-ship in time of war.

ear of the birds. The ears of a young homing-pigeon and the nostrils of another were tightly sealed, cocaine being applied to prevent the bird from feeling the cotton wad. Care was taken that the breathing should not be interfered with. A third pigeon was left free. Blindfolded, the pigeons, in a dark basket, were transported 300 miles to a strange place. All flew briskly away. In a few hours the free bird, and scarcely later the deaf bird, arrived at their haunt. Two days later the pigeon that had its nostrils closed reached the cote. It was nearly starved, but its nostrils were open. The bird, bewildered, had failed to find its way when the air could not strike its nose. Evidently the bird gets its bearings from the air itself, for it cannot see far enough for guidance. Its nostrils first catch the wind. The delicate membranes, acting as barometer, hygrometer, and thermometer should instantly register any change in the moisture, the temperature, the weight, or the vibration of the current. This should enable the bird to tell when the wind is no longer uniform. Now, an air-navigator, with his still imperfect knowledge of the air, has learned that any change in moisture and temperature means a sudden shifting in the direction and speed of an air-current. It is evident that the bird does not lose the wind in which it wants to travel. The

tattler, the sanderling, the turnstone, and the pintail annually travel from islands in Bering Sea, over the Pacific, to the Hawaiian and Fanning Islands, a distance of 2200 miles, which must be made in a single flight. The slightest deviation in the course at the point of departure would make the birds miss the Hawaiian Islands. Of course the birds must make their way over the ocean with the precision of a rifle-bullet and at tremendous speed.

The plover needs the same localizing faculty to accomplish the feat of crossing the strong west-to-east planetary drift. This could not be done unless navigable lanes were opened by the cyclones. They are the switches that shift the aërial trackage. Many balloonists have learned that this switching of the air-currents is as systematic as any railroad terminal yard. Cyclones completely control the winds up to a mile. While the lower winds veer almost directly toward the storm's path, the planetary circulation above a mile is deflected only a few degrees from its regular course. Up beyond two miles the air-drift is too strong for interference. Cyclones happen all the year in temperate latitudes; but in the tropics tempests generally occur at the time of the plover's great flight in late August; therefore the air is carried toward the equator at tremendous speed. The currents between one and

Drawn by W. T. Benda.   Half-tone plate engraved by C W. Chadwick

THE SWOOP OF AN AIR-SHIP WHILE FIRING MACHINE GUNS AT ARTILLERY

two miles, in which the bird often flies, are turned south; those underneath a mile are flowing southwest. Abreast of the Bermudas the bird can drop into the winds nearer the earth. These are being pulled more directly toward the storm as it approaches the ocean. A descent shifts the traveler's course more toward South America. In other words, a voyager would then be flying in air that was being drained with great rapidity toward the storm-center. If the cyclone were met in the gulf, it might be used for a fast-turning movement into the Antilles, which are the bird's stepping-stones to the continent. If a cyclone arrived at the ocean ahead of the bird, it could stay aloft in the currents above a mile, where the storm had less effect, dropping into the trade-winds afterward. Then the remaining short stretch of tropical sea having no adverse winds, the sturdy plover would be independent of the assistance of favorable winds. This is exactly what an air-ship will do when navigating between the two Americas.

BIRDS AS TEACHERS OF AËRIAL WARFARE

THE bird's art in mastering the air has become vitally important in creating that new element in international politics—air-power. Aërial battle-ships must not only be perfectly navigated to gain strategic positions to the windward of an enemy, but practice has shown that birds even point the way to aggressive tactics in aërial warfare. Herr Gaetke says:

The way birds descend from the sky is striking; many precipitate themselves with a rushing sound like a sky-rocket and with almost incredible speed. First, a black dot is seen; almost at the same second, it shoots past in the form of a bird. On turning the head, the bird is noticed quietly skimming over the ground or resting. In the darkness, at the Heligoland lighthouses, birds are sometimes impaled on lightning-rods, and found skewered through the breast and back.

A hawk, attacking a chicken, folds its wings while high above the ground, and drops like a bullet on its prey, for the same reason that tigers and lions, after stealing upon their victims, pounce on them in one irresistible leap. These tactics prevent flight or defense. Animals that are the natural quarry of birds of prey seem to have a dread of any object hovering above them. Instinct evidently warns them that the suddenness of such an attack is almost always overwhelming. Mr. Dienstbach suggests that the swoop will be the most effective feature of the tactics of aërial warfare.

The Wrights, Paulhan, and Latham have found that while descending from great heights their flying-machines involuntarily swoop. One of Paulhan's passengers recently said that coming down was "awful—like shooting the chutes." The more conservative Wrights have tried to check this speed of descent. To avoid swooping, Orville Wright made a spiralized descent when ending his highest flights over Potsdam in the summer of 1909. But the high-fliers, Paulhan and Latham, make a practice of swooping from great altitudes. Paulhan, who is less of the daredevil than the far-seeing aviator, found that the very force of the plunge sends the aëroplane up again when the rudders are manipulated near the ground, lifting the machine's front edges.

In swooping, an aëroplane's supporting planes, instead of being driven at an inclination against the air, cut downward like a knife. In cutting swiftly through the air, the machine does not yield except in the direction of its flight, any more than a knife yields sidewise in cutting through cheese. Birds that swoop have no advantage, for an aëroplane, driven on a downward slant by propellers, would of course develop greater speed than a body falling by its own weight. Then, a swooping aëroplane might attack like a dirigible bullet from the height of a mile while flying a horizontal distance of two miles. In thirty seconds it could descend on men at the ground before they realized that they were the objects of attack. During the entire descent one machine-gun could fire four hundred shots a minute. In France, machine-guns have been mounted on the military Antoinette aëroplanes. Near the enemy, bombs may be released at the instant the flying-machine makes its upward sweep. In the recent exhibitions at Los Angeles, Lieutenant Foulois threw counterfeit bombs with deadly aim from a height of 200 feet.

Though an aëroplane's swoop will be irresistible, the attack cannot cover much space, owing to its essentially limited capacity for carrying ammunition. A squadron of aëroplanes would be nearly as easy to hit with volleys as a covey of ducks with a shot-gun. Many aëroplanes might get into one another's way. Therefore, the greatest damage may be inflicted by the air-ship, because of its capacity for mounting twenty or more machine-guns, in addition to light cannon, bombs, and torpedoes. In 1909, it became known that Krupp had invented a light, semi-automatic cannon, with a caliber of one and two thirds inches, and sixty shots a minute, for arming the Zeppelin air-ship, from which it was successfully fired; and that Krupp had also acquired the rights to the Unge aërial torpedo and tube, the invention of a Swedish artillery officer. This torpedo can be launched with an initial velocity of 164 feet a second, quickly increasing by the law of fall to 656 feet a second, making the missile strike like a shell. In the same year the invention of the Maxim "silencer" stopped the noise, and extinguished the flash of firearms, thus permitting large gas-inflated air-ships to carry guns and make the most destructive swoop.

THE ZEPPELINS BORE THE AIR

VISITORS to the Frankfort Aëronautical Exposition in 1909 were astonished at seeing the Zeppelin air-ship dipping its bow and rushing down to land in half the time of the non-rigid Parseval air-ship, which had to descend in spirals. On another occasion, over Lake Constance, the Zeppelin plunged so rapidly that spectators believed they were witnessing a disastrous chute. Though it does not cut through the air like a knife or an aëroplane, a rigid air-ship can bore the air like a punch. A needle-like Zeppelin, when permitted to fall headforemost from a great height, would plunge like a bullet, if its weight were only slightly heavier than its buoyancy. A round balloon often falls with fatal rapidity when it becomes only a little heavier than the air it displaces. A Zeppelin, driven on a downward slant, can be made to behave like an aëroplane. The air-ship might swoop so suddenly toward the ground that an enemy would be annihilated by the end-on fire from some twenty machine-guns, which could be mounted in small sponsons around the larger Zeppelin's waist of 250 feet. But in descending at high speed from a height of more than a mile, where the air-ship is virtually beyond range, it would be exposed to fire for the shortest time. An eagle swoops so suddenly on a cat that the prey fails to locate the point from which to expect the attack. For the same reason, men upon whom an air-craft might swoop with the eagle's speed would fail to fire efficiently. This situation would be similar to a cavalry charge, the nature of the surprise preventing the directing and concentrating of the fire on an aërial foe. Under the most favorable conditions, cavalry requires more than a minute to deliver a charge. In comparison, the air-craft will swoop like a falling stone.

ATTACKS MADE WITH THE WIND

SUCH an attack might be made with a favorable wind at a speed of 100 miles an hour. From a steady air-ship, moving at that speed, long-range guns could be fired with more exactness than from a destroyer running thirty-two knots an hour. Thus the swoop seems destined to become vastly superior to any similar attack in land- or sea-fighting, whether a charge by cavalry or by a torpedo-boat. When surprised, an enemy's discomfiture should become intolerable, because of the leaden hail beginning with the inception of the swoop, and increasing furiously during the entire advance. Aiming back might then become highly improbable. In a few seconds one machine-gun could concentrate a tremendous fire, which suggests that this weapon is an ideal one for the swoop. In Germany, two machine-rifles are regarded as equaling the concentrated rapid fire of 200 expert marksmen. Again, guns on an air-craft need not be carefully aimed, because the shots will all fly in the direction of the advance. To increase the possibility of hitting, the modern manufacturer of rifles strives to make the bullets travel in nearly a straight line, instead of in an arc. It goes without saying that on an air-ship any gun will send its bullets downward in a straight line. It is equally evident that the gunners would see to aim behind any cover, observe the effect of their shots, and, if necessary, correct them. A large, inflammable air-ship would not swoop so close to the enemy as the aëroplane, its heavier guns reaching farther. Like the flying-machine, its momentum will send it up out of danger as fast as the advance. Two light, quick-firing cannon, swiveled in turrets in the extreme bow and stern, would be well adapted for both the swoop and its recession. Of course the entire military situation will be spread out beneath the air-ship like the pawns on a chess-board, so that the craft may always swoop upon any place at the most propitious moment.

STRIKING VITALLY WITHOUT RISK

Air-craft, flying out of range at great height, may easily get in an enemy's rear, and then, with no risk, by suddenly swooping, annihilate all food and ammunition transports, camps, and marching columns. Tests by observations from balloons have indicated that men on the ground are excellent marks. Instead of one file concealing many files behind, all the files become visible at once. A single man, though as small as a dot, can be hit, because a machine-gun has the same effect as a shotgun. This point should offset any possibility that a slanting fire will fail to score chance hits far behind the target. The appearance of an air-craft far above would cause nearly as much terror and confusion as a hawk above a barn-yard. Hitting the air-ship would be difficult, because, while swooping end-on, it would show only its prow, eighty feet in diameter, armored with a bullet-proof cloth that has been invented and successfully tested in public by Dowe, a German. The size of the air-ship's prow does not increase at the rate at which a larger air-ship provides greater lifting capacity for armor and guns.

Shooting on land, under the same conditions that should always prevail in the air, has established the superiority of "dominating" fire. Batteries on elevations that overlook strongholds have inevitably compelled capitulation. This was the repeated story of Ticonderoga, Sedan, and Port Arthur.

8.
The Menace of
Aerial Warfare
(1909)

THE MENACE OF AËRIAL WARFARE

ALL GREAT NATIONS ARE PREPARING FOR IT—GREAT BRITAIN AS
EXPOSED AS ANY OTHER COUNTRY TO SUCH ATTACK—THE
UNITED STATES MUST PREPARE FOR AËRIAL DEFENSE—PROBABLE
INCIDENTS OF AËRIAL ATTACK, AND CONFLICTS IN THE SKY

BY HENRY B. HERSEY [1]

Inspector, United States Weather Bureau

WHEN, a few weeks ago, Sir Hiram Maxim, in a lecture which he delivered before the Society of Arts in London, arraigned the British nation for its lack of interest in the possibilities of aërial warfare, he made the cold shivers run up and down the British spine, and it is safe to say that our transatlantic cousins have been doing a lot of thinking about it since. At first some of the military and naval authorities were inclined to make light of Sir Hiram's warnings, but in view of his eminence as an inventor and scientist, one not given to wild imaginings, but a practical, hard-headed, logical thinker and analyst, they must admit the threatening attitude, if not the gravity, of the situation. Isolated by seas from all foes, their shipping protected in all quarters of the globe by the frowning *Dreadnaughts* of a navy whose strength, according to plan, must exceed that of the combined navies of any two possible enemies, they have felt a sense of security. But now a new danger in war arises against which they are not prepared. These silent cruisers of the air, hovering like vultures over cities, harbors, and fortifications, dealing, with hawk-like swiftness, death and destruction, and then disappearing as suddenly, only to strike some other unexpected point, are most certainly a menace which must be taken into account.

England alone of all the great European powers has done but little experimentation with aërial war-craft. Yet she is of all nations the most threatened by the recent inventions and improvements in aërial work, because she has depended largely for security on her splendid isolation, protected by her powerful navy. Now she realizes that this isolation cannot be maintained against aërial attack by any present means of defense, and that such defense must be prepared in the form of a fleet of air-cruisers.

Great Britain's situation gives point to the question of the possibilities of aërial attack on this country in case of war, and of what should be done that we may be properly prepared to meet such attack. Our needs are not so pressing as those of England because we have no such powerful neighbors near enough for aërial expeditions to be started out from their own countries as a base of operations.

Still, in any future war two general plans of attack will be open to our antagonists. Bases of operations could be established in Canada or Mexico, either by agreement or force, from which aërial fleets could be operated; also aërial sorties could be made ·from ships fitted up specially for the purpose. With a suitable base established in the vicinity of Montreal, attacks by dirigible balloons of the Zeppelin type could be made on Boston, or New York, or the inland cities of the

[1] Major Hersey's voyages by balloon across the English Channel and in the St. Louis balloon contest are described in his illustrated paper "Experiences in the Sky," printed in THE CENTURY for March, 1908. See also Edmund Clarence Stedman's paper on aërial navigation as a menace to British supremacy, "The Prince of the Power of the Air," in THE CENTURY for May, 1908.—THE EDITOR.

nearby States. From bases in Canada located along the Great Lakes, Buffalo, Detroit, Chicago, Milwaukee, and Duluth could be reached, while British Columbia would afford a good point from which Seattle and Portland could be threatened. Such attacks are not visionary, but actually could be made with a reasonable chance of success with dirigible balloons now in the hands of some of the European nations.

And if not used for independent attack, war-balloons would become formidable additions to an army invading this country from Canada or Mexico. They would not only act as scouts, securing complete information of the location and movements of the defending armies, but could join in an attack, especially on fortifications, by dropping aërial torpedoes inside lines of defense, exploding magazines, and dealing death in all directions among the defenders. The moral effect of such an attack during a battle would be tremendous and hard to overcome.

To much the same effect, attacks might be made from aëronautic ships accompanying battle fleets. These ships are now being added to all the principal European navies except the British. Germany has two converted aëronautic transports, and another large one is being built specially for this work. This one is so planned that the masts, smokestacks, and other upper works, will not interfere with the inflation of large dirigible balloons or the launching into the air of aëroplanes. It will be fitted with the finest apparatus for producing hydrogen gas rapidly, also with a special arrangement for the storage of an enormous quantity of hydrogen compressed in steel cylinders. These will be connected with pipes running to the deck, so that by turning stop-cocks the gas may flow into the balloon for inflation as rapidly as wished, without disturbing the storage-cylinders. There will be special facilities for storing aëroplanes, and arrangements for assembling them quickly on deck for flight; also complete workshops for repairs and alterations; and, still more important, there will be magazines for storing special aërial torpedoes. This ship will have great speed and will be protected like an armored cruiser.

The Germans have been doing a great amount of experimental work in connection with aërial torpedoes recently. Trials have been made of many different patterns with various kinds of high explosives, dropping them from balloons at different heights at prearranged targets below. They are of course not giving the world the benefit of the experience they have acquired, but the accuracy with which they were able to place the torpedoes on these targets, and the effect of the explosions were such that they have taken up aërial work with renewed energy. The French navy has two converted aëronautic transports and the Italians one. These three nations are the only ones in Europe who are prepared at present to make aërial work an important feature of their navies, but as the indirect result of their enterprise it will be only a comparatively short time before all important navies of other countries are equipped for this work.

Japan has recently placed orders for two ships, one in an English shipyard and the other with a German firm. With genuine Oriental wisdom she has placed the veil of secrecy around these orders, and what they are to be used for can only be guessed, but it has been known for some time in the aëronautic world that Japan, true to her custom in recent years to learn everything new and hold all she finds good, has been anxious to take up aërial work in a thorough and serious manner.

Now, let us consider for a moment the possibilities of an attack on New York city by a war-fleet superior in strength to any which we would have available for defense at the time. It would then be necessary to rely largely on land defenses. If the attacking fleet were accompanied by thoroughly equipped aëronautic transports, dirigibles might be inflated and sent in over our fortifications, dropping torpedoes into them from the sky at the same time that the fleet would be making the attack from the water. Due notice having been given of bombardment, these same dirigibles might sail over the skyscrapers of New York, dropping bombs or torpedoes into the very light-shafts of the proud structures, and wrecking them completely. If the dirigibles should be disabled by shots from the land and destroyed or captured, we should thereby inflict on the enemy a loss of perhaps five men, and possibly a hundred thousand dollars—a loss trivial as compared with the damage done by one explosive dropped from the sky. What is true of New York applies with greater force to San Francisco or Seattle.

All these possibilities are based partly on the supposition that this country would not be prepared for serious aërial warfare. If, however, we were as well prepared as we ought to be within the next few years, the probabilities would be different. At the approach of a hostile fleet, our air-cruisers would be on the alert. Every move of the enemy would be reported, and, as night drew on, our air-craft would hover near, and under cover of darkness make a sudden attack, dropping torpedoes on their ships, perhaps down the smokestacks into the very vitals of the ship, destroying it instantly. Or, if both sides were equipped for aërial battle, the ships of the air might meet in the sky for the death-struggle— and a battle royal it would be. Each would be armed with light guns carrying a bullet or shell which would explode on striking even the silk of the gas-bag and throw fire in all directions. This would ignite the gas in the balloon, causing a terrific explosion and sending the wreckage and crew hurtling through space back to mother-earth, which always receives calmly the wrecks we give her.

So far I have spoken only of the work of dirigible balloons, generally referred to as air-ships, but the simple spherical balloon is of great value for use on naval vessels. It can be inflated and sent to a height of five hundred or a thousand feet as a captive balloon from a ship, with one or two officers in the basket. From this altitude a splendid lookout can be maintained, and being equipped with telephones, any information secured can be promptly communicated to the commander of the fleet. If our fleet at Santiago had been provided with such a balloon and the necessary equipment, it could easily have determined whether the Spanish fleet was in the harbor during that trying period of uncertainty preceding the land operations of the Santiago campaign.

Within the last year another great invention has entered the field of aërial achievement. I refer to the aëroplane, which has attracted the attention of the world by its mechanical flight. Henry Farman, an English resident of Paris, was the first to demonstrate publicly its success; but since then our own Wright brothers of Ohio, who had been able to preserve a degree of secrecy in regard to a long series of experiments, have so far eclipsed the work of all others in this line that they are in a class by themselves. The European governments have promptly taken up this invention. Russia and France through their agents have secured the rights to the patents of the Wright brothers for their respective war departments. How extensive the field is for aëroplanes in military work cannot be determined now, for it must be remembered that their operators are at present only fledglings, mostly standing on the edge of the nest, while a few of the venturesome ones are essaying short flights to strengthen their young pinions, others recovering from the sore bruises of falls, and others lying still in death. But, undaunted, the little band will continue to win success, flight by flight, until the conquest of the air is complete.

Judging from the present outlook, it seems that the field of the aëroplane in military work will be distinct from that of the dirigible balloon. It will not be able to carry great weight, like the dirigible, but it will be much swifter. Being smaller and more compact and requiring no gas-making apparatus, it will be more easily transported. A single supply-ship could carry a whole fleet of them, and they could be quickly put in action. They will probably become the cavalry of the aërial army, while the heavier and more formidable dirigibles will constitute a combination of infantry and artillery.

This country has been backward in aërial work simply because the people have not realized how important a part it will play in the warfare of the future. The European nations appreciate this and are putting forth their greatest efforts to get the best equipment possible and thoroughly to train a large corps of men in the work. Already France and Germany have very respectable fleets of aërial cruisers and are actively training men in the work of handling them. England, Russia, and Italy are all working on the problem. They all realize that in the wars of the future an army or navy not equipped for aërial work will be badly handicapped, if not at the mercy of an enemy having a strong corps of trained men well equipped with modern air-ships. It is not a work that can be taken up when the occasion arises, for it is of a technical nature and can be acquired only by experience.

The Signal Corps, under General James Allen, has charge of this work for our army, and the progress made has been remarkable, considering the small amount of funds available. It is, however, only the beginning. Ample funds should be provided for the construction of at least two large air-cruisers suitable for training-ships. On these, men could be trained thoroughly in the practical work of dropping torpedoes and manœuvering the ship. Some experimental work should be done in the construction of special torpedoes or bombs for use in this work. Different types of large rifles or small cannon with special sights should be devised and thoroughly tried out, with a view to becoming expert in hitting balloons or air-ships in the sky.

The organization of aëronautic corps or detachments in the National Guard should be encouraged, and when such an organization from any State is shown to be ready for active work, regular officers should be detailed temporarily to give them the necessary instructions. At the annual manœuvers where the regulars and the National Guard are brought together for instruction, demonstrations of the working of dirigible and spherical balloons should be provided for, and members of the National Guard should be instructed in handling them. Portable gas-making outfits should be supplied and the men trained in their use. Balloon clubs in different cities should be invited to coöperate, and the names of members becoming

expert in the work should be enrolled on a list of those available for duty as officers in case of war.

For the present the work could be managed to good advantage by the Signal Corps, as it is now being done; but after a few years it would probably be better to have a separate corps devoted entirely to aërial work. We have the best material in the world for the organization of an aërial force, and at present lack only the necessary funds and authority from Congress. To be unprepared is to invite aggression, which may force us into a war costing blood and money beyond estimate. Our navy to-day is proving itself to be one of the greatest peacemakers in the world.

Through the long ages past and gone, man has climbed up slowly step by step from out the dark caverns which formed his home and lair, from which he prowled forth to prey on his weaker neighbors of the animal kingdom. Slowly step by step under patriarch, feudal baron, dukes, and kings, he has advanced in national organization until now he owes allegiance not to his ruler, but to his country. Just so surely will he continue to climb, but always slowly, until he owes allegiance to all his brothers over the earth, and not until then will there be an end of war. But that desired amity is in the distant future. We must be patient and wait for the development that will come to us slowly as it has in the past. As a nation we have only feelings of good-will and friendship toward all our neighbors. We wish for peace; but, as nations exist to-day, to ensure that peace we must be prepared to wage a victorious war, if it be forced upon us.

9.
The Wright Brothers' Aeroplane
(1908)

THE CENTURY MAGAZINE

SEPTEMBER, 1908

THE WRIGHT BROTHERS' AËROPLANE

BY ORVILLE AND WILBUR WRIGHT

WITH PICTURES FROM PHOTOGRAPHS SUPPLIED BY THE AUTHORS

THE article which follows is the first popular account of their experiments prepared by the inventors. Their accounts heretofore have been brief statements of bare accomplishments, without explanation of the manner in which results were attained. The article will be found of special interest, in view of the fact that they have contracted to deliver to the United States Government a complete machine, the trials of which are expected to take place about the time of the appearance of this number of THE CENTURY.— THE EDITOR.

THOUGH the subject of aërial navigation is generally considered new, it has occupied the minds of men more or less from the earliest ages. Our personal interest in it dates from our childhood days. Late in the autumn of 1878, our father came into the house one evening with some object partly concealed in his hands, and before we could see what it was, he tossed it into the air. Instead of falling to the floor, as we expected, it flew across the room till it struck the ceiling, where it fluttered awhile, and finally sank to the floor. It was a little toy, known to scientists as a "hélicoptère," but which we, with sublime disregard for science, at once dubbed a "bat." It was a light frame of cork and bamboo, covered with paper, which formed two screws, driven in opposite directions by rubber bands under torsion. A toy so delicate lasted only a short time in the hands of small boys, but its memory was abiding.

Several years later we began building these hélicoptères for ourselves, making each one larger than that preceding. But, to our astonishment, we found that the larger the "bat," the less it flew. We did not know that a machine having only twice the linear dimensions of another would require eight times the power. We finally became discouraged, and returned to kite-flying, a sport to which we had devoted so much attention that we were regarded as experts. But as we became older, we had to give up this fascinating sport as unbecoming to boys of our ages.

It was not till the news of the sad death of Lilienthal reached America in the summer of 1896 that we again gave more than passing attention to the subject of flying. We then studied with great interest Chanute's "Progress in Flying Machines," Langley's "Experiments in Aërodynamics," the "Aëronautical Annuals" of 1905, 1906, and 1907, and several pamphlets published by the Smithsonian Institution, especially articles by Lilienthal and extracts from Mouillard's "Empire of the Air." The larger works gave us a good understanding of the nature of the flying problem, and the difficulties in past attempts to solve it, while Mouillard and Lilienthal, the great missionaries of the flying cause, infected us with their own unquenchable enthusiasm, and transformed idle curiosity into the active zeal of workers.

In the field of aviation there were two schools. The first, represented by such men as Professor Langley and Sir Hiram Maxim, gave chief attention to power flight; the second, represented by Lilienthal, Mouillard, and Chanute, to soaring flight. Our sympathies were with the latter school, partly from impatience at the wasteful extravagance of mounting delicate and costly machinery on wings which no one knew how to manage, and partly, no doubt, from the extraordinary charm and enthusiasm with which the apostles of soaring flight set forth the beauties of sailing through the air on fixed wings, deriving the motive power from the wind itself.

The balancing of a flyer may seem, at first thought, to be a very simple matter, yet almost every experimenter had found in this the one point which he could not satisfactorily master. Many different methods were tried. Some experimenters placed the center of gravity far below the wings, in the belief that the weight would naturally seek to remain at the lowest point. It was true, that, like the pendulum, it tended to seek the lowest point; but also, like the pendulum, it tended to oscillate in a manner destructive of all stability. A more satisfactory system, especially for lateral balance, was that of arranging the wings in the shape of a

A GLIDING FLIGHT (WITHOUT MOTOR) FROM KILL DEVIL HILL, NEAR
KITTY HAWK, NORTH CAROLINA, OCTOBER 21, 1903

These flights lasted from forty-five seconds to a minute and ten seconds. The inventors'
camp and the ocean are observable in the distance.

ORVILLE WRIGHT   From photographs by Hollinger   WILBUR WRIGHT

broad ⋁, to form a dihedral angle, with the center low and the wing-tips elevated. In theory this was an automatic system, but in practice it had two serious defects: first, it tended to keep the machine oscillating; and, second, its usefulness was restricted to calm air.

In a slightly modified form the same system was applied to the fore-and-aft balance. The main aëroplane was set at a positive angle, and a horizontal tail at a negative angle, while the center of gravity was placed far forward. As in the case of lateral control, there was a tendency to constant undulation, and the very forces which caused a restoration of balance in calms, caused a disturbance of the balance in winds. Notwithstanding the known limitations of this principle, it had been embodied in almost every prominent flying-machine which had been built.

After considering the practical effect of the dihedral principle, we reached the conclusion that a flyer founded upon it might be of interest from a scientific point of view, but could be of no value in a practical way. We therefore resolved to try a fundamentally different principle.

We would arrange the machine so that it would not tend to right itself. We would make it as inert as possible to the effects of change of direction or speed, and thus reduce the effects of wind-gusts to a minimum. We would do this in the fore-and-aft stability by giving the aëroplanes a peculiar shape; and in the lateral balance, by arching the surfaces from tip to tip, just ·the reverse of what our predecessors had done. Then by some suitable contrivance, actuated by the operator, forces should be brought into play to regulate the balance.

Lilienthal and Chanute had guided and balanced their machines by shifting the weight of the operator's body. But this method seemed to us incapable of expansion to meet large conditions, because the weight to be moved and the distance of possible motion were limited, while the disturbing forces steadily increased, both with wing area and with wind velocity. In order to meet the needs of large machines, we wished to employ some system whereby the operator could vary at will the inclination of different parts of the wings, and thus obtain from the wind forces to restore the balance which the wind itself had disturbed. This could easily be done by using wings capable of being warped, and by supplementary adjustable surfaces in the shape of rudders. As the forces obtainable for control would necessarily increase in the same ratio as the disturbing forces, the method seemed capable of expansion to an almost unlimited extent. A happy device was discovered whereby the apparently rigid system of superposed surfaces, invented by Wenham, and improved by Stringfellow and Chanute, could be warped in a most unexpected way, so that the aëroplanes could be presented on the right and left sides at different angles to the wind. This, with an adjustable, horizontal front rudder, formed the main feature of our first glider.

The period from 1885 to 1900 was one of unexampled activity in aëronautics, and for a time there was high hope that the age of flying was at hand. But Maxim, after spending $100,000, abandoned the work; the Ader machine, built at the expense of the French Government, was a failure; Lilienthal and Pilcher were killed in experiments; and Chanute and many others, from one cause or another, had relaxed their efforts, though it subsequently became known that Professor Langley was still secretly at work on a machine for the United States Government. The public, discouraged by the failures and tragedies just witnessed, considered flight beyond the reach of man,

FIRST FLIGHT OF THE WRIGHT BROTHERS' FIRST MOTOR MACHINE,
AT KILL DEVIL HILL, DECEMBER 17, 1903
This picture shows the machine just after lifting from the track, flying against a
wind of twenty-four miles an hour.

and classed its adherents with the inventors of perpetual motion.

We began our active experiments at the close of this period, in October, 1900, at Kitty Hawk, North Carolina. Our machine was designed to be flown as a kite, with a man on board, in winds of from fifteen to twenty miles an hour. But, upon trial, it was found that much stronger winds were required to lift it. Suitable winds not being plentiful, we found it necessary, in order to test the new balancing system, to fly the machine as a kite without a man on board, operating the levers through cords from the ground. This did not give the practice anticipated, but it inspired confidence in the new system of balance.

In the summer of 1901 we became personally acquainted with Mr. Chanute. When he learned that we were interested in flying as a sport, and not with any expectation of recovering the money we were expending on it, he gave us much encouragement. At our invitation, he spent several weeks with us at our camp at Kill Devil Hill, four miles south of Kitty Hawk, during our experiments of that and the two succeeding years. He also witnessed one flight of the power machine near Dayton, Ohio, in October, 1904.

The machine of 1901 was built with the shape of surface used by Lilienthal, curved from front to rear like the segment of a parabola, with a curvature $\frac{1}{12}$ the depth of its cord; but to make doubly sure that it would have sufficient lifting capacity when flown as a kite in fifteen- or twenty-mile winds, we increased the area from 165 square feet, used in 1900, to 308 square feet—a size much larger than Lilienthal, Pilcher, or Chanute had deemed safe. Upon trial,

FLIGHT AT SIMMS STATION, NEAR DAYTON, OHIO, NOVEMBER 9, 1904

The machine described almost four complete circles, covering a distance of three miles in five minutes and four seconds.

however, the lifting capacity again fell very far short of calculation, so that the idea of securing practice while flying as a kite, had to be abandoned. Mr. Chanute, who witnessed the experiments, told us that the trouble was not due to poor construction of the machine. We saw only one other explanation—that the tables of air-pressures in general use were incorrect.

We then turned to gliding—coasting down hill on the air—as the only method of getting the desired practice in balancing a machine. After a few minutes' practice we were able to make glides of over 300 feet, and in a few days were safely operating in twenty-seven-mile [1] winds. In these experiments we met with several unexpected phenomena. We found that, contrary to the teachings of the books, the center of pressure on a curved surface traveled backward when the surface was inclined, at small angles, more and more edgewise to the wind. We also discovered that in free flight, when the wing on one side of the machine was presented to the wind at a greater angle than the one on the other side, the wing with

[1] The gliding flights were all made against the wind. The difficulty in high winds is in maintaining balance, not in traveling against the wind.

THREE-QUARTER VIEW OF A FLIGHT AT SIMMS STATION, NOVEMBER 16, 1904

The location of the Springfield turnpike and the Springfield electric road is indicated by the trees.

THE START OF THE FIRST FLIGHT OF 1905

The machine is seen just leaving the track, the initial velocity being obtained by its own motive power,
assisted by a cable with falling weight, rigged to the derrick, especially for use in calm weather.

the greater angle descended, and the machine turned in a direction just the reverse of what we were led to expect when flying the machine as a kite. The larger angle gave more resistance to forward motion, and reduced the speed of the wing on that side. The decrease in speed more than counterbalanced the effect of the larger angle. The addition of a fixed vertical vane in the rear increased the trouble, and made the machine absolutely dangerous. It was some time before a remedy was discovered. This consisted of movable rudders working in conjunction with the twisting of the wings. The details of this arrangement are given in our patent specifications, published several years ago.

The experiments of 1901 were far from encouraging. Although Mr. Chanute assured us that, both in control and in weight carried per horse-power, the results obtained were better than those of any of our predecessors, yet we saw that the calculations upon which all flying-machines had been based were unreliable, and that all were simply groping in the dark. Having set out with absolute faith in the existing scientific data, we were driven to doubt one thing after another, till finally, after two years of experiment, we cast it all aside, and decided to rely entirely upon our own investigations. Truth and error were everywhere so intimately mixed as to be undistinguishable. Nevertheless, the time expended in preliminary study of books was not misspent, for they gave us a good general understanding of the subject, and enabled us at the outset to avoid effort in many directions in which results would have been hopeless.

The standard for measurements of wind-pressures is the force produced by a current of air of one mile per hour velocity striking square against a plane of one square-foot area. The practical difficulties of obtaining an exact measurement of this force have been great. The measurements by different recognized authorities vary fifty per cent. When this simplest of measurements presents so great difficulties, what shall be said of the troubles encountered by those who attempt to find the pressure at each angle as the plane is inclined more and more edgewise to the wind? In the eighteenth century the French Academy prepared tables giving such information, and at a later date the Aëronautical Society of Great Britain made similar experiments. Many persons likewise published measurements and formulas; but the results were so discordant that Professor Langley undertook a new series of measurements, the results of which form the basis of his celebrated work, "Experiments in Aërodynamics." Yet a critical examination of the data upon which he based his conclusions as to the pressures at small angles shows results so various as to make many of his conclusions little better than guess-work.

To work intelligently, one needs to know the effects of a multitude of variations that could be incorporated in the surfaces of flying-machines. The pressures on squares are different from those on rectangles, circles, triangles, or ellipses; arched surfaces differ from planes, and vary among themselves according to the depth of curvature; true arcs differ from parabolas, and the latter differ among themselves; thick surfaces differ from thin, and surfaces thicker in one place than another vary in pressure when the positions of maximum thickness are different; some surfaces are most efficient at one angle, others at other angles. The shape of the edge also makes a difference, so that thousands of combinations are possible in so simple a thing as a wing.

We had taken up aëronautics merely as a sport. We reluctantly entered upon the scientific side of it. But we soon found the work so fascinating that we were drawn into it deeper and deeper. Two testing-machines were built, which we believed would avoid the errors to which the measurements of others had been subject. After making preliminary measurements on a great number of different-shaped surfaces, to secure a general understanding of the subject, we began systematic measurements of standard surfaces, so varied in design as to bring out the underlying causes of differences noted in their pressures. Measurements were tabulated on nearly fifty of these at all angles from zero to 45 degrees, at intervals of 2½ degrees. Measurements were also secured showing the effects on each other when surfaces are superposed, or when they follow one another.

Some strange results were obtained. One surface, with a heavy roll at the front edge, showed the same lift for all angles from 7½ to 45 degrees. A square plane, contrary to the measurements of all our predecessors, gave a greater pressure at 30 degrees than at 45 degrees. This seemed so anomalous that we were almost

SIDE VIEW, SHOWING THE MACHINE TRAVELING TO THE RIGHT, WITH DOUBLE HORIZONTAL RUDDER IN FRONT, AND DOUBLE VERTICAL RUDDER BEHIND

This flight was made September 29, 1905, and the distance covered was twelve miles.

ready to doubt our own measurements, when a simple test was suggested. A weather-vane, with two planes attached to the pointer at an angle of 80 degrees with each other, was made. According to our tables, such a vane would be in unstable equilibrium when pointing directly into the wind; for if by chance the wind should happen to strike one plane at 39 degrees and the other at 41 degrees, the plane with the smaller angle would have the greater pressure, and the pointer would be turned still farther out of the course of the wind until the two vanes again secured equal pressures, which would be at approximately 30 and 50 degrees. But the vane performed in this very manner. Further corroboration of the tables was obtained in experiments with a new glider at Kill Devil Hill the next season.

In September and October, 1902, nearly one thousand gliding flights were made, several of which covered distances of over 600 feet. Some, made against a wind of thirty-six miles an hour, gave proof of the effectiveness of the devices for control. With this machine, in the autumn of 1903, we made a number of flights in which we remained in the air for over a minute, often soaring for a considerable time in one spot, without any descent at all. Little wonder that our unscientific assistant should think the only thing needed to keep it indefinitely in the air would be a coat of feathers to make it light!

With accurate data for making calculations, and a system of balance effective in winds as well as in calms, we were now in a position, we thought, to build a successful power-flyer. The first designs provided for a total weight of 600 pounds, including the operator and an eight horse-power motor. But, upon completion, the motor gave more power than had been estimated, and this allowed 150 pounds to be added for strengthening the wings and other parts.

Our tables made the designing of the wings an easy matter; and as screw-propellers are simply wings traveling in a spiral course, we anticipated no trouble from this source. We had thought of getting the theory of the screw-propeller from the marine engineers, and then, by applying our tables of air-pressures to their formulas of designing air-propellers suitable for our purpose. But so far as we could learn, the marine engineers possessed only empirical formulas, and the exact action of the screw-propeller, after a century of use, was still very obscure. As we were not in a position to undertake

the other's side, with no more agreement than when the discussion began.

It was not till several months had passed, and every phase of the problem had been thrashed over and over, that the various reactions began to untangle themselves. When once a clear understanding had been obtained, there was no difficulty in designing suitable propellers, with proper diameter, pitch, and area of blade, to meet the requirements of the flyer.

FRONT VIEW OF THE FLIGHT
OF OCTOBER 4, 1905

a long series of practical experiments to discover a propeller suitable for our machine, it seemed necessary to obtain such a thorough understanding of the theory of its reactions as would enable us to design them from calculation alone. What at first seemed a simple problem became more complex the longer we studied it. With the machine moving forward, the air flying backward, the propellers turning sidewise, and nothing standing still, it seemed impossible to find a starting-point from which to trace the various simultaneous reactions. Contemplation of it was confusing. After long arguments, we often found ourselves in the ludicrous position of each having been converted to

REAR VIEW OF THE FLIGHT OF OCTOBER 4, 1905

In this flight twenty miles were accomplished in thirty-three minutes and seventeen seconds. The machine used in the extensive experiments at Kitty Hawk, North Carolina, last spring, was virtually of similar construction, adapted to two passengers.

High efficiency in a screw-propeller is not dependent upon any particular or peculiar shape, and there is no such thing as a "best" screw. A propeller giving a high dynamic efficiency when used upon one machine, may be almost worthless when used upon another. The propeller should in every case be designed to meet the particular conditions of the machine to which it is to be applied. Our first propellers, built entirely from calculation, gave in useful work 66 per cent. of the power expended. This was about one third more than had been secured by Maxim or Langley.

The first flights with the power-machine were made on the 17th of December, 1903. Only five persons besides ourselves were present. These were Messrs. John T. Daniels, W. S. Dough, and A. D. Etheridge of the Kill Devil Life Saving Station; Mr. W. C. Brinkley of Manteo, and Mr. John Ward of Naghead. Although a general invitation had been extended to the people living within five or six miles, not many were willing to face the rigors of a cold December wind in order to see, as they no doubt thought, another flying-machine *not* fly. The first flight lasted only twelve seconds, a flight very modest compared with that of birds, but it was, nevertheless, the first in the history of the world in which a machine carrying a man had raised itself by its own power into the air in free flight, had sailed forward on a level course without reduction of speed, and had finally landed without being wrecked. The second and third flights were a little longer, and the fourth lasted fifty-nine seconds, covering a distance of 852 feet over the ground against a twenty-mile wind.

After the last flight, the machine was carried back to camp and set down in what was thought to be a safe place. But a few minutes later, while we were engaged in conversation about the flights, a sudden gust of wind struck the machine, and started to turn it over. All made a rush to stop it, but we were too late. Mr. Daniels, a giant in stature and strength, was lifted off his feet, and falling inside, between the surfaces, was shaken about like a rattle in a box as the machine rolled over and over. He finally fell out upon the sand with nothing worse than painful bruises, but the damage to the machine caused a discontinuance of experiments.

In the spring of 1904, through the kindness of Mr. Torrence Huffman of Dayton, Ohio, we were permitted to erect a shed, and to continue experiments, on what is known as the Huffman Prairie, at Simms Station, eight miles east of Dayton. The new machine was heavier and stronger, but similar to the one flown at Kill Devil Hill. When it was ready for its first trial, every newspaper in Dayton

was notified, and about a dozen representatives of the press were present. Our only request was that no pictures be taken, and that the reports be unsensational, so as not to attract crowds to our experiment-grounds. There were probably fifty persons altogether on the ground. When preparations had been completed, a wind of only three or four miles was blowing, —insufficient for starting on so short a track,—but since many had come a long way to see the machine in action, an attempt was made. To add to the other difficulty, the engine refused to work properly. The machine, after running the length of the track, slid off the end without rising into the air at all. Several of the newspaper men returned the next day, but were again disappointed. The engine performed badly, and after a glide of only sixty feet, the machine came to the ground. Further trial was postponed till the motor could be put in better running condition. The reporters had now, no doubt, lost confidence in the machine, though their reports, in kindness, concealed it. Later, when they heard that we were making flights of several minutes' duration, knowing that longer flights had been made with air-ships, and not knowing any essential difference between air-ships and flying-machines, they were but little interested.

We had not been flying long in 1904 before we found that the problem of equilibrium had not as yet been entirely solved. Sometimes, in making a circle, the machine would turn over sidewise despite anything the operator could do, although, under the same conditions in ordinary straight flight, it could have been righted in an instant. In one flight, in 1905, while circling around a honey locust-tree at a height of about fifty feet, the machine suddenly began to turn up on one wing, and took a course toward the tree. The operator, not relishing the idea of landing in a thorn-tree, attempted to reach the ground. The left wing, however, struck the tree at a height of ten or twelve feet from the ground, and carried away several branches; but the flight, which had already covered a distance of six miles, was continued to the starting-point.

The causes of these troubles—too technical for explanation here—were not entirely overcome till the end of September, 1905. The flights then rapidly increased in length, till experiments were discontinued after the 5th of October, on account of the number of people attracted to the field. Although made on a ground open on every side, and bordered on two sides by much traveled thoroughfares, with electric cars passing every hour, and seen by all the people living in the neighborhood for miles around, and by several hundred others, yet these flights have been made by some newspapers the subject of a great "mystery."

A practical flyer having been finally realized, we spent the years 1906 and 1907 in constructing new machines and in business negotiations. It was not till May of this year that experiments (discontinued in October, 1905) were resumed at Kill Devil Hill, North Carolina. The recent flights were made to test the ability of our machine to meet the requirements of a contract with the United States Government to furnish a flyer capable of carrying two men and sufficient fuel supplies for a flight of 125 miles, with a speed of forty miles an hour. The machine used in these tests was the same one with which the flights were made at Simms Station in 1905, though several changes had been made to meet present requirements. The operator assumed a sitting position, instead of lying prone, as in 1905, and a seat was added for a passenger. A larger motor was installed, and radiators and gasolene reservoirs of larger capacity replaced those previously used. No attempt was made to make high or long flights.

In order to show the general reader the way in which the machine operates, let us fancy ourselves ready for the start. The machine is placed upon a single rail track facing the wind, and is securely fastened with a cable. The engine is put in motion, and the propellers in the rear whir. You take your seat at the center of the machine beside the operator. He slips the cable, and you shoot forward. An assistant who has been holding the machine in balance on the rail, starts forward with you, but before you have gone fifty feet the speed is too great for him, and he lets go. Before reaching the end of the track the operator moves the front rudder, and the machine lifts from the rail like a kite supported by the pressure of the air underneath it. The ground under you is at first a perfect blur, but as you rise the objects become clearer. At a height of one hundred feet you feel hardly any motion at all, except for the wind which strikes your face. If you did not take the precaution to fasten your hat before starting, you have probably lost it by this time. The operator moves a lever: the right wing rises, and the machine swings about to the left. You make a very short turn, yet you do not feel the sensation of being thrown from your seat, so often experienced in automobile and railway travel. You find yourself facing toward the point from which you started. The objects on the ground now seem to be moving at much higher speed, though you perceive no change in the pressure of the wind on your face. You know then that you are traveling with the wind. When you near the starting-point, the operator stops the motor while still high in the air. The machine coasts down at on oblique angle to the ground, and after sliding fifty or a hundred feet comes to rest. Although the machine often lands when traveling at a speed of a mile a minute, you feel no shock whatever, and cannot, in fact, tell the exact moment at which it first touched the ground. The motor close beside you kept up an almost deafening roar during the whole flight, yet in your excitement, you did not notice it till it stopped!

Our experiments have been conducted entirely at our own expense. In the beginning we had no thought of recovering what we were expending, which was not great, and was limited to what we could afford for recreation. Later, when a successful flight had been made with a motor, we gave up the business in which we were engaged, to devote our entire time and capital to the development of a machine for practical uses. As soon as our condition is such that constant attention to business is not required, we expect to prepare for publication the results of our laboratory experiments, which alone made an early solution of the flying problem possible.

10.
The Man-Bird and His Wings
(1910)

Cosmopolitan Magazine

MAY, 1910

The Man-Bird and His Wings

By Augustus Post

Editor's Note.—Few men identified with the science of aviation are so well qualified to write about the general subject of flying-machines and those who pilot them as is the author of this article. Mr. Post has for many years been a student and practical demonstrator of aerial flight and an active member of the Aero Club of America. His statements are authoritative, albeit they are couched in terms non-technical and intelligible to the most uninformed among us who have taken the dirigible balloon, the monoplane, the biplane, and the rest of those interesting types of uplifting apparatus as a sheer matter of course in the every-day evolution of civilization.

IT was just at daybreak on the eighth of September, 1908, that I left my room in the Cosmos Club at Washington, crossed the corridor, and tapped gently on the bedroom door of Mr. Orville Wright. He appeared at once, dressed and ready; and with scarcely a word we started for the parade-ground at Fort Myer. The air was perfectly still. It was so early that we could not break-fast at the club, but caught up coffee and rolls at a little restaurant along the way; so early that the only ones to see us arrive were a few soldiers grooming cavalry horses or cleaning field-pieces in the gun-sheds. Swiftly the aeroplane was run out of its shed, the signal-corps men, who had slept in tents, around it helping Mr. Taylor, the mechanician. Mr. Wright slipped into the seat, the weights fell, the machine sped down the rail, rose rapidly, and began to speed in a great circle over our heads. I pulled out my watch and noted the instant it left the ground, and with each circuit of the aeroplane I made a mark upon the back of an old envelope that proved to be the first paper at hand. Round and round the machine

LILIENTHAL, ORIGINATOR OF THE AEROPLANE, IN HIS DOUBLE-DECKED GLIDER

flew, and as the twenty-fourth mark went down I realized that the world's record for continuous flight—made by the Wrights at Dayton two years before—had been smashed. After it passed forty we scarcely breathed; no one dared make a sign, lest Mr. Wright should interpret it as a signal to descend. The circling whir became almost monotonous, the tension more acute, there were fifty-seven marks upon the paper—when Mr. Wright came easily to the ground. Then there was no more silence; everyone talked, shouted, at once; we were at last assured of the con-quest of the air. The old envelope had become an historical document; Mr. Wright endorsed it "O.K. —O.W." It was a witness that the dream of all the ages had come true.

It is no mere flower of speech to call man's de-sire to fly the dream of all the ages, nor is it neces-sary to rehearse the long catalogue of dreamers, from the days of Greek myth and Persian fable, past Leonardo da Vinci and Pascal, to the pathetic figures of Lilien-thal and Langley, dying almost in sight of the promised land. The desire for flight grew more

A SUCCESSFUL FLIGHT OF A ZEPPELIN DIRIGIBLE AT COLOGNE. COUNT ZEPPELIN BASES HIS HOPE OF
AERIAL NAVIGATION ON THE DIRIGIBLE BALLOON AND IS SAID TO BE PLANNING
LINES FOR REGULAR PASSENGER TRAFFIC

intense with the last decade; perhaps because with country after country opening before the explorer the restless spirit sought the unexplored regions of the air; more probably as a further development of the passion for speed that marks this epoch, which produced the express-train, the ocean-liner, and that triumph of individualism, the automobile. Travel in the air, where there are as yet no obstacles in the road, and where friction is reduced to a minimum, offers speed possibilities very attractive to the man for whom no automobile, no motor-boat, can ever go fast enough.

The development of the automobile, indeed, made possible that of the aeroplane, and yet in the construction and operation of the aeroplane one is confronted at once with new conditions, and even the old principles we must apply in a new way. The aeroplane starts from the fact that air, though invisible, has mass, and offers resistance to moving bodies. This property is utilized by broad surfaces moved by power and inclined at an angle to the direction of motion, the forward edges higher than the rear. The air resists this motion, and by pressing on the under side of the wing-surfaces holds them up. In the same way a flat stone skipped over the water

A ZEPPELIN DIRIGIBLE JUST OUT OF THE AERODOME. THE LONGEST AIR-JOURNEY ON RECORD—950
MILES—WAS MADE IN ONE OF THESE MONSTER AIR-CRAFT, AUG. 27 TO SEPT. 2, 1909

ORVILLE WRIGHT

GLENN H. CURTISS

LOUIS PAULHAN

WILBUR WRIGHT

HUBERT LATHAM, WHO
TWICE FAILED TO CROSS
THE ENGLISH
CHANNEL

LE BLON FLYING 3½ MILES IN 4 MINUTES 2
SECONDS AT HELIOPOLIS, EGYPT

LOUIS BLERIOT, WHO
CROSSED THE ENGLISH
CHANNEL, JULY 25,
1909

SANTOS-DUMONT, WHO
MADE THE FIRST
FLIGHTS IN
EUROPE

LEON DELAGRANGE,
KILLED AT BOR-
DEAUX, JAN.
4, 1910

LIEUTENANT SELF-
RIDGE, KILLED AT
FT. MYER, SEPT.
17, 1908

E. LEFEBVRE, KILLED
AT JUVISSY,
SEPT. 7,
1909

will sink if it is not moving swiftly or if it does not strike the water at the right angle. So the aeroplane, unless it is moving forward, will drop to the ground, and when the motor is stopped and its forward motion ceases, it must be allowed to glide down with its planes balanced exactly as when flying, gravity now taking the place of the motor. An aeroplane descending in still air from an altitude of one thousand feet can choose any landing-place within a radius of about a mile and a half; that is, it can come down at an angle of about one in seven; but in winds it takes the same sort of maneuvering that is used to land a rowboat on a swift-flowing stream.

All aeroplane construction is founded upon these principles of air-mass and air-resistance; all aeroplanes include certain vital parts—the surfaces, rudders, and motor, which includes the propellers. Of these the surfaces, first striking the eye, first claim the attention; their size, their shape and curvature, their bracing, the material of which they are made, are all important. One aeroplane may have double the amount of surface of another; it may differ just as widely in weight, but the other may be more speedy from having less resistance and a more effective thrust by its propeller. Two machines may have exactly the same extent of surfaces and the same speed, but one will lift almost twice as much weight because it has a more efficient curve to its surfaces. The popular idea that an aeroplane has planes is misleading, for they are really curved surfaces, "aero-curves"— so called because they are arched in the rear of the front edge. This allows the supporting surface of the aeroplane, which is passing forward with its broadest side, some thirty feet in width, set at an angle to the direction of its motion, so to act upon the air as to tend to compress it on its under side. The air natu-

THE LAST WORD IN AVIATION COSTUMES FOR WOMEN

rally resists for an infinitesimal period of time the attempt to change the direction of its motion. Meanwhile the aeroplane has penetrated into new and undisturbed air, where the same process is repeated.

The rudders are the next important point in any aeroplane. The first self-propelled vehicle, the railway locomotive, is bound to a track; no steering is necessary, the driver can only start and stop. Then the vehicle is freed from the rail, and becomes the automobile, in which the driver can steer in one plane of motion and to the right or left as well as control the speed. The third development is the dirigible balloon, which can be steered in two planes of direction, or up and down, as well as to the right or left. In this class is the aeroplane, which can be steered in four directions. Besides, and this is the hardest part of all, it must be balanced by the operator. It is at just this point that so many inventors have failed. The basic idea underlying the present system of balancing an aeroplane is to raise the lower side of the machine and make the higher side lower, in order to right it when it tips to one side or the other, either from wind gusts or because the machine tips at an angle when making a turn, as a bicycle tips when turning a sharp corner. This result is reached in two general ways: one, by changing the form of the wing itself, the other, by the use of entirely separate surfaces. The first method changes the form of the wing either by making one side lift more than the other, by being made to take a more curved form or by increasing the lifting surface of that wing by laterally extending its extremity. The second method of balancing is by means of separate surfaces that can be turned up or down far out on each side of the machine. These horizontal balancing-rudders are connected, so that they will work in an opposite manner, and while one is turned to lift one side, the other will act to depress the other side and thus bring the machine back to an even keel.

Balancing is, after all, the particular in which the characteristics of the different inventors are most clearly revealed. The wheel of an automobile and the tiller of a yacht are the points where man and machine are united, but the connection of aviator and aeroplane is much more close. The

peculiar charm. The flying-machine seems an extension of personality —the nearest thing to having wings oneself is to have a broad expanse of silk spreading on either side of you and know that you can bend and curve and adjust this to your will just as you might put out your hand or foot, or control your fingers. The aviator's mental development must be acute and his nervous system untiring. To operate such a deli-

governing-levers differ from these other two steering-devices, and are really more like the guiding-reins of a horse, for the aeroplane gives the most sensitive response to the slightest movement. This is one of the things that gives the sport its

cate piece of mechanism for over three hours without stopping, as did Henri Farman recently, taxes to the utmost every resource of endurance, and imperatively demands the closest and most uninterrupted concentration. The least

BARONESS DE LA ROCHE, PREMIER WOMAN FLIER— THE "ODIER-VENDÔME" IN FLIGHT AT ISSY—A FIFTY-HORSE-POWER GOUPY BIPLANE—CAPTAIN FERBER'S LAST FLIGHT AT JUVISSY WHEN HE WON THE SPEED PRIZE

relaxation of vigilance, the least miscalculation, would have dashed him to the ground. It is as if a great virtuoso should play for three hours steadily upon the piano, giving the finest shades of coloring and interpretation to every phrase, and without making a single false note. While he was passing other machines and rounding the signal-towers the greatest care was needed; after darkness had set in, it was necessary to use automobile search-lights to show the way. It was then that the mettle of the pilot was revealed; but even so, before the machine was exhausted he was forced to come down.

Next to the systems for maintaining stability come the motors and propellers. Here the connection between the development of the aeroplane and that of the automobile becomes apparent. The years of developing and refining the gas-engine for use by the automobile prepared it for its success in the future of the flying-machine. The first very light engine to be available, the Antoinette, built by Leon Levavasseur in France, was the immediate cause of the first successful flights made in public by Santos-Dumont, which convinced the public that the initial step toward solving the great problem had been taken. Until that time it was doubted that it was possible to get sufficient push against the air with a propeller to drive a machine with the required speed to rise; and even now it is marvelous that something revolving so fast that it can hardly be seen can push or pull a machine through the air at a speed of forty or fifty miles an hour, and that the column of air pushed back by the propeller is strong enough to blow another machine following in its wake out of its course backward, and possibly drive it to the ground. This actually did happen at Reims, and it shows how carefully machines must be held far enough apart to keep the wash of one from affecting the other.

These are the features common to all aeroplanes; beyond these begin the divergencies, the individual features that distinguish the different types, of which there are as many as there are inventors. The one feature by which more than another the Wright machine is distinguished is the warping wing-tips, of which so much has been written and around which so much litigation settles. Designed primarily for field-service, making its first appeal to governments, its structure, though as graceful as an instrument perfectly adapted to its uses is bound to be, impresses the spec-

tator at once by its substantial character, in contrast, for example, with the light, compact, sportsman's biplane of the Herring-Curtiss Company. Of the foreign biplanes, the Voisin retains, in general, the structural lines of a box-kite; the cellular construction at once strikes the eye in reality or in a photograph. Farman takes out all these vertical surfaces, and adds ailerons, or hinged wing-tips, to the outer rear edges of his surfaces, for use in turning and balancing. The Farman machine has also a combination of wheels and skids, or runners, for starting and landing.

The development of the monoplane is conditioned by the position of the various inventors upon the question whether, to assist in maintaining automatic stability, the center of gravity shall be below the center of support, as in a pendulum, or whether the center of gravity and the center of support shall coincide; that is, whether the aviator and the motor are to be suspended underneath the machine or balanced upon its structure. Latham sits on top of the *Antoinette;* Bleriot, in his late machines, such as the *Number Twelve,* far down underneath. The *Antoinette* is built like a boat, the aviator sitting in a cock-pit on top. The *Demoiselle,* Santos-Dumont's machine, follows the general lines of the *Antoinette,* but is distinguished by its very small size.

Everyone is familiar with the general lines of the two divisions of aeroplanes—the monoplane, having single large surfaces like the wings of a bird; and the biplane, having two large surfaces braced together, one over the other. This is as far as classification has gone, although there will undoubtedly be others relating to differences in size, power, and weight, as the industry develops, examples multiply, and sporting meets become more frequent.

In America there are two manufacturing firms with machines on the market, the Wright Brothers, at Dayton, Ohio, and the Herring-Curtiss Company, at Hammondsport, N. Y. These both make biplanes; their points of difference have been often explained in print, especially since the opening of the Wright Brothers' suit for infringement of patents. In France there are seven firms that have already delivered a number of machines to buyers, not to speak of the many inventors who have built machines to develop their ideas. The industry has grown more rapidly than did that of the automobile. So far the principal buyers of aeroplanes have been men who built the first successful machines, used by Farman and Delagrange in 1908, and by Paulhan and Rougier in 1909. These aeroplanes of 40 square meters surface (a meter equals 39.37 inches), 10 meters wide, weighing 500 kilos (a kilo equals 2.204 pounds), cost 12,000 francs (a franc equals twenty cents).

The Société Antoinette, builders of the famous Antoinette motors, made

SANTOS-DUMONT EXPERIMENT-
ING AT ISSY IN SPITE
OF THE SNOW

taking advantage of the feverish interest in aviation to give exhibitions of flying; then come the sportsmen, especially automobilists. The commercial and special uses of the aeroplane are only just beginning to open up; as usual, the qualities of the instrument suggest further uses. The oldest firm in France is Voisin Frères,

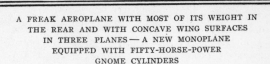

A FREAK AEROPLANE WITH MOST OF ITS WEIGHT IN
THE REAR AND WITH CONCAVE WING SURFACES
IN THREE PLANES — A NEW MONOPLANE
EQUIPPED WITH FIFTY-HORSE-POWER
GNOME CYLINDERS

LATHAM WINNING THE PRIZE
FOR ALTITUDE—508
FEET—AT REIMS

the beautiful bird-like monoplane used by Latham in his attempts to cross the English Channel and in his flights at Reims, where he captivated the crowds by his exceedingly graceful flights. Here he won the altitude prize and flew at times without touching a hand to the steering-wheel, his polished machine of the type that crossed the channel, as well as for the larger model, the *Number Twelve*, that can carry two people. This machine has several unique features, and is the fastest yet made, having beaten the time made by Mr. Glenn H. Curtiss in his biplane with its 60 horse-power motor. The fourth important French machine that can be purchased is that built by M. Henri Farman. This is the model in which he made the world's duration record by a flight of three hours and fifteen minutes at Reims. These machines are the least expensive, costing, without the motor, 6000 francs. They have 25 square meters surface, are 7½ meters wide and 8 meters long and weigh 140 kilos; motors of from 24 to 50 horse-power can be installed.

The most successful company is that of the Wrights, whose machine is in great demand. The rights to manufacture this machine were purchased by a syndicate headed by M. Weiler, for $100,000. It is offered at 30,000 francs with a four-cylinder motor of 30 horse-power. The aeroplane contains 30 square meters, is 12½ meters wide and 9 meters 35 centimeters long, and weighs 400 kilos. It is the only aeroplane of its class using two propellers. The price of these machines in this country is $7,500, and a duty of forty-five per cent. must be paid on foreign machines when they are brought into the United States. The

PAULHAN'S FIRST CROSS-COUNTRY FLIGHT—PASSING ABOVE THE VILLAGE LA VEUVE NEAR CHALONS

glistening in the sun like the sleek plumage of a raven. These machines are advertised for 25,000 francs, and are equipped with the Antoinette motor. The Bleriot machines can be purchased for 10,000 francs without the motor; the E. N. V. 35 horse-power and Anzani three-cylinder motors are usually used in these aeroplanes, however. The factory is swamped with orders for monoplanes

DE LESSEPS COMPETING FOR AN ALTITUDE PRIZE. HILL AND VALLEY ARE AS ONE LEVEL TO THE NEW LORDS OF THE AIR

Wright Brothers expect to establish a manu-facturing-plant here next year; at present they have only a small shop in Dayton, where the motors and demonstration machines have been made. The only other machine that has proved a pronounced success that is made in this country is made by the Herring-Curtiss Company at Hammondsport, N. Y. The Curtiss machine sells for $5000 and is fitted with the well-known Curtiss motor, that has so many world's records to its credit, both in aeroplane events and with dirigible balloons. New buildings are going up, and the first company to be manufacturing aeroplanes in any quantity in America will soon be turning them out like any other commodity.

This necessarily brief statement of the con-dition of the industry leaves out of account the innumerable inventors and individual build-ers, and deals only with aeroplanes, saying nothing so far of the large concerns that have an immense amount of capital invested in the manufacture of dirigibles. In Germany alone the amount invested is enormous; the Zeppelin Company has prepared for the building of ten Zeppelins, each valued at over $100,000; and the establishment of an air-line route connecting the principal cities of the German empire, which is one of the immedi-ate aims, reveals possibilities of transporta-tion yet undreamed of. Aeronautics in Ger-

PAULHAN PASSING OVER THE RIVER ORGA IN A CROSS-COUNTRY FLIGHT NEAR PARIS

WILBUR WRIGHT IN ITALY. ONE OF THE LONG SERIES OF FLIGHTS BY WHICH HE DEMONSTRATED THE PRACTICABILITY OF AIR-NAVIGATION

many, while perhaps less spectacular than in France or America, have an ele-ment of practicality that puts the Germans at pres-ent in the lead in the field of the air. There is every reason for the intense in-terest shown, not only by the people but by the gov-ernment of Germany, in aeronautics; as evidence of how far this has gone, witness the Zeppelin Arctic Air-ship Expedition,

GLENN H. CURTISS AT LOS ANGELES, WHERE
HE WON ALL THE SPEED EVENTS AND
MADE NEW RECORDS IN STARTING,
CIRCLING, AND LANDING

WILBUR WRIGHT WITH
MME. O'BERG AS A
PASSENGER

LATHAM IN ONE OF HIS
UNSUCCESSFUL AT-
TEMPTS TO CROSS
THE ENGLISH
CHANNEL

Polar Regions. It has been decided to send an advance party to Spitzbergen during the summer of 1910 with a complete equipment to prepare for the operation of the air-ship under polar conditions. An improved type is to be constructed for trial flights in 1911, and tests will be made between various German ports; the ship is now being developed with a view especially to long voyages over the sea. It is to be hoped that this country may see a type of war air-ship of rigid construction, and also the French type of semi-rigid dirigible. These great ships, costing from fifty to seventy-five thousand dollars, give an idea of the importance of these craft in the field of aeronautics, and show how great the value and the possibilities are of the buoyant air-craft, whose advantages have been in this country temporarily eclipsed in the public eye by the performances of racing-aeroplanes. The buoyant craft are becoming more and more efficient and better able to cope with storms and severe weather as they increase in size. The principle upon which this improvement depends is that the volume increases as the cube of the dimensions, while the surface increases only as their square; this means that the volume of gas that an air-ship can contain becomes very much greater as it increases in size, while the proportional weight of the structure is less. In the case of the aeroplane, as its material structure is increased

organized and under the direct patronage of the Emperor and his son. Prince Henry of Prussia has presided over the meetings of the board of directors at Fried-richshafen, in whose hands the detailed arrangements are placed. This expedition is undertaken under the auspices of the German Society for Exploration of the

in size, its braces strengthened, and its surfaces made larger, it becomes much heavier in proportion. This fact will limit development in this direction.

Every public flight of an aeroplane makes more enthusiasts for the sport; every passenger who tries to tell "how it feels" makes more people determined to know for themselves. There is no

York, St. Louis, and Los Angeles. So far aviation is largely in the hands of professionals, but soon will come the army of amateur aeronauts making cross-country flights for the sake of the fascinating sport. This is the history of the bicycle and of the automobile, and there is no doubt that the same elements of human nature will crop out to develop aviation.

doubt that there will be thousands of small aeroplanes flying about in all places and at all times much sooner than would be supposed; already nearly all large cities have had aeroplane flights at or near them, and within the last year contests or demonstrations have attracted thousands to Le Mans, Pau, Rome, Reims, Brescia, Berlin, Washington, Chicago, New

As long as the builder operates the machine his mind will be bent upon its perfection. His reputation is bound up in the success of his creation, and he cannot afford to take chances, especially with crowds of people watching his every move as if he were some new kind of bird or some strange, rare creature. When the aeroplane gets into the hands of the aviator pure and simple,

NOTHING TO HOLD TO WHEN SOMETHING GOES WRONG—
REMAINS OF MACHINES DRIVEN BY BLERIOT, DE
LESSEPS, DELAGRANGE, AND BRÉGUET

who thinks very little about the machine it-self, who lies awake nights conjuring up new stunts to astonish the world, he is likely to accomplish startling things and find latent possibilities in the machine that no one, not even the inventor, has dreamed existed there. The aviator attacks even the winds, the worst foes of the aeroplane; Hubert Latham flew against a gale of thirty-seven miles an hour. When the signal went up that indicated there would be a flight, Latham's friends looked doubtful; the machine rose into the air without a start, the speed of the wind taking the place of speed in the machine, and went swaying from side to side, at first hardly seeming to make headway. This feat has done more to encourage avia-tion than almost anything else, for winds have been so far the greatest source of danger to the aviator. The thousands that watched day after day for the appearance of Wilbur Wright during the Hudson-Fulton celebration grew surprisingly weather-wise and wind-wise in the course of those days of waiting, and when the aeroplane has really taken its place as a vehicle in common use, we will no longer look only at the clouds to see if it looks like rain, but at the flag-poles, to see how much of a wind is blowing, and how fitfully. The balloonist wants a good wind blowing steadily in one direction, to carry him far out over the country, but for some time to come the wind will furnish the most serious problem for aeroplane-makers and driv-ers to solve.

But there can be no doubt that as the main problem of flight has been brought to a solution, the weather condi-tions will in time be understood, so that the now baf-fling winds will be turned to advan-tage. All progress demands a certain amount of desperate daring to enter new

AEROPLANE ROUNDING A SIGNAL-TOWER, WHICH IS EQUIPPED WITH SIGNALS FOR EVERY
CONTINGENCY OF THE AIR—GOBRON IN A VOISIN BIPLANE WINNING
A PRIZE DURING THE AVIATION WEEK AT REIMS

LOUIS PAULHAN STARTING ON HIS WORLD'S-RECORD FLIGHT OF FORTY-SIX
HUNDRED FEET INTO THE AIR AT LOS ANGELES, JAN. 12, 1910

fields, to contend against the mighty untried forces of nature. Man is brought into conflict with great powers when he faces gravity and the turbulent air. That he is sometimes beaten in the fight is no wonder, nor that the history of aviation holds a long roll of the dead; the wonder is that it is not much longer. Many of these were killed in attempts to learn the principles of mechanical flight by actual experiment: Letour in London in 1854, De Groof in Belgium in 1874, and Lilienthal, the father of modern aviation, who perished in a flight on the tenth of August, 1896, but not until he had made over two thousand successful gliding flights, and by his experiments and records laid the foundations of the future science of aviation.

The death, on September 17, 1908, of Lieut. Thomas E. Selfridge, a passenger on Orville Wright's machine, sounded the first note of warning to the aeronautic world as to the danger attending breaks in the machinery during flight. Up to this time fatal accidents or those resulting in serious injury had arisen from defects in construction itself, or in some misapplication of principle, but this was the first case to show the public the possibilities arising from breaks in machines properly

constructed, but giving way from some cause or other while in flight. Since then breaks in the mechanism have furnished the cause for the greater number of serious accidents. And such accidents have happened to well-known aviators—LeFebvre, one of the most daring of the new school, who had been fined for reckless piloting at the Reims races, met death at Juvissy, and Captain Ferber, known professionally as M. de Rue, who had done much important work for the development of military aeronautics, was killed near Boulogne. The death of Delagrange, which occurred near Bordeaux on January 4, 1910, removed one of the most brilliant figures in modern sport.

But neither death nor danger deters the aviator or retards the progress of aviation. Nor need they, for each accident, unless it be the result of the useless recklessness arising from over-familiarity, inspires fresh efforts on the part of inventor or of aviator, either to correct the imperfection or to perfect the control. All progress is paid for by its martyrs, and so far aviation has had surprisingly few, considering that its progress has been made in the face of forces believed unconquerable—the forces of gravitation and of the unfettered winds.

11.
Why
Flying-Machines Fly
(1911)

Why Flying-Machines Fly

BY WALDEMAR KAEMPFFERT

ASK a scientist, "What is an aeroplane?" and he will reply, "Any flat or slightly curved surface propelled horizontally through the air." That, being merely a definition of a thing, and not an explanation of flight, tells little of what is most wonderful about a flying-machine. Time and time again we have all asked ourselves: Why is it that this combination of planes, propellers, motors, and rudders does not fall? Why is it that a machine many times heavier than the air stays aloft?

It is the air pressure beneath it, and its motion, that keep up a plane. If it is to remain in the air, an aeroplane must constantly move like a skater on thin ice. The skater must move fast enough to reach a new section of ice before he falls; the aeroplane must move fast enough to reach a new section of air before it falls. Both are constantly struggling with gravitation.

The simplest and most familiar example of an aeroplane is the kite of our boyhood days. By holding it against the wind, or by running with it, if there happens to be only a gentle breeze, this oldest of flying-machines is kept aloft. Invent a substitute for the string, some device, in other words, which will enable you to hold the kite in the proper direction, and you have invented a flying-machine. The pull or the thrust of an engine-driven propeller is that substitute.

In order to steer the aeroplane, after it is launched, two sets of rudders are required. A steamboat is a vehicle that travels in two dimensions only; hence it requires only a single, vertical rudder, which serves to guide it from side to side. An aeroplane moves not only from side to side, but up and down as well; hence it is equipped not only with a vertical rudder similar to that of a steamboat, but also with a horizontal rudder, which serves to alter its course up or down, and which is becoming more widely known as an "elevator."

If only these simple principles were involved in a solution of the age-old problem of artificial flight, aeroplanes would have skimmed the air decades ago. Some way must also be found of starting the machine on its voyage through the atmosphere. Like a kite or a soaring bird, an aeroplane must rise in the very teeth of the wind. What is more, it must be in motion before it can fly. How this preliminary motion was to be obtained long baffled the flying-machine inventor. Eagles, condors, and other soaring birds launch themselves either by leaping from the limb of a tree or the edge of a cliff, or by running along the ground with wings outspread, until they have acquired sufficient speed. Many of us have disturbed wild ducks on the water and noticed them run along it, flapping their wings, for some distance, to get velocity before they can fly. A vulture can be confined in a small cage which is entirely open at the top, simply because he cannot make a preliminary run. The necessity of initial velocity is as great with an artificial flying-machine as it is with a bird.

With the gliders or motorless aeroplanes of Lilienthal, Pilcher, and Chanute, it was no difficult matter for the aeronaut to launch himself into the air. He simply carried his apparatus to the top of a hill, grasped the handle-bar, ran down the hill at top speed for a short distance, and then drew up his legs, like any bird. Thus he would slide down the air for several hundred feet as if upon an invisible track.

It is difficult to launch a ship, although gravity keeps it down upon the ways. Here the problem is much more difficult of solution. The aeroplane on the ground is as much out of its element as a feather that has fallen from a bird's wing. It is ready, like the feather, to obey any chance gust, and to fly hither and thither instead of in the direction intended. A ship glides into the water along definite ways, but there are no definite ways on which an aeroplane rises into the air. After repeated failures, Langley succeeded in launching his craft, somewhat as a ship is launched into the water, the machine resting on a car, which fell down at the end of a track, and released the aeroplane for its freer flight.

In their earlier experiments the Wright brothers employed an inclined track. The machine was placed upon a car which ran upon a single rail. By means of a falling weight, connected by ropes with the car, the machine was propelled down the rail at high speed and thus given its preliminary motion.

Even before the Wright brothers threw aside all secrecy and flew publicly in the United States and in France during the summer of 1908, Curtiss and Farman had made short flights on machines which were mounted on bicycle wheels. The machines would run on the wheels for several hundred feet before leaping into the air. So successful has this system been that in somewhat improved form it is embodied in every successful aeroplane. Even the Wright brothers, who long persisted in using the starting-rail in the face of the obvious advantages of wheels, have followed the example of their rivals.

Once in the air, the pilot must see to it that he keeps his balance so that the aeroplane will glide on an even keel, an art so difficult that even a hawk sways from side to side as he soars, in the constant effort to steady himself, like an acrobat on a tight rope. An aeroplane has weight; that is, it is always falling. It is kept aloft because the upward air pressure is greater than the falling force. The weight or falling tendency is theoretically concentrated in a point known as the "centre of gravity." Opposed to this gravitative tendency is the upward pressure of the air against the under surface of the plane, which effect is theoretically concentrated in a point known as the "centre of air pressure." Gravitation (weight) is constant; the air pressure, because of the many puffs and gusts of which even a zephyr is composed, is decidedly inconstant. Hence,

while the centre of gravity remains in approximately the same place, the centre of air pressure is more restless than a drop of quicksilver on an unsteady glass plate.

The whole art of maintaining the side-to-side balance of an aeroplane consists in keeping the centre of gravity and the centre of air pressure on the same vertical line. If the centre of air pressure should wander too far away from that line of coincidence, the aeroplane is capsized. The upward air pressure being greater than the falling tendency, and having been all thrown to one side, the aeroplane is naturally upset. Because of the wind's capriciousness, the aeroplane drops more on one side than on the other. To maintain his balance the aeronaut must in some way lift the falling side or lower the rising side, or do both. Human flight would have been practicable long ago if there had only been some mechanical way of mimicking the swaying vulture that circles in the blue, watching for carrion below. It was not until the Wrights found a way of doing what the vulture does—a way of meeting the countless little blasts unheeded by most of us—that flying became possible at all. They hit upon a means of bending the planes, so that if one side of the machine were tilted up the resistance could be increased beneath the falling side to lift it. In other words, they made of the aeroplane a kind of seesaw, which is so distorted that upward pressure is brought to bear upon the falling end. To prevent skidding, during this warping of the wings, the vertical rudder is suitably manipulated. This principle which they discovered—of increasing the pressure beneath the falling side and of simultaneously employing the vertical rudder —is embodied in every successful flying-machine of the day. Clearly, the vertical rudder of a flying-machine serves not only for steering the aeroplane from side to side, like the rudder of a ship, but to keep it on an even keel as well.

Instead of bending or twisting the wings, as the Wrights do, many designers, among them Curtiss and Farman, employ what the French call "ailerons"—small flaps hinged to the rear edges of the main planes, and so manipulated as to bring about the same result. By lowering such an aileron, or flap, on the falling side of a flying-machine the upward air pressure beneath that side is increased and the machine righted. Whether or not it is necessary to employ the vertical rudder to correct any skidding tendency is the chief point at issue in the various patent infringement suits brought by the Wright brothers.

The aviator of the present day is somewhat in the position of the bicycle-rider on a slack wire, armed with a parasol. He must exercise incessant vigilance lest he lose his balance. The strain upon nerves and muscles, for the beginner at least, is tremendous. Hence, even now, we hear of automatic devices which will prevent the loss of a flying-machine's equilibrium and which will enable the aviator to soar in the sky more blithely than he can at present. When Louis Brennan exhibited to the world a monorail car which was kept on an even keel merely by gyroscopes—in other words, by swiftly revolving fly-wheels—it seemed almost obvious to apply the same device to the flying-machine. Yet the attempt had been made long before Brennan came to the front. Sir Hiram Maxim made promising experiments with the gyroscope some years ago. Paul Regnard, a French experimenter, has recently been testing a flying-machine which is perfectly controlled by a little wheel measuring only a few inches in diameter, but turning 10,000 times a minute. The success of the gyroscope in preventing the rolling of ships at sea and in guiding Whitehead torpedoes on their course would seem to augur well for the automatically controlled aeroplane.

When a line of soldiers wheels around a street corner the man at the inner end of the line does little more than mark time; the man in the centre of the line marches along at a steady pace; while the man on the outside all but runs. In order that the line may be straight the movement must be progressively faster from the inner to the outer end. An aeroplane as it turns horizontally is in exactly the same predicament as a line of soldiers. The outer end of the machine must move faster than the inner end.

As the speed of an aeroplane increases, its lifting power also increases. Hence the more rapidly moving outer end of an aeroplane will be subjected to a greater lifting effort than the slowly moving inner end, and hence the entire machine is canted at a more or less sharp angle on a turn. This natural canting or banking has its advantages. It counteracts the effects of centrifugal force which are unavoidable in any rotary movement.

What centrifugal force means we see when a weight at the end of a cord is whirled around. If swung fast enough, the weight will describe a circle, because the centrifugal force is very much greater than the force of gravitation. If the whirling be slackened below a certain critical point, the weight will drop back to the hand. A flying-machine is like the whirling stone. It has a very large centrifugal force as it turns. So great is that force that it must be checked by the gravitation—in other words, by the weight of the machine. The more the machine is heeled over, the more marked will be the action of gravitation.

The same principle is applied on bicycle tracks and railway curves. In order that the bicyclist may race around curves at high speed, the track is banked, so that he can oppose his weight to the centrifugal force which tends to throw him off the track. In order that the train may round a curve at high speed, the outer rail is raised above the inner, so that the cars lean in.

If the canting of a flying-machine be very pronounced, it is possible that gravitation may overcome the centrifugal force, so that the machine will slide down to the ground. To forestall that possibility the aviator may either sweep his circle on so long a radius that there will be but little canting, or he may employ wing-warping devices or ailerons to counterbalance the canting action. Since most aeroplanes are provided with either warping devices or ailerons, it is the usual practice to depend upon them in turning. The result is that we see skilful pilots swinging in an arc at a speed that cants their machines at an angle which may be more than sixty degrees to the horizontal, and which almost causes the spectator's heart to stop beating, so perilous does the exploit seem.

All this sounds very easy; yet, even after a successful aeroplane had been invented, many machines were wrecked before the trick of making a turn was learned. It took the French two years to acquire the art. Indeed, a wealthy Parisian, named Armengaud, offered a prize to the first Frenchman who flew in a circle. Henry Farman won that prize so recently as July 6, 1908. The Wright brothers spent the whole flying season of 1904 in learning how to sweep a circle when the wind was blowing.

A sharp turn on an aeroplane is like one of those moments on a yacht when you slack away quickly on the main-sheet and prepare for the boom to jibe. There is none of the yacht's hesitancy, however; for the machine slides away on the new slant without a quiver. An inexperienced passenger on an aeroplane is tempted to right the machine as it swings around and tilts. In a canoe or on a bicycle it would be natural to use the body. In an aeroplane the movement is unnecessary, because the machine does its own banking.

In the Curtiss and Santos-Dumont machines any instinctive movement on the part of the aviator to right the careening machine actuates the ailerons or wing-warping devices in the proper way. In the Curtiss biplane the seat-back is pivoted at the bottom and is connected by cables with the ailerons. Should the pilot involuntarily throw his weight over to right the machine, the cables are pulled, and the ailerons are almost automatically tilted to regulate the air pressure beneath the planes in the proper manner. In the Santos-Dumont monoplane, the cables that warp the wings lead to a piece of metal sewed to the back of the pilot's coat.

The flying creatures of nature—insects, birds, fishes, and bats—spread wings that lie in a single plane. Because these wings are thus disposed, birds may be properly regarded as single-decked flying-machines, or "monoplanes," in aviation parlance, and because the earliest attempts at flying were more or less slavish imitations of bird-flight, it was but natural that the monoplane was man's first conception of a flying-machine.

It is a circumstance of considerable scientific moment that the wings of a gliding bird, such as an eagle, a buzzard, or a vulture, are wide in spread and narrow in width. Much painstaking experimenting by Langley and others has shown that the best shape of plane is that which is oblong; the span must be considerably greater than the width. In other words, science has experimentally approved the design of a bird's wings.

Long spans are unwieldy, often too unwieldy for practical, artificial flight. Suppose we cut a long plane in half and mount one half over the other. The result is a two-decked machine, a "biplane." Such a biplane has somewhat less lifting power than the original monoplane, and yet it has the same amount of surface. But the biplane is a little steadier in the air than the monoplane, and therefore a little safer, just as a box-kite is steadier than the old-fashioned single-surface kite. Still, the difference in stability between biplane and monoplane is so slight that designers base their preferences on other considerations. Both types are inherently so unstable that it requires a skilled hand to correct their capsizing tendencies.

By placing one plane over another certain structural advantages are obtained. It is comparatively easy to tie two superposed planes together and to form a strong, bridge-like truss. The proper support of the outstretched surfaces of a monoplane, on the other hand, is a matter of some concern.

If a monoplane were to fall vertically like a parachute, it would offer the resistance of its entire surface to the fall; if a biplane were to fall, it would offer the resistance of only one of its planes to the fall. Hence the monoplane is a better parachute than the biplane. The point is of slight value. If an aviator is high enough when his motor fails him, he can always glide to the ground on a slant, which may be two miles in length. Paradoxical as it may seem, the greater the distance through which he may fall, the better are an aviator's chances of reaching the ground with an unbroken neck. At a slight elevation from the ground, both monoplanes and biplanes are in a precarious position in case the motor breaks down. There is no distance to glide, for which reason they must fall.

Since an aeroplane, whether it be of single-deck or two-deck construction, must be driven at considerable speed to keep it in the air, and must, furthermore, get up a certain preliminary speed before it can fly at all, some inventors have thought of rotating the planes, as if they were huge propellers, instead of driving them along in a straight line. Such screw propellers, to push a machine from the ground, are mounted on a vertical shaft, the whole constituting a machine which goes by the name "helicopter." A helicopter should theoretically screw its way up into the air. Because no screw propeller can at present support a weight in air with anything like the aeroplane's economy of power, the helicopter has not been a practical success. Indeed, the pathway of aeronautic invention is strewn with wrecked helicopters. Many dreamers have pinned their faith to the blades of their revolving screws. In France, where fashions in flying-machines are created with the same facility as fashions in clothes, the type still engages the attention of a few enthusiasts, despite the brilliant success of the aeroplane.

Far less encouraging than these experiments with helicopters have been the efforts of a few misguided aviators who have sought to build what are known as ornithopters—machines that flap wings like a sparrow. It seems very natural to adopt the flapping-wing principle, because all birds depend upon it more or less. The most earnest experimenter with the flapping wing was Hargrave, who ultimately gave the world the box-kite, the prototype of the biplane. He built eighteen flapping-wing models between 1883 and 1893. With one of these, at least, a flight of 343 feet was made in 1891. It must be said that Hargrave relied on flapping wings solely for propulsion and not for support. His efforts to devise an efficient sustaining surface gave us the box-kite. Only a few French inventors still persist in working on the flapping-wing principle.

In most forms of locomotion increased speed is obtained at the expense of power. When you run, you expend more energy than when you walk. A locomotive driven at high speed utilizes more power than at low speed. Paradoxically enough, the aeroplane follows no such rule. Professor Langley discovered that the higher the speed of an aeroplane, the less power is required to drive it. Theoretically at least, it seemed to him that a speed could be reached where the power received would be nil.

It might be supposed from all this that the flying-machines of man are far more efficient contrivances than the eagle or the hawk. Marvel as we may at the wonderful ingenuity displayed in the modern flying-machine, we have still much to learn from soaring birds. Little as we know of the efficiency of flat and curved surfaces in the air, we know still less how to drive those surfaces without an inordinate expenditure of power, fuel, and lubricant. We have only to compare the amount of energy expended by the great flying creatures of the earth with that required by our machines to realize how much we have to learn.

Professor Langley long ago pointed out that the greatest flying creature which the earth has ever known was the extinct pterodactyl. Its spread of wing was probably as much as twenty feet; its wing surface was in the neighborhood of twenty-five square feet; its weight was about thirty pounds. Yet this huge creature was driven at an expenditure of energy of probably less than 0.05 horsepower. The condor, which is preeminently a soaring bird, has a stretch of wing that varies from nine to ten feet, a supporting area of nearly ten square feet, and a weight of seventeen pounds. Its approximate horse-power has been placed by Professor Langley at scarcely 0.05. The turkey-buzzard, with a stretch of wing of six feet, a supporting area of a little over five square feet, and a weight of five pounds, uses about 0.015 horsepower. Langley's own successful, small, steam-driven model had a supporting area of fifty-four feet and a weight of thirty pounds. Yet it required one and a half horse-power to drive it. How much power is needed to fly at high speeds in machines may be gathered from the fact that although Blériot crossed the Channel with a 25 horse-power Anzani motor, and the Wright machine uses a 25 or 30 horsepower motor, most aeroplanes have engines of 50 horse-power and upward. When we consider that one horse-power is equal to the power of at least ten men, we see that even the smallest power successfully used in an aeroplane represents the combined continuous effort of more than two hundred men. To be sure, our flying-machines are very much larger than any flying creature that ever existed; but comparing their weights and supporting surfaces with the corresponding elements of a bird, their relative inefficiency becomes immediately apparent.

The memorable experiments of Professor Langley on the Potomac River gave rise to the idea that only an engine of extreme lightness could be employed if the flying-machine was ever to become a reality. Since his time biplanes have lifted as many as six passengers, besides the pilot, over short distances. While the ultimate achievement of flight was due to the lightness of the gasoline motor in relation to the power developed, subsequent experiment has demonstrated how the efficiency of the sustaining surfaces can be increased so as to diminish head resistance and to make extreme lightness in the motor desirable only on the score of freight-carrying capacity. The original motor used by the Wrights was comparatively heavy for the power developed.

Because lightness and durability are antagonistic qualities, and because the more trustworthy the machine, the heavier must be its construction, it may well be inferred that the aeroplane motor is not a model of durability or reliability. The aeroplane-builder appears at present willing to tolerate very little reliability, largely because the aeroplane is still in the hands of record-breakers and prize-winners, rather than of ordinary tourists.

The need of improvement in motors was strikingly evinced in the famous Circuit de l'Est of 1910, a circular cross-country race which started from Paris and finished there, and which included the towns of Troyes, Mézières, Douai, and Amiens. The contest was remarkable because the air-men were expected to perform what they had never attempted before. They had to fly over a given course on specified days without being able to choose weather conditions most favorable to them. Eight machines started from Paris, but after the second day the only competitors left were Leblanc and Aubrun on their Blériot monoplanes. The failure of the others was due solely to engine troubles.

It is probable that the future aeroplane will carry two motors instead of one, each motor independently operative, so that if one fails, the other will still be able to drive the machine safely through the air. For military purposes, at least, such a double-motor aeroplane is absolutely necessary. Imagine a spy in the air compelled to glide ignominiously down into an enemy's camp, because his engine failed him! Mere considerations of safety also demand the installation of two motors on a flying-machine. In March, 1910, the French aviator Crochon fell to the ground in a cross-country flight from Mourmelon to Châlons, because his motor broke down. Le Blon was killed at San Sebastian on April 2, 1910, as a result of a similar motor trouble. During the Nice meeting in April, 1910, Chavez and Latham mercifully dropped into the Mediterranean, also because of motor trouble. All of these accidents might have been avoided if the aviators could have relied upon a second motor.

It is likely that in the near future we may be able to economize motive power by practically applying the discovery of Langley that at high speed less supporting surface and less power are required than at low speeds. A machine may yet be constructed which, taking advantage of this law, will be provided with a supporting surface adjustable in area, so that it can start with a large surface, and reduce it, when travelling at full speed, to a mere fin.

What will this flying-machine of the future be like? He would be a wise man indeed who could predict with any degree of accuracy its exact form and dimensions. The dreams of the old-time imaginative novelist seem almost to be realized now. Mr. R. W. A. Brewer, an English authority, sees a larger and a heavier machine than we have at present, a kind of air-yacht, weighing at least three tons, and built with a boat body. The craft of his fancy will be decked in. It will carry several persons conveniently, and will be provided with living and sleeping accommodations. He prophesies that it will fly at speeds of 150 to 200 miles an hour, for the reason that high speeds in flying mean less expenditure of power than lower speeds. Mr. F. W. Lancaster, another authority, entertains similar views on the necessity of high speed. He argues that the aeroplane speed must be twice that of the maximum wind in which the machine is to be driven. A certain amount of automatic stability is thus obtained; for a machine travelling at a hundred miles an hour is practically uninfluenced by gusts and eddies that might prove disastrous at thirty-five miles an hour. A modern *Lusitania* plunges undaunted through waves that would be perilous to a schooner. If it is ever possible for an aeroplane to travel at such terrific velocities, the United States will become the playground of the Chicago aviator. Daily trips of one thousand miles would not be extraordinary.

It seems certain that special starting and alighting grounds will be ultimately provided throughout the world. If street-cars must have their stables and their yards, it is not unreasonable to demand the provision of suitable aeroplane stations. Depots or towers will be erected for the storage of fuel and oil—garages on stilts, in a word. The aviator in need of supplies may some day signal his wants, lower a trailing line, and pick up gasoline by some such device as we now employ to catch mail-sacks on express trains.

The early days of the bicycle and the automobile industries offer a close parallel to the present position of the aeroplane industry. The pioneers having shown the way, the machine immediately became an instrument of sport. Speed was the thing first desired, and the speed of anything that moves can best be demonstrated in competition. Bicycle and automobile races became and still are, to some extent, the manufacturer's opportunity of testing and demonstrating the quality of his machines. Long before the manufacture of either touring-bicycles or touring-automobiles assumed its present proportions, the production of the racing-machine was all-important. The flying-machine is now in this stage. Races and endurance tests will be the battles from which will emerge the flying-machine of the future—the machine capable of sustained flights, at high speed, many hours in duration. The racer will give birth to the touring-flyer, just as the touring-car of to-day was evolved from the racing-car of ten years ago.

Compared with the flying-machine of the future, the motor-car will seem as tame and dull as a cart drawn by a weary nag on a dusty country road. Confined to no route in particular, free as a bird, an adventurous pilot can satisfy his craving for speed in the high-powered monoplane of the future. Even the most leisurely of air-touring machines will travel at velocities that only a racing-automobile now attains, while the air racer will flit over us, a mere blur to the eye and a buzz to the ear. In an hour or two a whole province will be traversed; in a day half a continent. Swifter than any storm will be the flight of its pilot. If the black, whirling maelstrom of a cyclone looms up before him, he can make a détour or even outspeed it; for the velocity of his machine will be greater than that of the fiercest of howling, wintry blasts. At a gale which now drives every aviator timorously to cover, he snaps a contemptuous finger, plunges through it in a breathless dash, and emerges again in the sunshine, as indifferent to his experience as a locomotive engineer after running through a drizzling rain.

12.
Cross Country in the Aeroplane (1910)

WILBUR WRIGHT FLYING WITH A PASSENGER OVER THE MOORLAND NEAR PAU.

CROSS COUNTRY IN
THE AEROPLANE
by W. F. Bradley

Illustrated with Photographs

WILBUR Wright was the idol of France. The incomprehensible American had been popularly described as a "bluffeur" when he invaded the land of the Gaul with his crudely constructed flyer and his unmechanical looking motor. But the stranger proved his worth so thoroughly as to arouse the enthusiasm of the Frenchmen to such a pitch that they could see no good in their own aviators.

An act of daring was needed to prove that the Frenchman was not three years behind the American. It must be more than an ordinary flight over a prepared ground and under ideal weather conditions. It must be that sort of daring that the French denominate "culot"—a combination of cheek and pure daredeviltry.

Henry Farman decided to provide it when he gave the order to Marcel Herbster, his faithful mechanic, to verify motor and aëroplane with more than usual care. There was suppressed excitement among the knot of people gathered around his Voisin biplane standing on a corner of the aviation ground at Châlons-sur-Marne, for the

153

PAULHAN FLYING FROM MOURMELON TO CHALONS-
SUR-MARNE.

vast plain on the outskirts of the city of Rheims, after covering twenty miles above the tree tops, villages, streams, highroads, railways, and other natural and artificial obstructions. France was amazed, for until then the pilots of artificial birds had considered an aviary necessary for their evolutions. Their aëroplanes had been built for the upper regions, but until that hour not even the best of them had dared to escape beyond the limits of an unobstructed plain or a sandy military drill ground upon which they could descend at the slightest sign of danger.

Farman's exploit brought renewed hope to the French school. Wilbur Wright was taken off the pedestal and the Anglo-Frenchman put in his place. But behind all the popular applause the voice of the scientific expert could be heard in disapproval. Even Farman admitted that it was a terrible moment when he found himself above the tall poplar trees and wondered if he would clear them.

The following day, in another part of France, Louis Bleriot broke away from the restraining aviation ground and attempted a free flight over hill and valley. But the echoes of the Farman flight were still too loud for much attention to be paid to the Bleriot exploit, and though the most persistent and coolly daring aviator in France had traveled twenty-one miles, starting from his garage and returning there, after two voluntary stops, without any outside assistance, he did not receive all the credit to which he was fully entitled for his exploit.

It is to Henry Farman, then, that the honor must be awarded for giving the aëroplane its true application. But

rumor had leaked out that something sensational was about to happen.

The usual pull on the propeller and a run over the ground with the sound of the motor growing less and less was followed by the gradual rising of the aëroplane and the cessation of the suspense which always accompanies the start of a flight. Instead of skimming partridge-like, Farman quickly rose to a level with the tops of the tall poplar trees lining the course, then still higher until he was far above the monument on the high ground at the opposite end of the field. Then he disappeared, escaping from the narrow limits of the aërodrome like a huge bird that has at last realized the full power of its wings.

The first cross-country flight had begun. It ended half an hour later when the big machine fluttered down upon a

for his daring exploit aviators might still have been rolling the ground before attempting to fly over it, and the artificial bird might still have had the same relation to the natural bird as the river boat has to the ocean-going yacht. When aviators had secured sufficient confidence in their mounts to soar away unfettered by any ties to Mother Earth, the flying machine became a practical instrument. Incidentally, the showman's business received a severe blow, for how could he secure spectators if his birds were likely at any minute to escape from the boundaries he had traced for them, or to rise so high in the air that penniless Peter outside would have as clear a view as the grand-stand occupant within?

Less than six months after the first free flight it became evident that aërodromes were useless except for learners and as starting and landing grounds. This was never more clearly proved than on the day when Count de Lambert rose from the aërodrome at Juvisy, a few miles to the south of Paris, and after encircling the field twice, disappeared from the view of the spectators who had paid to see flights. While the grand stand saw an aëroplane rise from the ground, disappear behind the hill, then return and settle down quietly after an absence of about one hour, the Parisian, merely by coming to his door, could enjoy the thrilling sight of an aëroplane soaring round the Eiffel tower, the highest monument in the world, at a height of a quarter of a mile from the ground.

The cool audacity of a man who would dare to fly over one of the most crowded cities in the world, to rise to a height that had never before

been attained by a power-driven machine, held the spectators spellbound, too astounded to cheer, too amazed to utter more than wordless exclamations.

In addition to Farman, Bleriot, and De Lambert, there are not more than half a dozen others who have as yet made free flights over land and water. Hubert Latham has to his credit two attempts to fly across the twenty-one miles of salt water separating France from England. Three weeks had been spent in waiting for a calm that the natives declared would never come. From an hour before daybreak to the hour of sunset the tricolor flag had been watched in the hope that it would fall limp and lifeless.

At last, in the early hours of a July morning, the standing corn ceased to

LOUIS BLERIOT CROSSING THE CHANNEL FROM FRANCE TO ENGLAND.

bend its head before the breeze, and in a few minutes a well-prepared white-winged flyer had soared above the French cliffs and for the first time in the history of man was speeding above the open sea. Half the distance had been covered when a mechanical defect —a mere trifle that would have delayed an automobile but a few seconds—

to a shooting party on his estate sixteen miles away.

"Come on your aëroplane," laughingly added the marquis.

"I will," replied Latham.

And he kept his word. A rifle and cartridges were placed in the boat-like body of the flyer, Latham mounted, started the engine, rose from the ground,

COMTE DE LAMBERT CIRCLING THE EIFFEL TOWER.

caused the engine to stop and allowed the aëroplane to glide into the sea.

Then Bleriot appeared, made his preparations quietly, took advantage of a calm moment, flew over the Channel, and landed safely in England. Undaunted, Latham made another attempt to fly to the English coast, but was again stopped when within one hundred yards of the shore.

Hubert Latham, if he failed to fly the Channel, has the honor of being the first man to keep an appointment by aëroplane. He was at Châlons, testing new machines and training pupils, when Marquis de Polignac invited him

and directed the nose of his aëroplane in the direction of the shooting lodge sixteen miles to windward. When a servant announced that a flying machine was in sight, the guests rushed out in excitement, the marquis with a smile on his face, for he knew that his invitation had been accepted. After a successful day's shooting, Latham placed the game in the body of the aëroplane, mounted, and disappeared with a wave of his hand, landing twenty minutes later at the door of his shed after passing directly over the roof of his own hotel.

Louis Paulhan is another daring

COMTE DE LAMBERT FLYING OVER A STREAM.

SANTOS-DUMONT ON A CROSS COUNTRY FLIGHT WITH HIS LITTLE "DEMOISELLE."

cross-country flyer, who is naturally as much at home in the air as is a sailor at sea. He and Latham are rivals. They are of the same age, their sheds are only a few yards apart, both commenced to fly at the same period, and both are unusually skilled. Paulhan, an ordinary mechanic who would have remained unknown but for the aëroplane, graduated in the dirigible balloon service. From a youth he was connected with airships; even when he accomplished his compulsory military service, he was in the dirigible balloon corps.

He built a model aëroplane and was later provided with a man-carrying flyer. From the first he showed a preference for high altitudes. When flying before the president of the republic at Juvisy in the late fall of 1909, he broke away from the aërodrome, flew over the Seine, the highroads packed with automobiles, and the market gardens. Then he returned and landed within a few feet of the presidential box.

Later he made a trip from the aviation ground of Châlons to the military

town of the same name, eighteen miles away. There was a strong breeze behind him when he started, making possible a speed of sixty miles an hour, at which rate the automobiles, obliged to follow the sinuosities of the road, were unable to follow. A circuit of the town was made, thus giving an object lesson to the military occupants of the ease with which all their fortifications could have been discovered and their plans laid bare. The return was a beat to windward, with the aëroplane obliged to tack like a sailing ship, while the accompanying automobiles rushed ahead and won the race home.

The future doubtless reserves curious adventures for those who travel by air. This was shown by an incident which occurred to Santos-Dumont. He had started a little before nightfall and while a storm was brewing. Without any well-defined object in view, he let his aëroplane carry him where it willed, only to awake suddenly to the fact that he had lost his bearings.

As there was a large forest ahead and

HUBERT LATHAM PASSING OVER MOURMELON ON HIS WAY TO A SHOOTING PARTY.

the gathering storm was behind him, he decided to land on the lawn of a country residence near at hand. The lady of the house and her daughter urged the unexpected visitor to take dinner and pass the night at the chateau. While the meal was in progress, an automobile drove up to the door, and a young man jumped out and rushed into the house with the news that Santos-Dumont had set out on a flight and never returned.

"Allow me to present him to you," replied his mother.

Newspaper men and intimate friends spent half the night scouring the country for the lost aviator. Next morning Santos-Dumont drove back to his shed with his aëroplane attached to the rear of his host's automobile.

Maurice Farman, brother of the better known Henry, is proud of the fact that he has never made a flight except over open country; he is still prouder of the fact that he holds the world's long-distance cross-country record for a journey from his shed at Buc, ten miles from Paris, to the town of Chartres. The distance is forty-four miles, which were covered in fifty-nine minutes, at an average height of about three hundred feet. On the whole, the country is level, with the exception of a portion at the outset and another part near Chartres, where a deep valley has to be crossed.

On the trip Farman guided himself by the main road and the railway line from Paris to Bordeaux. As he sped along in a southwesterly direction he was clearly visible to the occupants of the trains.

In all probability Farman will continue his southwesterly flight in stages as far as Bordeaux, 350 miles from Paris. There is a fascination about a flight to the capital of the wine country, for it is over this route that the early bicycle and automobile races were held. Farman himself, in the days when he was a cyclist, riding tandem with his brother Henry, and later when he drove powerful automobiles, has many a time raced over the smooth roads from Paris to Bordeaux.

Already one of the greatest difficul-

ties of the cross-country flyer is in finding his course. It will be necessary to cultivate a homing instinct, or, better, as is already being done in France, to erect conspicuous landmarks and establish landing grounds for the benefit of travelers in the air. Louis Paulhan has had to abandon his projected flight in England from London to Manchester, owing to the impossibility of finding his way through the air of the fog-bound country.

Count de Lambert, although he had studied his course thoroughly, was in difficulties for a few seconds after he had rounded the Eiffel tower and found himself over Paris and desirous of returning to his garage at Juvisy. Bleriot says that he was completely lost for a few seconds during his cross-channel flight, for he had shot ahead of the destroyer, and yet was not near enough to the English coast to see it. In order to pick up his bearings he had to describe a huge circle in midchannel, out of sight of any land, until the destroyer arrived and showed him the course to follow.

Although the first instances of cross-country flying have taken place in France, the most notable instance of free flight in America being that of Wilbur Wright up the Hudson at the time of the Hudson-Fulton celebration, it is likely that its greatest development will be in such countries as the United States. The vast tracts of open country remove all danger in case of an enforced landing. The greater the distance, too, the greater the utility of the aëroplane. As speed is likely to increase enormously, transcontinental and other long-distance trips will be undertaken by the aërial way when time is of value.

France intends that the year 1910 shall be one of cross-country flights. An aëroplane race from Paris to Brussels, a distance of two hundred miles, is being planned and the English Channel will doubtless be crossed several times during the year. Several aviators hope to fly from the capital to Bordeaux, and numerous trips along the shores of the Mediterranean are projected.

13.
The Unsolved Problem of Human Flight
(1912)

THE UNSOLVED PROBLEM OF HUMAN FLIGHT

By AUGUSTUS POST

ILLUSTRATED WITH DIAGRAMS AND PHOTOGRAPHS

A Record of Failures That May Yet Point the Way to a Glorious Success

WITH aerial flotillas forming part of the military equipment of the most conservative nations, with millions pouring in from popular subscriptions to strengthen these air fleets in France and Germany, with at least six thousand air-going aeroplanes leaving the world's factories this year, some to make the tremendous distance of 7,800 miles from Peking to Paris, some to carry government mail on regular schedule, it may sound absurd to say that the problem of human flight is yet unsolved. But this is literally true. Not yet has man succeeded, at least publicly, in propelling himself through the air with no other motive force than he can himself supply. We have machines that fly and take up men with them as manipulators or passengers, but, in the strict sense, human flight we have not, nor have ever had. The dream of Leonardo da Vinci is still as far from realization as that of Icarus. He who has watched a vulture, a sea gull or a hummingbird knows that if this be flight man does not fly.

This is no mere twisting of definitions. One of the last letters written by Wilbur Wright, speaking of the new type of aeroplane upon which the brothers were at that time engaged, says, "Everybody who has ever seen a buzzard flying knows there must be some method whereby a human being can also remain in the air, once he really finds himself aloft. The sole difficulty is that nature has provided the birds with the means of soaring without exertion to themselves, while human beings must devise an artificial means of achieving the same result. The real problem now confronting us is to find out whether we, too, like the birds, once we are in the air, can stay in it indefinitely."

In other words, the problem of human flight must really be solved if aviation is really to progress. Aviation has come to the point where it must face this question squarely; if for no other reason, commercial considerations make it imperative. A crisis is imminent. It is not putting the matter too strongly to say that the whole future of the industry rests upon the solution of this problem. The attention of constructors has been directed for so long to the motor, with the object of developing power and speed —power that will force almost anything into the air and keep it there until it tears itself to pieces—that the aeroplane is fast becoming "a brief-lived, dangerous toy for colossal fortunes." The automobile "developed" in this one direction until it was a ghastly projectile tearing around a track in the gray of early morning, bearing men, for the time scarcely human, through a mad mob of speed fiends. If it had developed only in this direction, there would not be upon every road of the country the thousands of touring cars bearing whole families through the broad country at a rate that does not reduce the landscape to a blur.

There will always be use for the aeroplane of tremendous speed and high power, just as we still have automobiles

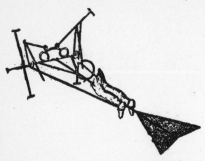

Leonardo da Vinci (*circ*. 1500) had the idea of mechanical flight in which the legs should be used to depress the wings and the arms to elevate them.

Besnier's plan (1678) was for wings operated by feet and hands that should open on the up stroke and close on the down.

Launoy and Bienvenue (1784) exhibited this first helicopter before the Academy of Sciences, Paris. It is composed of two helices turning in opposite directions.

Le Bris (1857). The mechanism was to be operated by levers.

In this apparatus, made by De Groof (1864), operated by three levers, the inventor was killed.

such as those which made last year's records—of speed and mortality—but for reasons of simple mechanics, speeds practically utilizable in the air will not very greatly surpass those that can be reached on the ground, with the exception that these speeds can be attained on the ground only with great risk and discomfort, whereas they can be enjoyed in safety in the air owing to the elimination of roadbed, obstacles, and the blur of the near object. If the aeroplane is to develop only by developing power— it is a catchword of the profession that "you can ride on a shingle if you can apply enough power to it"—the sole avenue of usefulness that will soon remain to it will be that of warfare. The future of aviation as an industry, therefore, will rest upon the solution of the problem of constructing low-powered

MAN'S UNAVAILING DREAM

It is curious to see how human hopes and lowed similar lines of development and created

aeroplanes which will fly with even such a small engine as that used on a motorcycle. Then, and then only, will the manufacture of aeroplanes assume normal conditions and enter, as any industry must, into the general stream of civilization.

The aeroplane now seems to be in the class with thirteen-inch guns and military ordnance of the utmost value and necessity to the battleship—in fact, the whole ship is designed and arranged

A flight—of the fancy—attributed to de la Bretonne (date unknown).

Wings with which the inventor, de Baequeville (1742), actually attempted to fly across the Seine.

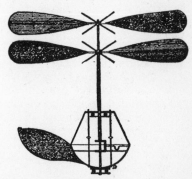

Bright (1859) devised a scheme of lifting helices operating in opposite directions.

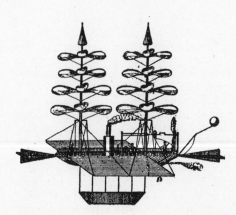

This apparatus, attributed to M. de la Landelle, was a combination of helices, planes and parachutes—with a steam engine to boot.

Penaud's aeroplane (1867) flew with the aid of a twisted rubber as the toy aeroplanes do to-day.

OF HUMAN FLIGHT

efforts from Leonardo da Vinci down, have followed here and there a hint of the modern aeroplane.

solely for the convenience and freedom of action of these big guns. Cannon are useless for private and individual purposes, and the development of the aeroplane seems to be tending in just this direction at this period of its existence.

In the same way that manufacturers place revolvers and small arms in the hands of the general public, some less powerful and less expensive form of flying machine should be put on the market to revive the interest of the individual

who would like to engage actively in this form of recreation or excitement, but now finds that it requires a prohibitive amount of both effort and money to keep an aeroplane in commission.

This is the real reason why strong interest attaches to the recent trials of the "aviette," or "cycloplane," in France and the attempts now being made to fly man-power machines. The "Prize of the Decametre" offered for a flight of only a little over thirty feet has a special importance because it marks a new line of progress. If a machine can be built that will get into the air and stay there for ever so short a time, with no greater motive force than a man can supply, its construction will throw a much-needed light on the more practical low-power-motor machine of the future. This is why the prize was established, why two trials have already been held, and why, though the public laughed at some of the contestants, its laughter was by no means sneering.

Almost every great aviator and constructor within reach of Paris attended the contests, where such men as Bleriot, Koechlin, the elder Farman, and Deutsch de la Meurthe gave applause, sympathy, and fellowship to the contestants, most of them humble workmen. For the bicycle is trying to fly; or, to put it in other words, the parents of the lofty "avion" were trying to arrange a marriage with the humble "bicyclette," from which at last the "aviette," or "cycloplane," may come into being.

The balloon has already gone through a similar stage of development, and the activities of the hot-air balloonist and the parachute jumper have kept aeronautics alive on many occasions when interest flagged in the nobler forms of gas ballooning and dirigible balloon activity. The parachute is a simple form of gliding machine and the new exhibition combination of aeroplane flight and parachute drop will undoubtedly develop a practical method of landing a passenger from an aeroplane. General James Allen, Chief of the U. S. Signal Corps, tells me that this will have a real value in war operations, which immediately calls attention to the practical application of aviation principles to the parachute or the substitution of a practical gliding machine for the parachute which can be attached to a hot-air balloon and raised into the air very quickly to a great altitude. After observations are made the operator could free himself from his balloon and glide down against the wind at such an angle that in almost all cases he could return to the starting point. This was the idea of Professor James Montgomery, of California, who was one of the early experimenters with gliders, and who lost his own life last year while gliding in one of his machines.

The Montgomery glider had remarkable spectacular features, for it could be so handled that it would turn over in the air and perform a complete revolution sideways without serious danger to the aeronaut. This was frequently done by one of Professor Montgomery's professional aviators to demonstrate his complete mastery of the machine.

Otto Lillienthal, who was experimenting in Germany just before this time and who is conceded by all the savants of aviation to be the father of practical and successful gliding, obtained such proficiency in the use of his apparatus that he felt perfectly at home in the air and was most firm in his conviction that he was on the verge of accomplishing human flight. He had built flapping wings to apply to his wing surfaces and had calculated that by applying all his power at proper moments he could ascend sufficiently, so that, combining his skill in gliding and taking advantage of every foot of altitude gained, he could accomplish indefinitely prolonged flight. It is unfortunate that Lillienthal was not able to carry out his experiments in this direction, for with his consummate skill and experience in the fundamental principles of flight he, above all others, seemed best equipped to make scientific and practical advancement in this direction.

Lillienthal looked forward to the time when gliding would be one of the regular youthful athletic sports, such as coasting and swimming; we emulate the fishes, so why not the birds? he said. Mr. Octave Chanute, of our own country, also looked forward to the time when gliding would be a real sport. He perfected an apparatus by which the aviator and machine could be towed or drawn through the air by means of a windlass operated by a motor to obtain an initial altitude. A wave of enthusiasm for this form of aerial activity passed over the college world a year ago and an intercollegiate contest was held by the Harvard Aeronautical Society at Boston. It was quite successful at that time. Competitive trials were held, the contestants gliding from a high platform or structure built to afford a suitable starting place, so arranged as to allow the apparatus always to start facing the wind.

This intensely interesting meeting seemed, however, to require the addition of some new element to make it a continued success. Some application of power seemed necessary to enable the skilful control obtained over the apparatus and the remarkable ability shown by many of the embryo aviators to keep its equilibrium to be utilized for an indefinite time. It is not enough to be limited by the pull of gravity; some

of ten minutes over the brow of a sand hill, at times descending at a very small angle and again being carried upward and backward over the starting point.

Of course the machine was falling in relation to the direction of the wind all this time, but the wind was blowing up

OTTO LILLIENTHAL SOUGHT THE SECRET OF MAN FLIGHT THROUGH THE GLIDER AND MET HIS DEATH

other power must be applied or secured in order to regain lost altitude, and thus prolong the flight and accomplish real sailing or soaring flight like that of the birds.

The Wright Brothers were seriously attracted to this phase of the problem of aviation, and Mr. Alexander Ogilvie, one of the most skilful, as well as intelligent, fliers of England, who piloted a Wright racer in the International Gordon Bennett contest, came over to accompany Orville and Wilbur to Kitty Hawk, S. C., last winter, where they studied and experimented for the solution of this very question. Mr. Orville Wright, with consummate skill, showed not only the possibilities of delicate adjustment of the controls of his gliding machine, but, at the same time, his personal ability to solve the secrets of the wind currents by hovering for a period

faster than the descent was allowed to take place, so the result was a rise relative to the surface of the ground.

A fine adjustment of controls and a utilization of the favoring currents of air is no doubt the very method that the bird itself uses whenever it sails or soars on motionless, or I should say, non-flapping wings, for there is no doubt that what would appear to one observing from the ground to be lack of motion in a bird's wing is really a continuous process of very subtle and minute changes and adjustments of the wing itself in order to enable the proper resulting action to take place.

In the study of the bird's soaring and sailing flight we can find three localities which seem to be most favorably adapted for this form of flying. First: in the region of mountains where the eagles and condors, the real kings of the air,

A MILITARY REPRESENTATIVE AT ISSY-LES-MOULINEAUX WHOSE UNIFORM AT LEAST GOT SPECIAL MENTION.   PROPELLER OPERATED BY PEDALS
NOTE THE SEPARATE RUDDER

usually reside and as a rule where they remain, flying at lofty altitudes, building their nests high up on the inaccessible crags and separate peaks, safe from intrusion, whose jutting rocks offer good landing places for these heavy bodied birds, and where they are able to get a good start by swooping down from these dizzy heights, to wheel and turn in any direction that it may be necessary to find the needful elevator current of air that must exist in a mountainous country. The winds that blow against the sloping side of the mountains receive an ascending direction, as is clearly perceived when approaching a mountain range in a balloon; the balloon which seems about to dash into the side of the rocky or forest-covered obstruction starts ascending as if ballast had been thrown out, and almost unperceived rises and slides over the top of the range as a canoe is carried around a rock in an eddying and swiftly flowing current of a river.

You must be very careful after gaining the summit, however, for on the leeward side, some distance away from the top of the ridges, there will be a down draft which sucks you down possibly to destruction if you are not very careful. This down draft, or eddy current, curls in back of the top of the mountain just as

dust curls around the back of the tonneau of a motor car going at high speed over a dusty road, or like an eddy of water back of the big rock in our trout stream, only the air eddy is in the vertical plane instead of the horizontal, as in the case of water flowing swiftly by a corner of rock which juts up abruptly.

When the eagle or condor gets this lifting breeze he rises high over the peaks and soars in great circles. If he descends on the lee side of the range, by coming in close to the side of the mountain he can be carried up on the eddying wind until he gets to the main flowing current and joins it to repeat the process over again, as do sticks and floating objects that get caught in eddies of water and circle round and round in the whirlpool. If they could adapt their shape and form to the current they could get out and float on as they wished, as the birds do in the whirls of air.

No doubt fishes that live in swift water make use of the eddy currents to help them stem the tide; ship captains also do the same thing when they out-maneuver the tidal and wind currents by hugging the shore.

Gulls may be seen playing around the side of a vessel or high cliff near the sea, where, as you lie prone near the

TRYING FOR THE DECIMETRE PRIZE OFFERED FOR A FLIGHT OVER TAPES FOUR
INCHES FROM THE GROUND AND ONE METRE APART

edge, you can watch them, as I have often done, as they are carried up on the wind eddy if it is blowing away from the face of the cliff. As they reach the top on apparently motionless wings the wind, blowing out, will carry them away at almost a right angle, and at some distance out, if they drop down, they will glide in close to the face of the cliff and be carried up again to repeat the journey. As you lie in the grass, almost concealed, these birds sometimes come within a distance of a few feet of where you are and their every movement can be studied in the most minute detail.

A second favorable locality for soaring and sailing flight is to be found over great stretches of level country, deserts and places in hot climates. Here the most famous of all air sailors, the buzzard, is to be found in great numbers; hawks and vultures are also found in these heated areas of the earth, where temperature plays such a great part in the creation of ascending air currents. Here the earth's surface is like the top of a great stove heated by the sun, which causes the warm air to rise. You can easily see it moving in undulating waves as you look over hot fields at the horizon or toward some dark background. This ascending air must be replaced in some way, for it is not possible for a vacuum

to exist in the air, notwithstanding the fact that a great deal is said about "holes in the air"—"Swiss cheese" atmosphere, as it is often called.

This term originated in a very interesting way, as many of our expressive phrases do. The originator of this phrase and catchword, as it proved to be, was Mr. Charles F. Willard, the first aeroplane pupil of Mr. Glenn H. Curtiss, and the son of Mr. A. P. Willard, who was thrown out of Miss Harriet Quimby's monoplane while flying as a passenger with her to the Boston Light and back during the recent Boston aviation meet.

Mr. Willard was flying in the early days of aviation at Los Angeles, Cal., and one day, when the air was very treacherous and rocked his machine so violently that it threatened to upset it, he landed after an exciting escape from what seemed like a desperate situation and said, "The wind nearly threw me out of the seat of my machine; I would go along a ways and suddenly my seat would drop from under me, leaving me sitting on air. It's like riding in an automobile with big holes in the road. In fact," he said, "it's all full of holes up there, just like Swiss cheese."

From this vivid description and happily or unhappily chosen simile, delivered on the spur of the moment, the world gath-

THIS TYPE OF AVIETTE HAS THE FRONT WHEEL FILLED IN AS STEERING
RUDDER AND A MOVABLE TAIL TO ELEVATE AND DESCEND
AS IN THE MONOPLANE

ered the impression that there are "holes in a hole," or in the air itself, or what would, in scientific terms, be known as a vacuum. Long dissertations are written on this subject. I have had many people say, "Does the air really have holes in it?" Their only scientific interest in aerology or meteorology seems to be to desire an explanation of how this impossibility can exist.

What appear to be holes in the air are simply descending currents which occur by the side of rising currents. When passing, as rapidly as an aeroplane does, from an ascending current into a very clearly defined current of air blowing downward, the wings of the aeroplane, caught by the quick change of the direction of the air, respond at once and the whole machine drops out from under you as if it were a veritable hole and there were no support at all. Naturally you are bounced up out of your seat, or rather the seat leaves you, and unless strapped in you find yourself sitting on air with nothing to purchase against to enable you to operate the controls. Almost all aviators strap themselves in either with a belt, which can be released instantly, or with two straps which go over the shoulders and can be readily shaken off in case of necessity.

These currents are very noticeable when you are in a balloon and drift into them; the sensitive instruments used for navigating these air craft record the sudden variations in altitude with great accuracy. In a balloon there are no complications caused by high speed, and the fact that, on account of the length of an aeroplane, the front end of the machine may be in a descending current of air while the tail is in an ascending current, which, as can be readily seen, would greatly increase the resulting action.

Anyone can very easily observe these varying currents in the early morning or when there is no apparent wind blowing over the water, the surface of which seems to be all streaked with glassy lines and little "cat's paws" playing here and there, "slants" of wind yachtsmen call them. Often a yacht race is won by skilful maneuvering among these little vagaries of wind. Often, too, the light topsails will draw when it seems that there is no wind at all on the surface of the water. These streaks are caused by the fact that just in that place the wind is either rising or descending perpendicularly and not blowing horizontally at all; in other words, it is the foot of a column of air.

On each side of these streaks, however, may be noticed small waves, perhaps getting larger the farther they are away from the calm streak. These are caused by the wind blowing into the foot of the column of rising and heated air, or possibly the descending current of cooler air spreading out to rise again after having become warmed by contact with the warm surface of the water.

In the calm spots at the foot of a column of air that is descending there will be an area at the surface of the water where the air is slightly under pressure, forming a cone and perhaps quite still, while at the height of the topsails the wind will be blowing to one side or the other, turning at the point of the cone of relatively still air. The same action takes place over heated areas of ground, such as over hot plains. Little whirlwinds in the dust may be seen ascending from different points where the conditions have caused the action to start. The buzzards sail around on these columns of rising air, wheeling or circling about, no doubt going from one to the other as their fancy suggests.

We, who casually observe the birds, are accustomed to think that they can go where they will, but it is quite possible, and in fact most probable, that they are just as much hampered as we are, and that they, too, must observe strict laws; so when we think they are sporting at their own sweet will they are in all probability being blown away or forced to take a very roundabout or circling method to get where they want to go, even if they know where they are bound, which I am sometimes inclined to doubt. Birds probably go where it is easiest to fly and where the wind eddies and currents are most favorable.

One other place, and the third, is naturally adapted to sailing flight. This is where, perhaps, the most marvelous and wonderful feats that are performed in the air occur, particularly those almost unbelievable flights of thousands of miles without resting, where the albatross is known to sleep on the wing while impelled by the rhythmic pulsations of the wind, which it must catch at just the right moment to check its fall and receive a proportionate part of its force

LAMOTTE, PARIS, AT THE STARTING LINE FOR THE DECIMETRE.   THE EXTREME ANGLE OF PLANES WAS A FEATURE OF HIS MACHINE

in such a way that it will be impelled forward at the same time. The most persistent observation fails to show anything like the beating of a wing in any of its agile movements. The only solution to the problem of this lack of orthodox action in these ocean-going birds is that the wind beats on their wings and by instinctive adjustment they resolve this force into sustaining and propelling power very much as a middleman lives off the difference between the buyer and the seller, where gravity and the bird's weight is the constant selling force and the intermittent pulsations of the wind are like the numerous buyers.

When the expert aeroplane builder can produce a machine so proportioned and so cleverly fashioned that the practiced artist of the air can lie back in his comfortable seat and by a rhythmic and monotonous motion synchronize the form of his broad wings to the undulations of the air, following the movements of the billows and beating on their surfaces with the same regularity that propeller blades beat the air in a power machine, then man's rivalry of the bird will be complete. Such a picture lulls us to sleep to dream of interminable flights which the albatross in reality makes before our very eyes. Are we going to stop our efforts at the very threshold of the problem of flight? The ancient query, "If the bird can fly, why can't I?" has become, "If the birds can sail the sky, why so can I!" and their secrets are teasing us on just as before. The powers in the wind itself are sought and the undeveloped abilities of men are finding free expression in the realm of air.

It was on the first of last February that the great bicycle firm of Peugeot Brothers, long known as generous prize givers, announced that they would award the sum of 10,000 francs to the first man to fly over two marks upon a flat surface, one decametre (thirty-three feet) apart, in a machine with no other motive power but what he could himself supply. The announcement made an excitement apparently out of proportion to the distance involved. Peking to Paris—7,800 miles—that was something to talk about; but a paltry thirty-three feet, what is that? The point is, and it is a point that Paris was not slow to see, that the 7,800 miles meant doing what we have already done for a longer time than we have yet done it; the thirty-three feet meant doing what nobody has yet done at all. This prize is a "peg to pull to." It is quality as opposed to quantity. And the French, whose world asset is quality rather than quantity, recognized the value of the undertaking and treated it with the deference due its importance.

When the prize was offered, on the first of February, the new types of machine were non-existent, even in experimental forms; when the lists opened fifteen days later twenty entrants were waiting at nine o'clock in the morning to be sure to get a good place on the list. Before the trial one hundred and ninety-eight had entered, including the familiar names of Gabriel Voisin, well known as one of the Voisin Brothers, builders of the "Voisin" aeroplanes, who were the first to build a successful flying machine in France; Colliex, Ladougne, Dutheil, Piat, Gabriel Poulain, de Kergarion, and M. Goupy, also an aeroplane builder.

The indefatigable prize-givers met the rush with the announcement that as soon as the first prize should be won a second would be offered with harder conditions. It was evident that somebody believed the first man to come to the line would win.

All over France extraordinary tales began to appear about human bats practicing in backyards and doing such wonders that the talk was not of decametres, but of kilometres. Hectic stories about a man that was flying all over the place in a winged bicycle actually scared off some Northern contestants until they found that the tale came from Marseilles, where, as everyone who reads Daudet knows, the southern sun makes mirages in the mind. Peugeot Brothers, however, had evidently seen some of the apparatus, for they announced another prize, that of the decimetre—a thousand francs for the first man to fly over two tapes stretched four inches from the ground and one metre (3 feet 7.9 inches) apart. A more modest flight could hardly be imagined, as if the just-fledged birdling were being tempted, as mother birds tempt their young, to just one little hop, for confidence in all its unused pinions. No one can say that France does not encourage aviation; if she does succeed in holding the empire of the air she will have deserved it; she floats the stately "avions" of war upon a popular subscription of over two and a half million francs and coaxes the timid aviette to flutter

"Aviette," is an improved gliding machine on wheels and includes attempts at such machines as Mouillard dreamed would furnish a simple and popular means of human locomotion, as he watched the great vultures of Cairo rising and falling for thousands of feet without the stroke of a wing, only by using the energy of the wind or of gravity. Apparatus of this kind brings our thought back to the very beginning of aviation, when Lillienthal and then the

A BIPLANE AVIETTE WITH TRICYCLE FUSILLAGE, BUILT BY THE SUPERINTENDENT OF THE VOISIN AEROPLANE FACTORY

at the rate of a thousand francs a metre.

A society for the encouragement of man-power machines has sprung into being with the suggestive name of "Icarus." Its membership includes celebrated patrons of sport, aviators and builders, men of letters, and military authorities. Under their auspices the first trials were held at the historic aviation fields of Issy-les-Moulineaux, on the level stretch between the hangars of the dirigibles and the fortifications, on the 27th of May. There was an assemblage of various types and four men exhibited their machines. The showing already indicated two distinct types of machines, which may be roughly characterized as soaring machines, or jumping machines, and machines fitted with a propeller driven by the aviator.

To give a more accurate description, the first class, which may be termed

Wrights were learning to fly, and the fact that, as we have seen, this was Wilbur Wright's last problem, reminds us that it has been all this time evaded rather than solved.

The second type, or "Cycloplane," as its name implies, is a bicycle equipped with a pair of wings and a tail. The angle of the wings being regulated, the operator pedals violently. When the speed is as high as possible, the elevating rudder is turned and the angle of the wings slightly increased, and the machine by the speed acquired is calculated to get up into the air. Most of the machines are of this type. This class approaches more nearly an aeroplane. It is a two-wheeled bicycle frame, whose pedals turn an aerial propeller at the same time that they make the rear wheel of the vehicle move.

Once in the air, the moving wheel of

the bicycle turns in space and all the energy produced by pedaling is absorbed by the propeller. The wings are placed very high above the bicycle so the center of gravity is low. Lateral stability is obtained either by vertical planes or by giving a very sharp dihedral angle to the wings. Of these Comte de Puiseux has constructed several models, one that looks like a box kite on a bicycle, another that suggests a large-sized "model" monoplane. Some are even made on the tricycle plan with biplane surfaces.

On the day of the Peugeot contest in Paris, June 2d, several thousand people, as many indeed as could crowd about the velodrome in the Parc des Princes, assembled early in the morning. Long before the appointed hour the curious machines began to be trundled out upon the course, and when the word to start was given, at nine o'clock, thirty machines were ready; of these twenty-three actually made the trials. The members of Icarus, the blue-badged committee, such heroes as Blèriot, Voisin, and Garros, and representatives of the paper in charge, L'Auto, and of the aviation daily, L'Aero, and of every leading Parisian paper, all were there.

One after another the contestants drove furiously at the barrier, reined up to hurdle over it—and fell. All the morning from nine to twelve, all the afternoon from two till five, there was not a pause. Not one met the conditions. The best machine of all, and one that will certainly bear watching, was that entered by the superintendent of the Voisin factory, a little "canard" with a highly interesting form of wing surface. One much desired machine, that of Ladougne, with which Lavalade had actually flown at Juvisy some days before, did not appear. To the chagrin of all, it had been broken the day before the contest in practice work and could not be brought into shape in time.

A soldier in full uniform manipulating aviette No. 151 received a personal and patriotic ovation, but the applause, the sympathy, and not a little of the laughter went to a fiery-eyed man of Montrouge, Vincent, who rode a bicycle equipped with two planes, upon which he charged the line like Don Quixote—only, unlike the Knight of the Rueful Countenance, he charged with the windmill on his back instead of against him. At intervals through the morning he contested for the Prize of the Decametre, and incessantly, until the close of the contest, rode furiously against the tape, reining up his steed like a witch on a broomstick, never once getting off the ground and never once losing his splendid courage.

When the contest was ended, by the watch, not only the Prize of the Decametre remained to be gained, but the modest decimetre prize was still for the winning. The newspaper in charge awarded each contestant actually appearing a silver medal and the thanks of the world of aviation, such as the great airmen had given them in person, saying that what the new art needed was brave fellows willing to make mistakes in public, so that the ground could be cleared at the beginning.

On July 5th Gabriel Poulain succeeded in winning the decimetre prize of one thousand francs ($200) flying in the presence of a commission from the Aero Club of France at Chatillon and clearing on his cycloplane two tapes three feet 7.9 inches apart and four inches from the ground. He made the distance twice, covering in all eleven feet nine inches at the first trial and ten feet nine inches at his second trial in the reverse direction.

The fact that so many had failed with their machines was not so surprising as that any of them should ever have thought they could succeeed, so completely lacking were they in evidence of even rudimentary knowledge of such principles as have been learned governing mechanical flight. The machines were much too heavy and the head resistance was such as no feeble motive power could overcome. The contestants were more athletes than aviators or even mechanics; they evidently thought the great thing was to be able to pedal furiously instead of paying attention to the construction of the machine, which is a matter of as much finesse as that of an aeroplane to be shot up into the air by a one hundred and eighty horsepower motor.

Every experienced and informed man can see by the very mistakes that were made that the big prize may be won and the problem of human flight, at least in its simplest form, at last fully solved. M. Blèriot is quoted as saying that this prize can be won, and he thought that a monoplane bicycle, with folding wings that could be instantly spread, would win it, but it would cost a good deal to build the machine—more than the amount of the prize. It is not a task for mere athletes, nor for dreamers, nor for inventors aiming to produce a brand-new revolutionary type of flying machine; it will undoubtedly be the result of a refinement of construction in the aeroplane itself.

The perseverance of Peugeot Brothers is equal to the needs of the case. They evidently want the big prize to be won, and they evidently earnestly desire that it shall be in another trial this month; if not won then, it will be tried for in April, 1913, and again in June.

It is to be wished that someone with a like true sportsman's spirit would endow a similar prize in America. There has been a curious interplay of ideas at the outset of aviation between France and America in more than one instance. It was a crippled French inventor, who, since he might not walk, longed to fly, that made flying toys thirty-five years ago, of such ingenuity and charm that they were exported to many lands. One of these Penaud models was the one that a certain Methodist bishop bought in New York and brought out to his boys in Ohio that had an incalculable though indirect influence upon the development of mechanical flight. For it started those boys upon a constantly increasing interest in these matters—and the boys were the Wright Brothers. It would mean much if Americans became interested in the solution of this special problem. I have shown that it affects the whole future of aviation, and that prizes do help, if not in furnishing brains, in hastening their action.

A celebrated American aviator said to me the other day, "Of course, they'll have aviettes up soon; there's a prize up, and if there's a prize offered for anything, and there's no string to it, somebody's going to win it." I do not believe that in a contest of American aviettists taken from the same class of mechanics there would be such a curious lack of understanding of the fundamental laws of aero-mechanics, and if anyone should make such a contest possible on this side of the water the aviette would find out how to use its wings very quickly in American air.

14.
The Men Who Flew at Rheims (1909)

LATHAM IN THE ANTOINETTE MONOPLANE, WHICH MADE A NEW RECORD FOR HEIGHT
AND FOR SPEED AND DISTANCE.

THE MEN WHO FLEW AT RHEIMS

IT'S a far cry from the days of Icarus and even the tale of Darius Green no longer falls with the same foreboding force on the ears of men. Men have flown—if not as birds, yet in a manner to convince skeptics that the conquest of the air has really begun. When France announced a "Week of Aviation" at Rheims from August 22d to 29th, there was much interest but little belief that any really important results would be accomplished. When

179

the week was over the world drew a long breath and sat down to contemplate the fact that practically every "flying" record had been broken and broken decisively—speed, distance, altitude—new marks had been set in all, and to crown the week's achievements the International Cup for speed had been won by Glenn H. Curtiss, the only American competitor at Rheims, thus insuring that the next contest will be held in the United States.

Curtiss's performance was made on the twenty-eighth, after a week of careful tuning and trial flights. Before starting on his two rounds of the $6\frac{1}{5}$-mile course, which he must cover, he made a trial round in 7 minutes $55\frac{1}{5}$ seconds—a world's record at that time. Then he was off for the record. A peculiarity of this flight was the height to which the aviator rose. Near the end of the second round he was nearly a hundred feet in the air. From this height he "coasted" down, crossing the finish line at tremendous speed. His

time for the two rounds was $15:30\frac{3}{5}$, and for the second round $7:53\frac{1}{5}$, breaking his own world's record made about half an hour before.

The time for the two rounds stood unbeaten to the end of the contest, but the single circuit mark was wiped out by Bleriot on the evening of the same day by a single lap in $7:47\frac{4}{5}$. This record stood, although it was not a part of the official program.

On the day following Curtiss added to his laurels by winning the special speed prize for three laps in an actual time of $23:26$, to which was added a penalty for not entering on previous days for the same race, making his official time $25:49$.

Next to the International Cup contest interest was concentrated on the Prix de la Champagne for speed and distance. The record for the week is one of constantly greater achievements in this event. On the twenty-fifth Paulhan, one of the youngest competitors and practically a beginner in the flying

COUNT LAMBERT IN HIS WRIGHT MACHINE, IN WHICH HE TOOK FOURTH PRIZE IN THE SPEED CONTEST.

game, covered nearly 81 miles, remaining in the air 2 hours, 43 minutes, 24⅘ seconds. Not for a whole day was this record disturbed. Then Latham flew 96½ miles in less than 2 hours and 18 minutes. ,

This in turn was destined to stand only 24 hours. Then Farman, the Englishman, swept the sky with his own biplane, traveling 112½ miles in 3 hours, 4 minutes, 56 seconds. This was the

Latham carried off the honors in the altitude contest on the last day of the tournament. The height which he attained with his monoplane, equipped with a Levasseur engine, was 155 meters, more than 505 feet. Farman made a bid for the prize in this event, but the best he could do was 110 meters, less than 330 feet.

As far as demonstration of relative values of different types is concerned

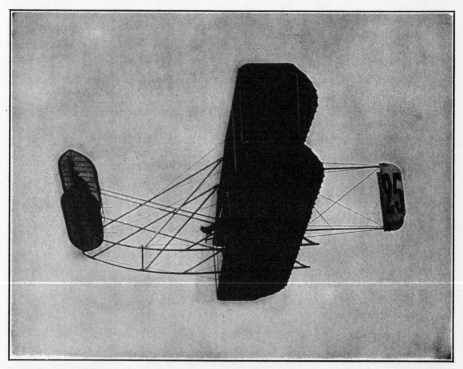

LEFEBVRE, ANOTHER PILOT OF THE WRIGHT BIPLANE; A FEW DAYS AFTER THE RHEIMS CONTEST HE WAS KILLED BY FALLING WITH HIS MACHINE AT JUVISSY.

last word for time and distance as far as Rheims was concerned.

Farman's biplane differs from the Voisin principally in having no upright divisions between the horizontal planes. He and Paulhan both used the Gnome motor, a peculiarity of which is its revolution around a fixed axle, thus effecting its own cooling. Paulhan used the Voisin biplane of the cellular or box-kite type. The engine was seven-cylinder. Latham's flight was made in an Antoinette machine with a sixty horsepower motor.

honors would seem to be about even. The greatest discussion was over the merits of the Wright biplane as against the cellular type as shown in the Voisin. Friends of the latter argue that in a simple biplane of the Wright type a lateral wind displaces the center of pressure, while leaving the center of gravity the same. This makes necessary wing-warping or some other similar device, whereas the action of the wind against the sides of the cells in the Voisin machine maintains the center of gravity at the point of pressure.

BLERIOT IN HIS MONOPLANE WHICH WON THE SPEED RECORD FOR A SINGLE CIRCUIT
OF THE COURSE.

FARMAN IN HIS OWN BIPLANE SETTING STILL ANOTHER NEW MARK IN THE DISTANCE
CONTEST BY FLYING NEARLY 115 MILES.

ROGER SOMMER, AN EX-RECORD MAN, NAVIGATING A FARMAN BIPLANE.

CURTISS, THE ONLY AMERICAN AT RHEIMS, WINNING THE INTERNATIONAL, WHICH
BRINGS THE NEXT CONTEST TO THIS COUNTRY.

15.
An Aerial Bivouac
(1907)

AN AERIAL BIVOUAC

THE LAST SURVIVOR'S STORY OF AN EXCITING ADVENTURE— TWENTY - SIX HOURS IN A BALLOON — THE LONGEST AERIAL VOYAGE, IN POINT OF HOURS, EVER MADE IN THE UNITED STATES, AND THE WORLD'S ENDURANCE RECORD UNTIL 1900

BY EDGAR BEECHER BRONSON

ILLUSTRATED BY GEORGE VARIAN AND WITH FACSIMILES

N the history of contests since man first began striving against his fellows, seldom has a record performance stood so long unbroken as that of the good airship "Barnum," made thirty-three years ago. Of her captain and crew of five men, six all told, the writer remains the sole survivor, the only one who may live to see that record broken in this country.

The "Barnum" rose at 4 P.M. July 26, 1874, from New York and made her last landing 9 miles north of Saratoga at 6:07 P.M. of the 27th, thus finishing a voyage of a total elapsed time of 26 hours and 7 minutes. In the interim she made four landings, the first of no more than ten minutes, the second twenty, the third ten, the fourth thirty - five minutes, and these descents cost an expenditure of gas and ballast which shortened her endurance capacity by at least two or three hours.

Tracing on a map her actual route traversed, gives a total distance of something over 400 miles, which gave her the record of second place in the history of long-distance ballooning in this country, which she still holds.

So far as my knowledge of the art goes, and I have tried to read all of its history, the "Barnum's" voyage of 26 hours and 7 minutes was then and remained the world's endurance record until 1900, and it still remains, in point of hours up, the longest balloon voyage ever made in the United States.*

The longest voyage in point of distance ever made in this country was that of John Wise and La Mountain, in the '50's, from St. Louis, Mo., to Jefferson County, N. Y., a distance credited under the old custom of a little less than 1200 miles, while the actual distance under the new rules is between 800 and 900 miles, the time being 19 hours. This voyage also remained, I believe, the world's record for distance until 1900, and still remains the American record—and lucky, indeed, will be the aeronaut who beats it.

As for the endurance record, I hope and fully expect to see it beaten by probably several of the 15 contestants in the International Cup Race at St. Louis in October, for with skillful handling, no bad luck, no frequent wide changes of temperature and no necessity for descent arising from near approach to the sea, the race regulations provide for balloons capable of remaining up at least 50 or 60 hours.

And if staying up until the last bag of ballast is spent or a nearing coast line calls a halt can win the race, all American aero-

* Under new rules lately adopted "endurance" means the time which elapses between ascent and first landing, and "distance" means the length of an air line between the point of starting and the point of first landing. Formerly "endurance" meant the time of voyage on one inflation, irrespective of the number of landings, and "distance" meant the whole number of miles covered by the balloon, swept here and there by varying air currents. Obviously, the new rules are more sportsmanlike, especially in the matter of "distance"; for, as the cleverest yachtsman brings his winning boat across the goal line by getting the best out of every shifting slant of wind, so the most skillful balloon pilot wins by superior knowledge of air currents.

nauts feel sure they can safely depend that either Lieut. Lahm, Jas. C. McCoy, or Allan R. Hawley will score a credit as the Cup's defender equal to the splendid record of Lahm as its original winner. But our champions have their work cut out; they know it and are preparing for it as best they may—they know the foreign entries include the most experienced and daring aeronauts now living.

P. T. Barnum's "Great Roman Hippodrome," now for many years Madison Square Garden, was never more densely crowded than on the afternoon of July 26, 1874. Early in the spring of that year Mr. Barnum had announced the building of a balloon larger than any theretofore made in this country. His purpose in building it was to attempt to break all previous records for time and distance, and he invited each of five daily city papers of that time to send representatives on the voyage. So when the day set for the ascent arrived, not only was the old Hippodrome packed to the doors, but adjacent streets and squares were solid black with people, as on a fête day like the Dewey parade.

Happily the day was one of brilliant sunshine and clear sky, with scarcely a cloud within the horizon.

The captain of the "Barnum" was Washington H. Donaldson, by far the most brilliant and daring professional aeronaut of his day, and a clever athlete and gymnast. For several weeks prior to the ascent of the "Barnum," Donaldson had been making daily short ascents of an hour or two from the Hippodrome in a small balloon—as a feature of the performance. Sometimes he ascended in a basket, at other times with naught but a trapeze swinging beneath the concentrating ring of his balloon, himself in tights perched easily upon the bar of the trapeze. And when at a height to suit his fancy, of a thousand feet or more, time and again have I seen him do every difficult feat of trapeze work ever done above the certain security of a net.

Such was Donaldson, a man utterly fearless, but reckless only when alone, of a steadfast, cool courage and resource when responsible for the safety of others that made him the man out of a million best worth tying to in any emergency where a bold heart and ready wit may avert disaster. Donaldson's days were never dull.

The day preceding our ascent his balloon was released with insufficient lifting power. Immediately he rose above neighboring roofs, a very high southeast wind caught him, and, before he had time to throw out ballast, drove his basket against the flagstaff on the Gilsey House with such violence that the staff was broken, the basket momentarily upset, dumping two ballast bags to the Broadway sidewalk and narrowly missing several pedestrians!

That he was not himself dashed to his death was a miracle. But to him this was no more than a bit unusual incident of the day's work.

The reporters assigned as mates on this skylark in the "Barnum" were Alfred Ford, of *The Graphic;* Edmund Lyons, of *The Sun;* Samuel MacKeever, of *The Herald;* W. W. Austin, of *The World,* every one of these good fellows now dead these many years, alas! and myself, representing *The Tribune.*

Lyons, MacKeever and myself were novices in ballooning, but the two others had scored their bit of aeronautic experience.

Austin had made an ascent a year or two before at San Francisco, was swept out over the bay before he could make a landing, and, through some mishap, dropped into the water midway of the bay and well out toward Golden Gate, but was rescued by a passing boat.

Ford had made several balloon voyages, the most notable in '73, in the great *Graphic* balloon.

After the voyage of the "Barnum" was first announced and it became known *The Tribune* would have a pass, everybody on the staff wanted to go. For weeks it was the talk of the office. Even grave gray beards of the editorial rooms were paying court for the preference to Mr. W. F. G. Shanks, that prince of an earlier generation of city editors, who of course controlled the assignment of the pass. But when at length the pass came, the enthusiasm and anxiety for the distinction waned, and it became plain the piece of paper "*Good for One Aerial Trip,*" etc., must go begging.

At the time I was assistant night city editor, and a special detail to interview the Man in the Moon was was not precisely in the line of my normal duties. I was therefore greatly surprised (to put it conservatively) when, the morning before the ascent, Mr. Shanks, in whose family I was then living, routed me out of bed to say:

"See here, Ted, you know Barnum's bal-

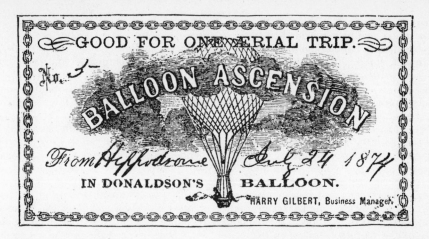

GOOD FOR ONE AERIAL TRIP.

No. 5

BALLOON ASCENSION

From Hippodrome July 24 1874

IN DONALDSON'S BALLOON.

HARRY GILBERT, Business Manager.

Mr E. B. Bronson
will represent the
Tribune

W. F. G. Shanks.
City Editor

July 23. 1874

Facsimile and Exact Size of Mr. Bronson's Pass and the Endorsement on the Back of it Appointing him to Represent "The Tribune"

loon starts to-morrow on her trial for the record, but what you don't know is that we are in a hole. Before the ticket came every one wanted to go, from John R. G. Hassard down to the office boy. Now no one will go—all have funked it, and I suppose you will want to follow suit!"

Thus diplomatically put, the hinted assignment was not to be refused without too much personal chagrin.

So it happened that about 3:30 P.M. the next day I arrived at the Hippodrome, loaded down with wraps and a heavy basket nigh bursting with good things to eat

and drink, which dear Mrs. Shanks had insisted on providing.

The "Barnum" was already filled with gas, tugging at her leash and swaying restlessly as if eager for the start. And right here, at first sight of the great sphere, I felt more nearly a downright fright than at any stage of the actual voyage; the balloon appeared such a hopelessly frail fabric to support even its own car and equipment. The light cord net enclosing the great gasbag looked aloft, where it towered above the roof, little more substantial than a film of lace, and appeared about as safe a proposition as to attempt to enmesh a lion in a cobweb.

Already my four mates for the voyage were assembled about the basket, and Donaldson himself was busy with the last details of the equipment. My weighty lunch basket had from my mates even a heartier reception than I received, but their joy over the prospect of delving into its generous depths was short-lived. The load as Donaldson had planned it was all aboard, weight carefully adjusted to what he considered a proper excess lifting power to carry us safely up above any chance of a collision with another flag-staff, like that he had the day before above the Gilsey House, and thus the basket and all its bounty (save only a small flask of brandy I smuggled into a hip pocket) were given to a passing acrobat.

At 4 P.M. the old Hippodrome rang with applause; a brilliant equestrian act had just been finished. Suddenly the applause ceased and that awful hush fell upon the vast audience which is rarely experienced except in the presence of death or of some impending disaster: we had been seen to enter the basket, and people held their breath.

Released, the ballon bounded 700 feet into the air, stood stationary for a moment, and then drifted northwest before the prevailing wind.

In this prodigious leap there was naught of the disagreeable sensation one experiences in a rapidly-rising elevator. Instead it rather seemed that we were standing motionless, stationary in space, and that the earth itself had gotten loose and was dropping away beneath us to depths unknown. Every cord and rope of the huge fabric was tensely taut, the basket firm and solid beneath our feet. Indeed, the balloon, with nothing more substantial in her construction than cloth and twine, and hempen ropes and willow wands (the latter forming the basket), has always, while floating in mid-air free of the drag-rope's tricks, the rigid homogeneity of a rock, a solidity that quickly inspires the most timid with perfect confidence in her security.

Ballast was thrown out by Donaldson, a little. At Seventh Avenue and 42d Street our altitude was 2000 feet.

The great city lay beneath us like an unrolled scroll. White and dusty, the streets looked like innumerable strips of Morse telegraph paper—the people the dots, the vehicles the dashes.

Central Park, with its winding waters, was transformed into a superb mantle of dark green velvet splashed with silver, worthy of a royal fête. Behind us lay the sea, a vast field of glittering silver. Before us lay a wide expanse of Jersey's hills and dales that from our height appeared a plain, with many a reddish-gray splash upon its verdant stretches that indicated a village or a town.

Above and about us lay an inmeasurable space of which we were the only tenants, and over which we began to feel a grand sense of dominion that wrapped us as in royal ermine: if we were not lords of this aerial manor, pray then who were? Beneath us, lay—home. Should we ever see it again? This thought I am sure came to all of us. I know it came to me. But the perfect steadiness of the balloon won our confidence, and we soon gave ourselves up to the gratification of our enviable position; and enviable indeed it was—for who has not envied the eagle his power to skim the tree-tops, to hover above Niagara, to circle mountain peaks, to poise himself aloft and survey creation, or to mount into the zenith and gaze at the sun?

Indeed our sense of confidence became such that, while sitting on the edge of the basket to reach and pass Donaldson a rope he asked for, I leaned so far over that the bottle of brandy resting in my hip pocket slipped out and fell into the Hudson.

Oddly, Ford, who was the most experienced balloonist of the party after Donaldson himself, seemed most nervous and timid, but it was naught but an expression of that constitutional trouble (dizziness) so many have when looking down from even the minor height of a step-ladder. In all the long hours he was with us, I do not recall his standing once erect in the basket, and when others of us perched upon the basket's edge, he would beg us to come down. But mind, there was no lack of stark courage in Alfred Ford, sufficiently proved by the fact that he never missed a chance for an ascent.

But safe? Confident? Why, before we were up ten minutes, Lyons and MacKeever were sitting on the edge of the basket, with one hand holding to a stay, tossing out handfuls of small tissue paper circulars bearing "*News from the Clouds.*" Many-colored, these little circulars as they fell beneath us looked like a flight of giant butterflies—and we kept on throwing out handfuls of them until our pilot warned us we were wasting so much weight we should soon be out of easy view of the earth! Indeed, the balance of the balloon is so extremely fine that when a single handful of these little tissue circulars was thrown out, ascent was shown on the dial of our aneroid barometer!

At 4:30 P.M. we drifted out over the Hudson at an altitude of 2500 feet. Here Donaldson descended from the airy perch on the concentrating ring which he had been occupying since our start, when one of us asked how long he expected the cruise to last. Donaldson replied that he hoped to be able to sail the "Barnum" at least three or four days.

"But," he added, "I shall certainly be unable to carry all of you for so long a journey, and shall be compelled to drop you one by one. So you had best draw lots to settle whom I shall drop first, and in what order the rest shall follow."

Sailing then 2500 feet above the earth, Lyons voiced a thought racing from my own brain for utterance when he blurted out:

"What the deuce do you mean by 'drop' us?" Indeed, the question must have been on three other tongues as well, for Donaldson's reply, "Oh, descend to the earth and let you step out then," was greeted by all five of

News from the Clouds.

P. T. BARNUM'S
Great Roman Hippodrome
NEW YORK.
Ascension of the Experimental Series by
PROF. DONALDSON.

Facsimile and Exact Size of the Tissue-Paper Circulars which were thrown from the Balloon

us with a salvo of deep, lusty sighs of relief.

Then we drew lots for the order of our going, MacKeever drawing 1, Austin 2, Lyons 3, Ford 4, and I 5.

Meantime, beneath us on the river vessels which from our height looked like the toy craft on the lake in Central Park were whistling a shrill salute that, toned down by the distance, was really not unmusical.

Having crossed the Hudson and swept above Weehawken, we found ourselves cruising northwest over the marshes of the Hackensack.

As the heat of the declining sun lessened, our cooling gas contracted and the balloon sank steadily until at 5:10 we were 250 feet above the earth and 100 feet of our great drag-rope was trailing on the ground.

Within hailing distance of people beneath us, a curious condition was observed. We could hear distinctly all they said at a height from which we could not make them understand a word: our voices had to fill a sphere of atmosphere; theirs, with the earth beneath them, only a hemisphere. Thus the modern megaphone is especially useful to aeronauts.

Hereabouts our fun began. Many countrymen thought the balloon running away with us and tried to stop and save us—always by grasping the drag-rope, bracing themselves and trying literally to hold us; when the slack of the rope straightened, they were tossed somersaults such as our pilot vowed no acrobat could equal. And yet the balance of the balloon is so fine that even a child of ten could pull us down, if only it had strength enough to withstand occasional momentary lifts off the ground. Occasionally one more clever would run and take a quick turn of the rope about a gate or fence—and then spend the rest of the evening gathering the scattered fragments and repairing the damage.

And when there was not fun enough below, Donaldson himself would take a hand and put his steed through some of her fancy paces—as when, approaching a large lake, he told us to hold tightly to the stays, let out gas and dropped us, bang! upon the lake. Running at a speed of 12 or 15 miles an hour, we hit the water with a tremendous shock, bounded 30 or 40 feet into the air, descended again and literally skipped in great leaps along the surface of the water, precisely like a well-thrown "skipping stone." Then out went ballast and up and on we went, no worse for the fun beyond a pretty thorough wetting!

At 6:20 P.M. we landed on the farm of Garrett Harper in Bergen County, 26 miles from New York. After drinking our fill of milk at the farm house, we rose again and drifted north over Ramapo until, at 7:35, a dead calm came upon us and we made another descent. We then found that we had landed near Bladentown on the farm of Miss Charlotte Thompson, a charming actress of the day whose "Jane Eyre" and

"Fanchon" are still pleasant memories to old theater-goers. Loading our balloon with stones to safely anchor it, our party paid her a visit and was cordially received. An invitation to join us hazarded by Donaldson, Miss Thompson accepted with delight. I do not know if she is still living, but if she is, she cannot have forgotten her half-hour's cruise in the good air-ship "Barnum," wafted silently by a gentle evening breeze, the lovely panorama beneath her half hid, half seen through the purple haze of twilight.

After landing Miss Thompson at 8:18 we ascended for the night—for a night's bivouac among the stars.

The moon rose early. We were soon sailing over the Highlands of the Hudson. Off in the east we could see the river, a winding ribbon of silver. We were running low, rarely more than 200 feet high. Below us the great drag-rope was hissing through meadows, roaring over fences, crashing through tree-tops. And all night long we were continually ascending and descending, sinking into valleys and rising over hills, following closely the contours of the local topography.

During the more equable temperature of night the balloon's height is governed by the drag-rope. Leaving a range of hills and floating out over a valley, the weight of the drag-rope pulls the balloon down until the same length of rope is trailing through the valley that had been dragging on the hill. This habit of the balloon produces startling effects. Drifting swiftly toward a rocky, precipitous hillside against which it seems inevitable you must dash to your death, suddenly the trailing drag-rope reaches the lower slopes and you soar like a bird over the hill, often so low that the bottom of the basket swishes through the tree-tops.

But, while useful in conserving the balloon's energy, the drag-rope is a source of constant peril to aeronauts, of terror to people on the earth and of damage to property. It has a nasty clinging habit, winding round trees or other objects, that may at any moment upset basket and aeronauts. On this trip our drag-rope tore sections out of scores of fences, upset many hay stacks, injured horses and cattle that tried to run across it, whipped off many a chimney, broke telegraph wires and seemed to take malicious delight in working some havoc with everything it touched.

At ten o'clock we sighted Cozzen's Hotel, and shortly drifted across the parade ground of West Point, its huge battlemented gray walls making one fancy he was looking down into the inner court of some great medieval castle. Then we drifted out over the Hudson toward Cold Spring until, caught by a different current, we were swept along the course of the river.

Sailing over mid-stream and 200 feet above it, with the tall cliffs and mysterious, dark recesses of the Highlands on either hand, the waters beneath turned to a livid gray under the feeble light of the waning moon. No part of our voyage was more impressive, no scene more awe-inspiring. It was a region of such weird lights and grewsome shadows as no fancy could people with aught but gaunt goblins and dread demons, come down to us through generations untold, an unspent legacy of terror, from half-savage, superstitious ancestors.

Suddenly Ford spoke in a low voice: "Boys, I was in nine or ten battles of the Civil War, from Gaines's Mill to Gettysburg, but in none of them was there a scene which impressed me as so terrible as this, no situation that seemed to me so threatening of irresistible perils."

Nearing Fishkill at eleven, a land breeze caught and whisked us off eastward. At midnight we struck the town of Wappinger's Falls—and struck it hard. Our visitation is doubtless remembered there yet. The town was in darkness and asleep. We were running low before a stiff breeze, half our drag-rope on the ground. The rope began to roar across roofs and upset chimneys with shrieks and crashes that set the folk within believing the end of the world had come. Instantly the streets were filled with flying white figures and the air with men's curses and women's screams. Three shots were fired beneath us. Two of our fellows said they heard the whistle of the balls, so Donaldson thought it prudent to throw out ballast and rise out of range.

Here the moon left us and we sailed on throughout the remainder of the night in utter darkness and without any extraordinary incident, all but the watch lying idly in the bottom of the basket viewing the stars and wondering what new mischief the drag-rope might be planning.

The only duty of the watch was to lighten ship upon too near descent to the earth, and for this purpose a handful of Hippodrome circulars usually proved sufficient. Indeed, only eight pounds of ballast were used from the time we left Miss Thompson till dawn, barring a half-sack spent in getting out of range of the Wappinger's Falls sportsmen who seemed to want to bag us.

Ford and Austin were assigned as the lookout from 12:00 to 2:00, Lyons and myself from 2:00 to 3:00, and Donaldson and MacKeever from 3:00 to 4:00.

From midnight till 3:00 A.M. Donaldson slept peaceful as a baby, curled up in the basket with a sand-bag for a pillow.

The rest of us slept little through the night and talked less, each absorbed in the reflections and speculations inspired by our novel experience.

At the approach of dawn we had the most unique and extraordinary experience ever given to man. The balloon was sailing low in a deep valley. To the east of us the Berkshires rose steeply to summits probably 1500 feet above us. Beneath us a little village lay, snuggled cosily between two small meeting brooks, all dim under the mists of early morning and the shadows of the hills. No flush of dawn yet lit the sky. Donaldson had been consulting his watch. Suddenly he rose and called, pointing eastward across the range:

"Watch, boys! Look there!"

He then quickly dumped overboard half the contents of a ballast bag. Flying upward like an arrow, the balloon soon shot up above the mountain top. When, lo! a miracle! The phenomenon of sunrise was reversed! We our very selves instead had risen on the sun! There he stood, full and round, peeping at us through the trees crowning a distant Berkshire hill, as if startled by our temerity.

Shortly thereafter, when we had descended to our usual level and were running swiftly before a stiff breeze over a rocky hillside, Donaldson yelled:

"Hang on, boys, for your lives!"

The end of the drag-rope had gotten a hitch about a large tree limb. Luckily Donaldson had seen it in time to warn us, else we had there finished our careers. We had barely time to seize the stays when the rope tautened with a shock that nearly turned the basket upside down, spilled out our water-bucket and some ballast, left MacKeever and myself hanging in space by our hands and the other four on the lower side of the basket, scrambling to save themselves. Instantly, of course, the basket righted and dropped back beneath us.

And then began a terrible struggle.

The pressure of the wind bore us down within 100 feet of the ragged rocks. Groaning under the strain, the rope seemed ready to snap. Like a huge leviathan trapped in a net, the gas-bag writhed, twisted, bulged, shrank, gathered into a ball and sprang fiercely out. The loose folds of canvas sucked up until half the netting stood empty, and then fold after fold darted out and back with all the angry menace of a serpent's tongue and with the ominous crash of musketry.

It seemed the canvas must inevitably burst and we be dashed to death. But Donaldson was cool and smiling, and, taking the only precaution possible, stood with a sheath-knife ready to cut away the drag-rope and relieve us of its weight in case our canvas burst.

Happily the struggle was brief. The limb that held us snapped, and the balloon sprang forward in mighty bounds that threw us off our feet and tossed the great drag-rope about like a whip-lash. But we were free, safe, and our stout vessel soon settled down to the velocity of the wind.

By this time we all were beginning to feel hungry, for we had supped the night before in mid-air from a lunch basket that held more delicacies than substantials. So Donaldson proposed a descent and began looking for a likely place. At last he chose a little village, which upon near approach we learned lay in Columbia County of our own good state.

We called to two farmers to pull us down—no easy task in the rather high wind then blowing. They grasped the rope and braced themselves as had others the night before, and presently were flying through the air in prodigious if ungraceful somersaults. Amazed but unhurt, they again seized the rope and got a turn about a stout board fence, only to see a section or two of the fence fly into the air as if in pursuit of us.

Presently the heat of the rising sun expanded our gas and sent us up again 2000 feet, making breakfast farther off than ever. Thus, it being clear that we must sacrifice either our stomachs or our gas, Donaldson held open the safety valve until we were once more safely landed on mother earth, but not until after we had received a pretty

"MANY COUNTRYMEN THOUGHT THE BALLOON RUNNING AWAY WITH US AND
TRIED TO STOP AND SAVE US—ALWAYS BY GRASPING THE DRAG-ROPE, BRA-
CING THEMSELVES AND TRYING LITERALLY TO HOLD US, WHEN, THE SLACK
OF THE ROPE STRAIGHTENED, THEY WERE TOSSED SOMERSAULTS SUCH AS
OUR PILOT VOWED NO ACROBAT COULD EQUAL"

severe pounding about, for such a high wind blew that the anchor was slow in holding.

This landing was made at 5:24 A.M. on the farm of John W. Coons near the village of Greenport, four miles from Hudson City, and about 130 miles from New York.

Here our pilot decided our vessel must be lightened of two men, and thus the lot drawn the night before compelled us to part, regretfully, with MacKeever of *The Herald* and Austin of *The World*. Ford, however, owing allegiance to an afternoon paper, *The Graphic*, and always bursting with honest journalistic zeal for a "beat," saw an opportunity to win satisfaction greater even than that of keeping on with us. So he, too, left us here, with the result that *The Graphic* published a full story of the voyage up to this point — Saturday afternoon, the 25th. The *Herald* and *World* trailed along for second place in their Sunday editions, while *Sun* and *Tribune* readers had to wait till Monday morning for such "*News from the Clouds*" as Lyons and I had to give them—for wires were not used as freely then as now.

Our departing mates brought us a rare good breakfast from Mr. Coons's generous kitchen—a fourteen-quart tin pail well-nigh filled with good things, among them two currant pies on yellow earthen plates, gigantic in size, pale of crust, though anything but anæmic of contents. Lyons finished nearly the half of one before our reascent, to his sorrow—for scarcely were we off the earth before he developed a colic that seemed to interest him more, right up to the finish of the trip, than the scenery.

Bidding our mates good-bye, we prepared to reascend. Many farmers had been about us holding to our ropes and leaning on the basket, and later we realized we had not taken in sufficient ballast to offset the weight of the three men who left us.

Released, the balloon sprang upward at a pace that all but took our breath away. Instantly the earth disappeared beneath us. We saw Donaldson pull the safety valve wide open, draw his sheath knife ready to cut the drag-rope, standing rigid, with his eyes riveted upon the aneroid barometer. The hand of the barometer was sweeping across the dial at a terrific rate. I glanced at Donaldson and saw him smile. Then I looked back at the barometer and saw the hand had stopped—at 10,200 feet! How long we were ascending we did not know.

Certain it is that the impressions described were all there was time for, and that when Donaldson turned and spoke we saw his lips move but could hear no sound. Our speed had been such that the pressure of the air, upon the tympanum of the ear, left us deaf for some minutes. We had made a dash of two miles into cloudland and had accomplished it, we three firmly believed, in little more than a minute!

Presently Donaldson observed the anchor and grapnel had come up badly clogged with sod, and a good heavy tug he and I had of it to pull them in, for Lyons was still much too busy with his currant pie to help us. Nor indeed were the currant pies yet done with us, for at the end of our tug at the anchor rope, I found I had been kneeling very precisely in the middle of pie No. 2, and had contrived to absorb most of it into the knees of my trousers. Thus at the end of the day, come to Saratoga after all shops were closed, I had to run the gauntlet of the porch and office crowd of visitors at the United States Hotel in a condition of costume that only needed moccasins and a war bonnet to make me a tolerable imitation of an Indian.

We remained aloft at an altitude of two to two and one-half miles for three hours and a half, stayed there until the silence became intolerable, until the buzz of a fly or the croak of a frog would have been music to our ears. Here was *absolute silence*, the silence of the grave and death—a silence never to be experienced by living man in any terrestrial condition.

Occasionally the misty clouds in which we hung enshrouded parted beneath us and gave us glimpses of the distant earth, opened and disclosed landscapes of infinite beauty set in gray nebulous frames.

Once we passed above a thunderstorm, saw the lightning play beneath us, felt our whole fabric tremble at its shock—and were glad enough when we had left it well behind.

Seen from a great height, the earth looked to be a vast expanse of dark-green velvet, sometimes shaded to a deeper hue by cloudlets floating beneath the sun, splashed here with the silver and there with the gold garniture reflected from rippling waters.

Toward noon we descended beneath the region of clouds into the realm of light and life, and found ourselves hovering above the Mountain House of the Catskills. And thereabouts we drifted in cross-currents until nearly 4:00 P.M., when a heavy south-

"HANG ON, BOYS, FOR YOUR LIVES!"

erly gale struck us and swept us rapidly northward past Albany at a pace faster than I have ever traveled on a railway.

We still had ballast enough left to assure ten or twelve hours more travel. But we did not like our course. The prospects were that we would end our voyage in the wilderness 200 or more miles north of Ottawa. So we rose to 12,500 feet, seeking an easterly or westerly current, but without avail. We could not escape the southerly gale. Prudence, therefore, dictated a landing before nightfall. Landing in the high gale prevailing was both difficult and dangerous, and was not accomplished until we were all much bruised and scratched in the oak thicket Donaldson chose for our descent.

Thus the first voyage of the good airship "Barnum" ended at 6:07 P.M. on the farm of E. R. Young, 9 miles north of Saratoga.

A year later the "Barnum" rose for the last time—from Chicago—and to this day the fate of the stanch craft and her brave captain remains an unsolved mystery.

16.
Hammondsport:
An Aeroplane
Laboratory
(1910)

HAMMONDSPORT AN AËRO-PLANE LABORATORY

by Arnold Kruckman

Photographs by H. M. Benner

ON a calm afternoon, ten summers ago, a group of skeptical Californians patiently submitted to a baking sunbath in order to witness the contortions of a balky dirigible balloon. The balloon bore a striking resemblance to a link of gigantic sausage, stuffed by a butcher with generous instincts, but lacking a nice sense of symmetry. On the frail wooden frame, suspended below the gas bag, a motor occasionally burst into a spasm of staccato explosions that would unexpectedly subside into a faint purr, the prelude to a dead stop.

To the amusement of the audience, each performance provoked an outburst of picturesque elocution from the stocky, athletic, square-visaged man who was urging the cranky airship to sail through space.

"Put th' spurs to thet buckin' cloud-jumper o' yourn, Captain Tom," counseled a grinning ranchman.

Capt. Thomas S. Baldwin turned to hurl an exasperated answer at his tormentor, but stopped short. His eyes strained over the glaring plain toward Los Angeles, and he listened acutely. Far in the distance the others saw a faint blur of yellow dust, the cloud rapidly approaching them with a rhythmical drumming noise.

"It's Harry White on his new-fangled motor bicycle thet he's just got from the East," announced the ranchman.

"Well, it's a wonder of a motor," commented Captain Baldwin.

The machine sped up to the group. Before the rider had dismounted Captain Baldwin was down in the dust eagerly examining the small motor in the bicycle. On one side of the frame it bore a small plate stenciled with the name "Curtiss."

"Where is this Curtiss outfit?" demanded Captain Baldwin.

The owner dug a small, cheaply printed, poorly illustrated catalog out of a pocket and pointed to the address:

GLENN H. CURTISS,
Hammondsport, New York.

The famous parachute jumper stuffed the leaflet into his pocket and turned to his helpers:

"Boys, dump the gas out of the bag and chuck that old junk pile of a motor. Smash it, bust it, sell it for old iron, but in the name of what-you'll-catch get rid of it. It's no good. I've found the motor we need. It's up here at this Ham-and-eggs-port town. I'm going right down to the city and catch the first train for the East, and I'm not coming back till I bring one of them Ham-ands-port motors with me. Then you fellows will see the big show," genially boomed the captain to the group which had been lingering to see if there would be any more fun that day.

Within three hours Captain Baldwin was rushing toward New York State. With a flash of insight he realized that the obscure mechanic who had built this crude but small motor was the man with the talent to build the spider-weight motor essential to the success of the dirigible balloon. Thus a chance incident on the Pacific slope started a train of events which shaped the destiny of a young man and a small town near the Atlantic seaboard, three thousand miles away. If the man and the motor had

A. L. PFITZNER, A "COSMOPOLITAN GENIUS," FURNISHES THE MONOPLANE
INTEREST AT HAMMONDSPORT.

not accidentally been brought in contact
on the plains near Los Angeles, it is
very doubtful whether Curtiss would
ever have become interested in airships
and whether Hammondsport would be
to-day to aëronautics what Nuremberg
is to toys.

Hammondsport is in the lake country
in the western part of New York State.
It is at the head of Lake Keuka about
sixty miles southeast of Buffalo, snug-
gling in a sheltered hollow on the lee
side of one of those miniature ranges
whose gentle, vine-draped slopes form
the peaceful Pleasant Valley where the
bulk of the wine made east of the Pacific coast is bottled. In the winter the
landscape reminds you of a baby Switzerland. This is not an original comparison. It was made by A. L. Pfitzner,
a cosmopolitan genius who has recently
produced one of the most novel aëroplanes that has emanated from Hammondsport.

The visitor from the outside world
penetrates to Hammondsport by means
of a typical backwoods branch line.
The main line deserts you at Bath. For

the next forty minutes you cover the
intervening eight miles on the Bath and
Hammondsport division train which
drowsily slips down into the valley
through the glories of the flats and the
hillsides where men, women, and children are picking grapes in the mellow
sunshine.

During these days it is very likely
that the man in the seat in front of
yours will start a conversation with the
neighborly conductor about the aërial exploits of "Glenn," or Pfitzner, or who-
ever may be the aëroplane hero of the
minute at Hammondsport; when the
train is wheezing along between Rheims
and the outskirts of Hammondsport it is
not improbable that you may see Pfitzner flying alongside, over the bald
meadows to the right, in his coal black
monoplane; or it may be Curtiss in his
trim yellow flyer or Captain Baldwin
with the birdlike machine, that flies
slower than any aëroplane ever built.
Aëroplane apparitions are so much a
part of the humdrum of everyday life
around Hammondsport that even the
horses in the fields calmly go about their

FIRST AËROPLANE TRIED IN PUBLIC; MADE BY CHAS. O. JONES, BUT WAS
UNSUCCESSFUL.

business without giving the slightest heed to the purring Thing that flashes over their heads.

The community is saturated with aëroplane knowledge. It talks in an aëroplane vernacular. The school children build fanciful kites and miniature flying machines and the older boys have built and flown innumerable full-grown gliders. When you stroll up or down the valley you can count at least a dozen wrecked gliders which have been abandoned on the hillside where the youthful experimenter's enthusiasm suddenly oozed away. In the cellars and back yards and garrets you may discover partially finished gliders that were built of lumber smuggled from Father's shop and covered with gingham or calico begged or borrowed from Mother.

Several of the youngsters who have had the advantage of helping to build the various important aëroplanes have done some surprisingly creditable work on their own initiative. As this is being written "Willie" Babcock, a son of a local physician, and "Mud" Brown, son of Editor Brown, are about to begin

experiments with a power-driven machine.

The keen interest felt by the average citizen in the novel industry which has developed in the community has caused him, unconsciously, to acquire a technical knowledge of the esoterics of flight and flying machines that dumfounds the visitor who is accustomed to the frank ignorance of even well-informed people. When a newcomer takes a dubious looking flyer out on the Kingsley flats to give it its initial spin it is certain that the butcher and the drygoods merchant and perhaps the barber will diagnose the ailments and shortcomings of that aëroplane with remarkable accuracy.

Pfitzner was trying out his new monoplane, an unusual type in America, last February. Pfitzner is a cultivated young Hungarian whose social graces and ability had won him many friends during his short residence in the town. The thermometer registered something like ten or twelve degrees below zero. But in spite of the discomforts of standing immersed in Arctic snow up to the knees, chilled by a cuttingly cold wind, there had gathered the usual company of townspeople augmented by sparkling eyed young girls and a group of youngsters just released from school.

"He has just a splendid curve to that plane," observed one young woman.

"Yes, indeed," replied her friend, a little blonde; "I think it looks as well balanced as any I ever saw."

Before the aëroplane was sent out to make its maiden flight a scale was attached to the machine by means of a

It seemed incredible that a child should know so much about a subject which is Greek to many engineers. Yet when the statistics on propeller efficiency were overhauled it was discovered that he was exactly right.

There is a reason for this. During the past ten years there have lived and worked in this little town many of the great minds which to-day are grappling with the problem of aërial navigation in America. Following the

SUMMER OR WINTER OVER THE SURFACE OF LAKE KEUKA IS A FAVORITE
PLACE FOR THE FLIGHTS.

long rope. The scale was held securely on the ground by two helpers while the propeller was set in motion. The largest number of pounds registered on the scale indicated the maximum pulling or pushing capability of the propeller. After several trials, for the sake of accuracy, it was announced that the propeller gave a thrust equal to $9\frac{4}{10}$ pounds for horsepower.

A young boy about twelve years old threw up his hat and shouted: "Whoopee! That's six tenths of a pound more than anybody else in the world has ever got out of a propeller."

lead of Captain Baldwin they came to see what he was doing or to follow his example. In a small community people easily become familiar with the other fellow's activities.

Almost anybody in the town can tell you in detail how Dr. Alexander Graham Bell and his associates of the Aërial Experiment Association constructed those five historic aëroplanes which gave the aëroplane business its start in Hammondsport. They'll tell you that they knew Oliver Jones was foredoomed to die a violent death if he persisted in riding that dirigible balloon which was made "of shoe strings and pasted together with chewing gum." Jones was originally a newspaper artist. He conceived an idea that he could build a novel aëroplane and came to Hammondsport to get in the atmosphere.

After several trials with his aëroplane he abandoned the heavier-than-air type and began the construction of a dirigible balloon along certain original lines. The first time he made an effort to fly from Palisades Park, opposite New York

tempt to launch the most impossible flying machines. Their efforts would have been shriekingly funny if their earnestness and reckless devotion of time and money to their projects had not made them pitifully pathetic. Captain Baldwin and his associates tried to save them, but the well-meant advice was received with suspicion and the givers were accused of attempting to purloin the property of those whom they were trying to protect.

CURTISS IN THE "JUNE BUG," FIRST AËROPLANE TO MAKE A SUCCESSFUL PUBLIC FLIGHT IN AMERICA.

City, he drifted across Harlem and narrowly escaped drowning in the Sound. The balloon finally collapsed in mid-air while Jones was giving an exhibition in New Hampshire. After the funeral the good folks of Hammondsport helped to raise a fund for the temporary relief of the widow and children.

Jones was a fatal exception among the misguided enthusiasts who used to swarm into the town. The majority of them didn't come to harm. Without the slightest conception of the fundamental principles of aërodynamics or aëronautic construction they would at-

There was, for instance, a cobbler from Chicago. A Pole, scarcely able to speak English or to write his own language, he had conceived a machine which was to make all the rest look like toys. It was the ultimate triumph of aëronautics. He brought it to Hammondsport, a complicated jumble of steel tubing and springs. It had cost him and others, as poor and ignorant as himself, more than five thousand dollars. When it was put together it looked like the steel framework of a crazily wrought one-room house. It was supposed to fly by mechanically reproducing the human function of breathing. The rapid and continuous concussion of the exhaust on the surrounding atmosphere was supposed to lift and drive the machine whither the operator willed.

The doe-eyed little cobbler had been inspired in a dream. He dreamed that by filling his lungs with air and rapidly expelling it his body floated like a bird's. Of course, it is not quite possible yet to pull yourself up by your bootstraps, so the "airship" didn't fly. After many heartbreaking attempts the little cobbler packed his pile of metal scraps and bought a ticket back to Chicago with the last bit of money he had left. He departed firmly convinced that, in some mysterious way, the other experimenters in Hammondsport had interfered with his success because they feared the triumph of his machine.

The cranks with freak machines are all that way. They are all obsessed by the hallucination that the rest of humanity is trying to steal their ideas. They had many of them in the early days up in Hammondsport. Some of them were as illiterate as the cobbler and others suffered from a plethora of knowledge. There were mechanics, artists, plumbers, milkmen, learned physicists, and business men otherwise canny.

They still come to Hammondsport, but not in such numbers. The natives are not so patient with them as they were during the experimental stage of the industry. Modern Hammondsport is the town whose principal points of interest are the dozen buildings "up on the hill" where Curtiss makes his aëroplanes and motors and the red workshop down beside the railroad tracks where Pfitzner built his monoplane, or the biplane shop where Baldwin is laboring in company with "Slim" Shriver the skilled mechanic who made history at Rheims last August by "letting her go" when Curtiss started on the championship race.

If you seem sincerely interested they will take you to the aërial garage at the head of the lake where they store the

" WHITE WINGS," THE FIRST MACHINE BUILT BY THE AËRIAL EXPERIMENT ASSOCIATION.

CAPT. THOS. BALDWIN, AN AIRSHIP PIONEER, IS NOW AN AËROPLANE
ENTHUSIAST.

machines that are about to be given a trial. It is the common property of all the aviators in the region of Hammondsport. Up in the rafters of this shed you will discover what is left of the famous "June Bug," the first aëroplane to make a successful public flight in America.

Although it is only two years old, its clumsy dimensions epitomize the marvelous development in aëronautics during the past two years. When Curtiss first made a circular mile flight with it the experts in all parts of the world hailed this apparatus as the supreme achievement. To-day it is kept only for sentimental reasons and the chattering birds make it their nesting place.

Another favorite roosting place for the little feathered folk is a rapidly decaying machine which was once the subject of national acclaim. It never flew, but it was so widely pictured on account of its resemblance to a bird that every reader of magazines became familiar with its trim outlines. It was built by inventor Gammeter of Cleveland, Ohio,

and was beautifully put together, but when it was tried at the aërial races in St. Louis in 1907 it refused to rise from the ground.

Rheims, two miles south of Hammondsport, in the very heart of the grape country of New York, offers ideal conditions for flying. There are treeless meadows and vineyards over a mile in breadth which extend all the way to Hammondsport. There is not an obstruction to interrupt flight and the place is protected by the miniature mountains from practically all heavy winds. In the summer the aëroplanes hop about on these fields like huge grasshoppers from dawn to dark. In the hope of seeing a record-smashing flight, such as they read about, the natives patiently keep watch from the shady hillsides day by day. Satisfied to witness any kind of flying, the summer resort visitors from the hotels and cottages many miles down the lake gather about the region in their automobiles.

Extraordinary as it may seem in the

THE "SILVER DART," CONSTRUCTED BY J. A. D. McCURDY.

face of the fact that more aëroplanes have come from Hammondsport than from any other locality in the world, the people of the community have never seen a continuous flight of more than a mile. There have been numerous flights but they have all been exceedingly abbreviated, made simply for experimental purposes. The longest flight Hammondsport has ever seen was made by Curtiss July 4, 1908, at Rheims. On this occasion, competing for the *Scientific American* Cup, he made the first public flight of a little more than one mile recorded in America.

It is a singular coincidence that just a little more than a year later Curtiss again made aëronautical history in winning the world's championship flight trophy by making the speediest flight over the vineyard plains at Rheims in France. The remarkable progress in aviation encompassed in that short interval marks one of the most amazing periods of evolution recorded in human history.

The ten eventful years that have elapsed since Captain Baldwin planted the first aëronautic idea in Hammondsport practically span the modern history of the aëroplane. In 1900 the Wrights built their first motorless aëroplane at Kittyhawk. That same month Baldwin came down through the rich grape country in search of the obscure builder who was to provide him an ideal motor. At that time Curtiss was but an obscure unit of the community.

The pride of the region was lavished upon the enormous wine cellars scattered through the valley. Indeed, the Wine Aristocracy dominated the society, commerce, and politics of the local world. Among its members were descendants of the pioneers who founded Hammondsport, many of the tender slips from which have sprung the miles of grapevines having been brought from the plains of Champagne by titled refugees who were obliged to flee the deadly wrath of the French Revolutionists or of Napoleon. With open-hearted, rural hospitality they made the captain welcome, but they looked upon his quest for an airship motor as the freakish whim of a crank. Even Curtiss was not very anxious to attempt it. He had just abandoned doorbell surgery to give first aid to injured bicycles and was laboriously turning out one or two motor

TRYING OUT "RED WING" ON THE ICE OF LAKE KEUKA.

cycles a year in spare moments.. He had recently married a schoolmate and lived in the same house that is the Curtiss home to-day, "up on the hill."

But in those days the little nest was not surrounded by a group of busy-looking workshops steaming and puffing day and night. These evidences of prosperity came later and gradually. Ten years ago the Curtiss workshop and office consisted of one very small room down on the Square. When Curtiss, his single helper, and Mrs. Curtiss, who took care of the books, all happened to be away at the same time James Smellie, a Scotch-Canadian who runs the drug store next door, would take the orders. Smellie is so proud of Curtiss that he has a picture of his hero hung in the window with the caption "He's Good Enough for Us." Indeed, you'll find evidences of personal pride in Curtiss plastered all over the business section of the town. Even the post office has an array of postals and posters pinned on its walls.

A stranger happened to be snowed in the town last February. He woke up one morning to find the Square lavishly decorated with flags. He asked the waitress in the Steuben House what holiday was being celebrated.

"Gracious!" ejaculated the young woman, jarred out of her professional calm. "Don't you know Glenn Curtiss flew six miles at the rate of fifty-five miles an hour yesterday at Los Angeles, and carried a passenger, too? Ain't that givin' the Frenchman something to think about? I guess you must be a friend of Paulhan's."

Curtiss began making motors for airships under protest. The Curtiss family was doing fairly well, thank you, and as bicycles promised to suffer contusions for some time to come there seemed to be considerable prosperity in sight. Those motor cycles were profitable, yes, but they were such a lot of bother that they didn't really pay in the long run.

The captain, however, has a way with him. He knows human nature as well as he knows airships. He paid generously for the motor he wanted before it was started, and in order to be handy if the builder needed more ready change he stayed right on the spot. The first motor was enthusiastic work and it was good, but it didn't exactly suit the fastidious tastes of Captain

G. H. CURTISS CARRYING A PASSENGER OVER THE ICE OF LAKE KEUKA.

Baldwin. So they put that dainty little two thousand dollar trifle in the woodshed and started on another; and still another; and then again another, until two years later the alert old airskipper's patience was rewarded with a motor that was just about as he wanted it.

Those jeering gentry on the blazing plains near Los Angeles were shown that a good motor could make that scorned airship perform. The news of the feat spread over the land. It filtered into Hammondsport and other small towns together with the cabled news about the sensational things Santos-Dumont was doing over in Paris. The successful flights on both sides of the ocean fostered public confidence. Incidentally in Hammondsport Curtiss's association with these events stirred the townspeople to feel a pride in the struggling young mechanic's achievement.

In order to be near his motor expert Captain Baldwin settled in Hammondsport to build his second airship. His success had attracted the attention of his old parachute-jumping rivals and they gradually drifted into the little vineyard town to discover what Captain Tom was doing. The exhibition possibilities in the dirigible balloon appealed strongly to the managers of fairs and parks and they urged the old hot-air balloon artists to get dirigibles. Consequently many strangely shaped airships sprang into being which their owners were anxious to equip with Hammondsport motors.

Curtiss, however, had just awakened to the possibilities in motor cycles and could see but small commercial prospects in building engines for aircraft. He had little faith in the future of flight and believed that his career lay along the line of developing motor cycles and automobiles. Of course if any person recklessly offered large premiums for a specially built motor, Curtiss was obliging. The extent to which he obliged may be gathered from a recent authentic report which indicates that over four hundred Hammondsport motors have been used exclusively for aërial craft during the past eight years.

Hammondsport rapidly became a rendezvous for people with airship projects. There came Roy Knabenshue, formerly a lineman, now manager for the Wright Exhibition Company, who then had just ridden the second Baldwin ship to glory at the St. Louis World's Fair. Then came Lincoln Beechy, a youth not of voting age but with a genius for piloting aircraft. He is one of the aviators in the employ of the Wright Company now. He served his novitiate with Captain Baldwin and broke away, like Knabenshue, to build his own craft. In their wake came professional aëronauts from the East and the West and even from over the seas. This species of birds came and went, but the scientists who were carrying on extensive experiments settled in the town.

During the winter of 1907 and 1908 the last dirigible balloon was built in Hammondsport. This was the airship which Captain Baldwin later sold to the United States Government. It was the supreme effort of the veteran aëronaut's life. In recognition of this achievement the Aëro Club of America awarded him

the first gold medal it ever bestowed on anyone for distinguished services. Before the balloon was taken to Fort Myer its trials were carefully rehearsed at Hammondsport. The captain was at the helm and Curtiss attended to the engine.

About the same time the Aërial Experiment Association began its eventful career. It was composed of Dr. Alexander Graham Bell, of telephone fame; Lieut. Thomas E. Selfridge, the American army officer who later was killed in the fall of the Wright aëroplane at Fort Myer; J. A. D. McCurdy, Dr. Bell's foster son, and F. W. Baldwin, who is not in any way related to Captain Baldwin. The last-named young men have since produced the heaviest aëroplane in the world, which they flew successfully at Baddeck, N. S., last winter. Curtiss was employed as motor expert.

The first machine built was called "White Wings." It was taken out on the ice of frozen Lake Keuka and skated off the smooth surface driven by its own power. The flight was exceedingly short, but it was supremely satisfactory to the small group of workers. Then followed the "Red Wing" and the "June Bug" and finally the "Silver Dart." Curtiss early developed an unusual skill as an aëroplane jockey and thus became prominent as the demonstrator.

How Curtiss Changed His Mind

While the Aërial Experiment Association was carrying on its work Capt. Newton Williams, of Derby, Conn., spent considerable time in the community endeavoring to fly with his helicopter. The helicopter is a machine which usually has two propellers surmounting a long, vertical shaft. These propellers revolve horizontally in opposite directions and are supposed to lift the machine vertically from the earth in the same fashion as the ordinary aëroplane pushes the plane surfaces horizontally through space. It is not the fashion to believe that this type of apparatus will ever be useful.

Curtiss had just come down from the hillside after a nasty spill in an attempt to glide with a motorless aëroplane. He was watching the men at work on the Williams machine.

"Do you know, Mr. Williams," he said, "I do not believe flight will come by the way of the box-kite. It is too dangerous. It depends so much on the speed. I pin my faith on the helicopter."

It must be remembered that Curtiss won the world's speed championship at Rheims last August on one of those motor-driven box-kites. He has been one of the most energetic promoters of this form of flying machine. The Curtiss biplane is known as one of the most perfect aircraft in the world. His remark to Captain Williams is an interesting sidelight on the immaturity of his knowledge two years ago. It is a significant indication of the remarkable manner in which the values in aëronautical experiments have been grasped by intelligent workers during the short interval.

What has happened to Curtiss has happened to almost every intelligent experimenter. The ornithopter of the Gammeter day and the helicopter have been abandoned in favor of the aëroplane, which constantly shows itself to be capable of increasing utility. Though it has flown far, it is still crude. But the adjuncts which will make it capable of soaring in high winds and of flying with little propulsion are in sight.

Hammondsport owes its commercial dominance in the flying-machine business to the development of the modern aëroplane. Skill in building these machines has developed among the young men of the village an expert class of mechanics whose services are in demand wherever aëroplanes are being built. It has attracted to the little town from all over the country eager young men who want to engage in the business. It has filled Hammondsport's boarding houses to such an extent that it has become a problem how to house the growing population.

Recently it was stated that the failures preceding the production of the successful machine in Hammondsport represented an expenditure of more than one hundred and fifty thousand dollars. The bulk of this money was spent in Hammondsport. But the most telling indication of the commercial value of the aëroplane industry to Hammondsport is the fact that the payroll of the Curtiss factory alone represents an aggregate of two thousand dollars a week.

17.
Monoplane
Versus Biplane
(1911)

LABOUCHERE IN THE NEW BIPLANE "ZODIAC" WHICH COMBINES MANY OF THE
FEATURES OF THE TWO TYPES

MONOPLANE VERSUS BIPLANE

By AUGUSTUS POST

ILLUSTRATED WITH PHOTOGRAPHS

*The Relative Merits of the Two Types of Aeroplanes Compared
on the Basis of Principles and Performances*

THERE is no question in the development of aviation more interesting to the average observer than the relative value of the biplane and the monoplane. Types of both have so multiplied and differentiated that the man on the street can no longer distinguish at sight, say, a Nieuport from any other of the monoplanes to which Bleriot accustomed him, or pick out a Farman, a Sommer, a Voisin, from other biplanes, however they may show their peculiarities to the initiate, but the two main divisions of the flying-machine remain distinct and distinguishable to the most casual gaze.

Distinct they have always been, even in the impulse that brought each into being. The dream of man for ages had been to fly; his one model in nature had been the bird; mechanical genius first set about to build a flying-machine on the bird's model. All birds are monoplanes, all insects, all flying-fish, all flying-squirrels are monoplanes, and the imitative genius of the mechanic seems to run naturally to the production of a machine of the monoplane type.

The biplane, on the other hand, starts from the kite. Originally a monoplane surface, the kite was developed and made more efficient by Mr. Hargrave, a well-known Australian scientist, who constructed the double-surface "Hargrave Kite," widely used for scientific purposes by the Weather Bureau, as well as by boys in their sports. This kite-form is not an imitation of anything in nature, but the creation of a scientific mind, worked out on engineering principles.

This fundamental difference extends all down the line of subsequent aeroplane construction. The monoplane is the development of mechanical genius,

THE NEW PAULHAN BIPLANE IN FLIGHT, SHOWING THE LATEST DEPARTURE
IN WING DESIGN

the biplane is the product of engineering skill and knowledge of the principles of aëro-dynamics and construction.

Otto Lilienthal, a German, a man of poetic nature and an enthusiast, studied the stork and its manner of flight and built a monoplane gliding surface on resultant lines. This inspired Octave Chanute to repeat some of Lilienthal's experiments near Chicago. Mr. Chanute was at that time chief engineer of the Erie Railroad, an engineer and scientist of the highest order, and just as Hargrave had improved the kite, Chanute finally improved the bird model of Lilienthal by building a "Chanute" gliding machine, founded on the basic principle of the Pratt truss used in all bridge building and engineering construction work.

The monoplane may thus be said to descend from Lilienthal's poetic model glider, the biplane from the glider of Chanute, scientifically constructed on engineering principles. The Wright Brothers were also experimenting at the time with a glider built with practically the same construction, but made flexible at the rear edge for the better maintenance of equilibrium.

The poet is, as the word implies, the "maker," the doer, the empiricist; the

scientist, as its derivation shows, the "Knower," one who works outward from basic principles. This shows not only in the types of machines but in the characters of the men who invent them. Bleriot, who has the best factory facilities and equipment in the world, is the typical monoplane inventor, the born mechanic; the Wrights created their biplane not so much in the shop as in the study, planning it out completely and working from data previously obtained.

The monoplane is, as everyone knows, an aëroplane with a single large supporting surface, while the biplane has the large or main supporting surfaces placed one over the other, usually strongly held together by struts and braced by cross-wires. However, I would put a number of machines into a third category, which I would call "double monoplanes" or "double planes," to include such machines as have two single planes tandem, or placed so that one follows the other, such as the Langley type. These have hitherto been considered monoplanes solely because all their surfaces were on the same general plane or level.

This class would also include machines with two single planes superimposed, which seem to be held apart from each other, but are not firmly built together as a unit. Such are the hydro-aëroplane recently used by Ferber in his experiments over the bay of Monaco, the Goupy machine, and the machine built by M. Louis Breguet, which has a monoplane fusillage with engine and propeller in front and two supporting surfaces held apart by single struts.

The case for the respective types, it would appear, resolves itself into a comparison of the claims of each to superiority in the qualities which flying-machines must possess—speed, adaptability for altitude, weight-carrying and duration, usefulness, especially in cross-country flight in war or peace, and safety. This may partly be indicated by performances, but at this early stage in aviation it must be forecast somewhat from the construction and consequent limitations of the types.

The speed record belongs to the monoplane and has done so from the beginning. At this writing it is held by the late E. Nieuport in a Nieuport at Mourmelon, France, with a speed of 82 miles an hour. Although the first Gordon Bennett race was won by a biplane, all others since have been won by monoplanes, and even when the biplane won the race, faster time was made in a single lap by the contesting monoplane.

Speed Not the Whole Story

In short, if all there were to flying were going swiftly straight through the air, it would be a clear case for the monoplane. But it is actually a debatable question whether in the final development of the art of flying, extreme speed is an entirely desirable quality. Extreme speed in flight is all right while in the air, and enables one to cut through wind disturbances with less chance of loss of equilibrium and consequent increase of safety, but it complicates seriously the problems of landing and maneuvering.

The altitude record shifts with surprising rapidity. Some idea of this may be obtained by a study of the records since only the beginning of the present year. Up to December 31, 1910, the world's record was held by Legagneux, in a Bleriot monoplane, with a trifle over 9,975 feet. He had wrested this from a Wright biplane flown by R. Johnstone to 9,714 feet. Loridan won from the monoplane in a Farman biplane at Mourmelon in July with 10,761 feet, and directly after Lincoln Beachey raised the figure to 11,642 feet in a Curtiss biplane at the Chicago meet. But before the end of the season it passed again to the monoplanes, and is now held by Rolland G. Garros in a Bleriot with 13,945 feet, over two and a half miles.

A high altitude record depends upon the ability to operate in air with not quite half, or at least much less than, the supporting power of air near the surface, and consequently furnishes an excellent test of general efficiency. This is one reason why altitude tests, to the layman often so purposeless, are so important to constructors of aëroplanes, especially just now in the experimental stage of building. The aviator's reason for exacting high altitude possibilities is his desire to get into the major currents, which may be favorable to speedy long-distance flight. If, to his tremendous engine power he can add the speed of the upper currents—well known to balloonists—there is no reason why he should not easily add to his machine's speed the velocity of upper air-currents, which have been recorded as high as one hundred miles an hour.

It also enables him to get out of disturbed conditions at lower altitudes and to cross high mountain ranges and—a very important point—gives him a much safer position for gliding down in case the motor gives out. The ultimate possibilities of altitude are by no means reached, and it is perhaps hazardous to forecast that the greater supporting surface of the biplane will finally count for more in the higher air, though there is reason for such a belief.

In weight-carrying, the biplane easily leads. Breguet holds the record with fourteen passengers, and though Bleriot has built a monoplane that carried seven, for demonstration purposes, this machine was not further developed. Weight-carrying power is a most important quality, not, as might be imagined, for possible passenger traffic, but because

Ready for the Start

In Full Flight

Gliding Down the Wire

Landing on the Water

Taking the Air

Back to Shore

LAUNCHING A CURTISS BIPLANE FROM A WIRE TO SHOW ITS AVAILABILITY IN
NAVAL USE

Photograph from Pictorial News Co.

THE NEW MAURICE FARMAN BIPLANE IN FLIGHT—THIS MACHINE HOLDS THE
WORLD'S RECORD FOR DURATION

it permits taking along a greater amount of fuel, much increasing the radius of action and permitting the aviator to stay up much longer. Aëroplane makers do not and will not consider passenger-carrying beyond a comparatively small number; it is the fuel, the life of the flight, that they wish to make possible to the aviator in increased quantity.

From this, it will not be surprising that the duration record should be held by the biplane—G. Fournay at Buc, France, September 2, 1911, flying a Maurice Farman biplane continuously for 11 hours 1 minute, and covering 720 kilometers, about 450 miles.

The aëroplane is now, roughly speaking, useful for two purposes,—military and naval uses in time of war and cross-country flight for sport or practical purposes in time of peace. For the army, both types may be, and are readily, utilized without encroaching upon each other's special usefulness. The speedy monoplane is used for messages where rapid personal communication must be established ; the biplane more for observation and reconnoitering, for locating impor-

tant dispositions of the enemy's troops, allowing by its lower speed an opportunity for passengers to sketch or photograph, something very difficult to do from a monoplane whose construction affords only a limited field of downward vision. This is a most important detail, and this is the position taken by all military officers and the Aeronautic Corps of France, England, and America, who have been training their military aviators for this kind of work. Biplanes have been the machines chosen for sketching or map-making, because by virtue of the position of the aviator, the field of vision is so much clearer below. The United States army has no monoplanes—which may or may not bear upon the question, according as one has had experience with the difficulty of getting American appropriations for military aeronautics—but the French army, with a remarkable governmental co-operation and a strong national predilection for the monoplane type, is equipped in about the proportion of sixty biplanes to thirty monoplanes.

For general scouting work, both machines are needed, and at the German

Photograph from Pictorial News Co.

THE BREGUET BIPLANE HAS THE PROPELLER IN FRONT AND TWO SUPPORTING
SURFACES HELD APART BY SINGLE STRUTS

maneuvers this year proved their efficiency so well as to earn the especial congratulations of the emperor. For wireless operations the biplane is better, on account of its construction, which is the reason why all experiments of this nature have been, as far as I know, conducted from biplanes. The biplane is able to make better landings on rough ground, an advantage in time of war, and though I have never known of actual experiments in such use, I do not see why the biplane could not be used to lay the "buzzer" wire, that marvelous development of field communication that comes nearest to actual wireless. The "buzzer" wire, now carried in a roll on the shoulders of a man who lays it as he goes, could be laid from an aeroplane over impassable ravines, swamps, or gorges in an incredibly short space of time.

As for naval uses, all the facts are on the side of the biplane, simply because it is the only type that successfully complies with naval conditions. These are that the machine should be capable of carrying the extra weight of pontoons or a boat for landing on water or for supplying flotation ; that it should possess exceptional qualities of duration and reliability, not only for the character, but for the range of the operations involved; that for the same reason it should have greater altitude possibilities than military uses require ; and, possibly most important, that it should be capable of landing on water and rising from it. To meet all these needs a new type has been evolved from the biplane,—the hydro-aëroplane, whose powers of rising and landing have been so developed that it has been actually launched from a wire. This shows that it could be readily launched from a ship, gaining its start by sliding down one of the stays of the vessel, aided by the ability of the ship to steer and steam into the wind. This launching from a wire was accomplished for the first time on September 17 of this year by the U. S. naval aëroplane built by Glenn H. Curtiss and operated by Lieut. Theodore G. Ellyson—one of the Hammondsport experiments at which I was so fortunate as to assist.

In the records for cross-country flight

Photograph from Pictorial News Co.

NIEUPORT ABOARD HIS 28-HORSEPOWER MONOPLANE WITH WHICH HE ESTAB-
LISHED THE WORLD'S SPEED RECORD—119 KILOMETERS AN HOUR

in Europe, the monoplane is pre-eminent, though some notable flights have been made by a passenger-carrying biplane, especially Renaux's Circuit of Europe flight and that from Paris to Puy-de-Dom. In the Circuit of England,—nearly one thousand miles, accomplished in three days of actual flying,—where eighteen monoplanes and twelve biplanes entered, monoplanes took both first and second place. In fact, they so outstripped the biplanes as to inspire Lord North-cliffe to give some fervent advice to his countrymen to pay all their attention to

Photograph from Pictorial News Co.

THREE-QUARTER VIEW OF ASTRA-BIPLANE BUILT FOR THE FRENCH ARMY;
SPAN 12 METERS, LENGTH 10 METERS, ENGINE 60-H.P., 8-CYL. RENAULT

Photograph from Pictorial News Co.

GASSIER IN HIS MONOPLANE WITH 70-HORSEPOWER GREGOIRE MOTOR

developing the single-surface machine as the aëroplane of the future, evidently in the belief that the biplane was already obsolescent. In the Paris-Rome race, there were only three biplanes out of over twenty entries, and these were far outclassed from the start. In the Circuit of Europe—France, Belgium and England, including two Channel crossings—monoplanes also made by far the best showing, though as already noted, one biplane did complete the course. A speedy machine may excel in such flights because it exposes the aviator to peril for a shorter space of time. For example, crossing Niagara River in a monoplane would

Photograph from Pictorial News Co.

PAULHAN'S NEW TRIPLANE, WHICH MADE ITS FIRST FLIGHT SEPTEMBER 20, 1911—DRIVEN BY A 70-HORSEPOWER GNOME MOTOR

expose the aviator to its dangers for a lesser time than a slower machine, although this very feat has, as it happens, been accomplished by a biplane that successfully navigated the turbulent air-currents.

In cross-country flights in America, on the other hand, the biplane is far ahead. Atwood's flight of over 1,200 miles from St. Louis to New York in a biplane establishes at this writing the world's record for long-distance cross-country flying, so this record, first made in Europe by a French monoplane, is now held in America by an American biplane.

Other conditions, however, govern cross-country flights when carrying a passenger, and here monoplanes are at a disadvantage for reasons already explained. The wings must be made much larger and this makes them too frail to withstand the shock of the machine's hard contact with the ground in a rough landing, such as cross-country flights often entail, and they are somewhat handicapped in landing by not being such good gliders, on account of lesser wing area.

It might seem as if the question of relative safety could be readily decided by comparing the number of fatal accidents to the score of each class, but it will be seen at once that such a course would have little value in this period of aëroplane building, which is still largely experimental. Our knowledge is not yet sufficiently exact always to determine whether a fall is due to structural deficiencies, to unusual strain, or—as is often the case,—to the recklessness of the aviator, or even to a momentary lapse of the constant, almost automatic vigilance required. However, the construc-

tion of the monoplane seems an evidence of greater safety because the engine is in front and the operator on top, and in case of a fall, it is on top of the engine that he falls. The biplane, unless the aviator is thrown to one side in falling, is likely to crush him under the engine. As a matter of fact, the machine is as likely to fall sideways as head-first, spilling the aviator free of the engine—and no direct fall from or with a machine is exactly what one would call safe. It is an interesting matter of record that the Wright Brothers started to experiment with monoplanes and gave it up because they could not get the factor of safety to a point that would satisfy them.

The evidence is in, as the case stands to-day, and the partisan of either type may—and will—use it to establish the claim of his own machine to pre-eminence, but there is no need for partisanship at all. Nor is there much among practical flyers, many of whom use the two types interchangeably, the monoplane being, according to the records of the French school, the easier for Frenchmen to learn, while Americans learn the biplane more readily. But the same qualities are needed to make a successful aviator in either, and every season the records shift back and forth with a rapidity that goes to show that there is no hard and fast line of demarcation, and that their uses do not develop so much along sharply diverging lines as students of construction believed at first would be the case. The main points of difference, as we have seen, develop from basic construction principles, but only the new age that produced the aëroplane, and that the aëroplane will in turn develop, can show which type will be better suited to its new civilization.

18.
The Highway
of the Air
(1909)

THE HIGHWAY OF THE AIR

By MAXIMILIAN FOSTER

Author of "Corrie Who?"

EDITOR'S NOTE.—Just "where are we at" in the flying game? The public has been surfeited with technicalities, vague descriptions, and ecstatic predictions. But how many of us have any real understanding of the situation in aeronautics? This article is intended clearly to explain the present status, and to make you sense the atmosphere, the spirit, of this, the oldest dream and the newest achievement of romance turned into fact.

OUT on the plains they used to tell the story of an old Pawnee buck who had just seen his first railroad engine. "Mebbe so. Injun plenty drunk now." Then he turned to his squaw. "You see um too?" Yes, she saw it. "Unh, squaw drunk too. Squaw steal um my whisky," he grunted, and stolidly knocked her down. In this way he not only disputed the improbable but asserted a policy of conservative doubt.

Say "flying machine" to the ordinary mortal, and you stand the chance of hearing a cackle of derision. On my way out to the parade ground at Fort Myer, Vir-

Photograph by D. A. Willey, Baltimore.

ginia, I said it to a man from Philadelphia, whereupon he regarded me with a fishy eye.

"Flying? Oh, they've got to show me first," said he. "Those Wrights may be doing it, but seeing's believing."

Pawnee and Philadelphian! The conservative, hidebound policy of doubt.

"Oh, well, I don't dispute they've done something," he went on to argue; "only—a hop, skip, and a jump off the ground, and back again, isn't flying. Not by a long chalk."

Nor was he wrong in that. He had in mind some of the hippodromists that have done much to bring aviation into ridicule. Flying is not a hop, skip, and a jump, and back to earth again.

But that afternoon, when the Wright aerodrome soared into the air from the Fort Myer parade ground, and wheeled, turning with the ease of a gull, I heard a gasping voice behind me. There was my friend from Philadelphia, his eyes starting like a cod's. "My God!" he said, and whispered it again, "we've lived to see it!"

So we had. Seeing was believing, and he didn't go home to beat his wife. One glance had convinced him.

But if you missed the sight, you may need convincing. I can't blame you. I wonder what the cave man thought who first struck fire. Or the first man to hear Bell's voice whisper through a length of copper line. Or what a Hottentot's impression is when he first hears a phonograph. The man from Philadelphia and I saw Wright fly at Fort Myer, and I don't think the cave man and the Hottentot have much the better of us in awe.

It was a fine day—sunny, almost cloudless, with a light air blowing across the parade ground. Away from the artillery sheds and close to the suburban trolley line, stood a sort of tower, a four-legged derrick; and in front of it, a thin wooden rail stretched for a hundred feet down the easy, open slope. This was the launching way. A shed at the other end of the field housed the flyer; and it must have tickled Orville Wright more than once to hear the onlookers glibly call this shed the aerodrome. It shows how flying has arrived before the public has even gripped its terms. They might have called it the aerodrome shed, or aerodrome barn, or, at a pinch, aerodome. But not aerodrome. That is the name of the machine itself. It was given to it by S. P. Langley, the first man ever to fly a power-driven man-bird. In his honor,

it ought to stand. Furthermore, "aeroplane" is a misnomer; for all the machines that fly have curved supporting surfaces—not planes. However, the man from Philadelphia and I went into the shed and took a look at the machine, and I heard him grunt with mild surprise, perhaps disdain.

For it was all so simple—there was so very little to see. One was prepared to view a complicated array of machinery—ganglia of wires, rods and gearing, an assemblage of planes, vanes, tails, and rudders, all set up in a manner designed to stagger the spectator. I suspect the machines we'd seen do a hop, skip, and a jump, and back to earth again, had led us to expect the fearful and wonderful in mechanism. What we saw was a machine of a simplicity that is positively absurd. It is so simple that you wonder how it has taken man till the twentieth century to learn to fly.

Here were two cloth-covered surfaces, one a man's height above the other, each one slightly curved, forty feet wide and six and one half feet fore and aft. Steel wires and wooden uprights trussed them together; and out in front, about where a bird would hold its head in flying, were two small horizontal planes, parallel and also cloth-covered. About where the bird would hold its tail was the rudder, consisting of two upright planes. A four-cylinder gasoline engine, not unlike the auto or marine type in looks, stood just a little to the right of midships on the lower wing and, by a plain bicycle attachment of chain and sprocket gearing, drove the two stern propellers. Beside the engine stood the radiators, flat, thin, sheet-brass pans set edgewise to the wind, their wide surfaces designed to cool rapidly the water from the motor cylinders' jackets. Then there were two small seats just at the left of the engine; and in front of them the three levers that guide the machine in flight. Under the flyer's body was a skid, a light wooden sledge with runners set widely apart. These few things were all one saw at a glance—and it was very little to see. But, please remember, it has taken man a few thousand years to reduce his schemes for flying to this plain, effective simplicity.

Lieutenant Selfridge explained Wright's flyer to me—that simple, brilliant, earnest young officer of the Signal Corps who was afterward to lose his life in the same machine. Singularly enough, my still dubious friend from Philadelphia asked this one question:

Photograph by Clinedinst, Washington, D. C.

ORVILLE WRIGHT GOING TO HIS FLYING MACHINE.

"What would happen if your propellers broke?" Selfridge smiled. "Nothing," he answered; "we'd simply glide to earth."

Orville Wright came in just then, and we were introduced to him. Wright had heard the question. "Yes," he added to Selfridge's answer, "we could remove the propellers entirely, and this machine would soar almost as easily as one of our lightest gliders."

And though it didn't do that when the propeller snapped, the mishap that cost Selfridge his life and crippled Wright, no more argues against the success of the machine than one wrecked motor car damns the whole utility of the automobile. A defect in building tumbled the flyer from the sky. A broken rail may wreck a railroad train, but the locomotive is not a failure.

The Wright machine must have gleaned something of its simplicity from its two creators. Orville Wright is a modest and unassuming person, as I am told his brother Wilbur is, as well. You would think him a plain business man, in his modest business clothes. Outside, two thousand onlookers gaped curiously, and he acted precisely as if he'd like to run around the corner of the shed and hide. And when the time came to fly—

"Haul her out," said he, casually, with a wave of his hand, as you and I might ask some one to bring out our bicycles. My Philadelphia friend raised his eyebrows. "Doesn't put on much lugs, does he?" he commented. "Now over in France——"

To be sure. They order this thing better in France.

"I saw it done over there," said Quaker City. "Some one blew a bugle, and a man in a leather suit, racing goggles, leather skullcap, puttees, and rubber gloves came out and was photographed. Then he got into a kind of machine shop with wings and had his picture taken again. Afterward, he made a short address to the crowd, looked up at the sky, shook hands all around, and then they let her go."

"What happened?" I asked, hanging on his words.

"Nothing. The machine did a hop, skip, and a jump across the field, and then stood on its head. The last I saw, they were taking it to the scrap heap, and the aviator was holding a reception in the grand stand."

A half dozen Signal Corps privates now hauled the flyer along the parade ground, and straddled it on a light, two-wheel truck set on top of the hundred-foot monorail. My Quaker City friend asked why. I happened to know, so I told him. "To give it a shove."

Selfridge, with a quiet, gentle patience, the patience of the enthusiast, explained further. "Every bird has to have a start," said he, "to get up off the ground. The little birds do it with a jump; big birds like the condor, the vulture and the turkey buzzard get it with a run. If you put a condor into a twenty-foot open pen, ten feet high, he couldn't get out. He couldn't get start enough to rise."

There was a fourteen-hundred-pound iron weight under the derrick. The Signalmen hauled it to the derrick top with a rope and tackle, and this rope was fastened to a wire that ran out to the farther end of the monorail, turned on a pulley, and came back to the flying machine. When the weight dropped, the flyer would be hauled forward at the speed of the falling weight. "The aerodrome requires a speed of twenty eight miles an hour," said Selfridge, "to support itself in the air."

Wright was standing inside the wire guys that brace the rudder frame. He looked around and nodded, and Taylor — his mechanician — and a helper cranked the engine by turning the two propellers. The motor coughed; the two turned again, and then the engine awoke, its exhaust making a staccato clatter, crackling sharply. Have you ever heard a

Photograph by A. Radclyffe Dugmore.

THE WRIGHT AERODROME
SOARED INTO THE AIR.

reaping machine clacking in the wheat fields on a still September day? This was like that. Keep it in mind now.

"Say, look at Wright," said my Philadelphia man. "I mean, look at his cap. He's got it tied on with string— common string."

Then Wright took off his coat, and next his cuffs—"Oh, I say!" protested my friend. He was right. You can't invest with much heroic glamor a man who calmly takes off his cuffs in the presence of two thousand gaping onlookers!

Wright climbed into his seat. "Let her go," he said. I think it was that; the motor made such an abominable clatter that I couldn't hear distinctly. Anyway, it was said about as you'd say to a man holding you up on a bicycle, "Say, give her a shove, will you." But "Let her go" will do.

The machine shot forward, two men running along with it and steadying it by the wings. At the end of a few feet, the outrunners stopped, unable to keep up; and there was a backward rush of air, a low murmur from the crowd, and I saw what I'd come all the way from the state of Maine to see —man at last vying with the birds in their mastery of the air.

I could have groaned with disappointment.

They warn you at Niagara that the only way to see the Falls the first time is to see them from below; that if you look at them from above you will have a quick, sinking sense of unfulfillment. My experience with the flyer was like that. There it was, barely skimming the tops of the grass and weeds of the parade ground, with only the edges of its broad wings visible, and its two propellers

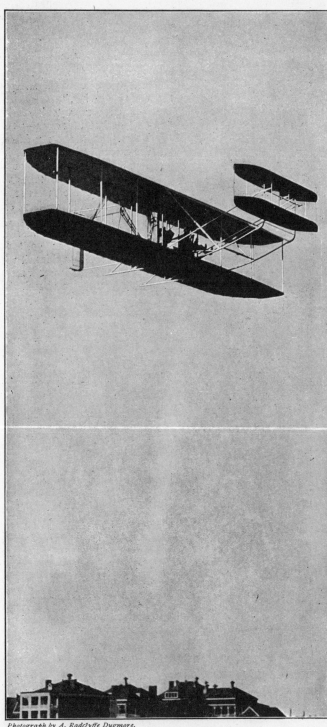

Photograph by A. Radclyffe Dugmore.

MAN VYING WITH THE BIRDS IN THEIR
MASTERY OF THE AIR.

flapping awkwardly behind. I saw no sublimity in that; no realized ideal of vast, white pinions gleaming in the sky; none of the grace and ease I'd dreamed about. Instead, there was what looked like a big, double-armed reaping machine trundling along, and the clack of its motor made but one sound in my ears—the noise of reaper knives hewing through the prairie wheat.

"Hunh!" drawled a voice behind me. I suspect it was disdainful Keystone State voicing its doubts again. But I didn't look around. I was watching closely now; for just ahead of the rising aerodrome stood its shed. It was going to be a touch-and-go, I thought, for the ugly, box-like reaper thing to clear it and the canvas tents that stood near. Somehow, the two flapping propellers looked uncommonly weak and incapable, and mind and eye worked quickly gauging where Wright was going to hit.

Something happened. The ugly, pitching frame swooped upward, as if my fancied reaper had galloped to a prairie rise. Then it careened on that circling, skyward shoot, and, edging over as it soared, turned its surfaces toward us with a flash of snowy wings. A murmur broke from the crowd, a whisper of admiration. "Oh!" Out over the distant tree-tops and the shed's peaked roof, above every background but the blue, rushed into view then the real picture—the one I'd dreamed about—

THE AERODROME "JUNE BUG," IN FLIGHT, OPERATED BY J. A. D. McCURDY

the vast bird-thing, wheeling in a long, lazy sweep of gracefulness through the profundity of the sky. Had it trailed a rope, a wire, even a single kite cord, the marvel of it might have failed—failed, because one would have realized then a bond between it and the earth. But there was nothing of that. Instead, it shot higher, free of all restraint; and with all the power of a great sea bird drove away upon its course.

"My God!" gasped the man from Philadelphia, "we've lived to see it."

And it was worth living for.

Again the white pinions tilted, and again the flyer turned, rushing onward, yet so certain in its movements that one had the feeling that it lived and flew of itself, guided by its own living will. One dreamed that its brain was its own, almost forgetting the man who sat there, skilfully fingering the levers. And then,

Photograph by A. Radclyffe Dugmore.

THE VAST BIRD-THING, WHEELING THROUGH THE PROFUNDITY OF THE SKY.

as if homeward bound to its aerie, it came rushing down the sky with the speed and poise of an albatross reaching along the trades.

I stood straight underneath the flyer as it went by. It was a hundred feet in the air then. I looked up and saw the small, crouched figure calmly handling the levers; and Wright's face was as unconcerned as the face of a farmer's boy gee-hawing a sleepy yoke of oxen along a country road. No doubt the sensation was old to him, but I felt the scalp creep beneath my hat. The broad surfaces of the flyer, the head planes, and the rudder were, at its height now, massed together into the real bird's form—a bird of inconceivable size, with white and stately plumage. If you have ever looked up from a clipper's decks and watched the sky-cloths drawing in a tops'l breeze, you may have some faint conception of its majesty. But to grasp the marvel, you must see the thing itself: blue sky overhead, white wings outspread, and that new wanderer of the air gliding smoothly onward. Oh, I cursed its busy motor for the noise it made. Sometime I should like to look up and see it go by silently along the highway of the air.

"Say," said the man from Philadelphia, "I'd like to get in and ride."

I felt as he felt. The ease and simplicity of the thing seemed incredible—more so when I recalled the history of flying. From what a graveyard of disaster this wonder springs, a graveyard whose tombstones are lettered with defeat. Langley, the first man to grasp the mastery of the air, died of a broken heart—success his, yet bursting like a bubble in his hands. I said so to Chief Clerk Dorsey, of the Smithsonian Institution, and he fished in a drawer of his desk.

"That's so," said he; "and here's what broke Langley's heart."

He brought out two small brass lugs tied together with twine. Langley's man-carrying machine, launched from its float, was tripped by them and thrown into the Potomac. The newspapers, unfriendly because of Langley's habitual brusqueness, set up a laugh; and Congress, ever timid of ridicule, refused him money to go on. Chanute, Bell, Zahm, Herring—all authorities in aviation—unite in telling me that Langley's machine, if tried

to-day, would fly. That's the history of flying. Darius Green broke his neck. Langley broke his heart. Two little pieces of brass tied together with a string! They found them when Langley's machine was taken apart.

The Wrights profited through others' errors. They learned, first of all, just what they had to deal with—namely, the air.

The average person regards air much as he regards water—as much lighter, of course, but like it otherwise. Calm air is precisely to him as calm water in a pool. If there is a wind, he pictures the air as a flowing river. And just so long as all men looked at it so, just so long the birds kept their monopoly. For the only state in which water approaches the condition of air is when water forms a maelstrom. Even then, water in its wildest turbulence falls far short of the unstable, incessant agitation of the atmosphere. Air is never still. It is filled with warm waves ascending, cold waves descending, and through it race cross shoots and diagonal shoots, with corkscrew whirlwinds wandering hither and yon, as they list. The warm air off a cornfield creates one kind of a disturbance; off ploughed land it creates another. A layer of cold air may hold down a layer of warmer air. Consider what happens when the warm air breaks through its envelope as a mill pond bursts its dam. A flowing stream churned to and fro and round

THE WRIGHT AERODROME ON THE STARTING TRACK JUST PRIOR TO MAKING AN ASCENT.

THE WRIGHT AERODROME IN FRANCE MAKING A FLIGHT AT NIGHTFALL.

and round and up and down would give a feeble idea of the air's inconstancy.

Now, a bird, circling with fixed wings, floats on a rising column of air. It maintains its altitude as to the earth, but it is constantly coasting down through the air's ascending volume. Once the bird loses the air column, it has to flap its wings, and it flaps till it finds another column, when it goes on wheeling again with fixed wings. Moreover, when it flies, the wind comes toward it in waves, rising and falling, like the billows of the sea. It meets them, and then it does precisely what a boat does: goes over them, or goes through them. The Wrights learned all this, and when they'd learned, they were about as near to flying as you and I would be to writing Chinese philosophy when we'd just learned the English alphabet. Furthermore, there were no teachers, living or dead, that could help them more than a few steps along the way.

Langley, to be sure, in this same year, 1896, had perfected an aerodrome, which, in the presence of Dr. Alexander Graham Bell, inventor of the telephone, had flown more than 3,000 feet. In addition, Wenham, Phillips, Lilienthal, Pilcher, and Chanute had experi-

mented widely in the art of gliding with wings. But the information to be derived from these sources was inexact. In many cases it was all wrong. Aside from a small part of the tables of Lilienthal and those of Langley, the world's written knowledge on flying was found to be useless. Listen: Do you know that a gnat spreads forty-nine square feet of wing surface per pound of its weight? Or that the condor spreads only 0.59? Or do you know that the condor exerts in flying 0.05 of a horse power? The pigeon 0.012? The humming bird only 0.001? Probably you don't care. But these are some of the facts that Science had laboriously garnered in its toiling effort toward the sky. It seems like trying to make a liner's engines by gathering iron dust with a spoon.

The Wrights chucked most of these facts overboard—tables of air pressures, velocities, cosines, π's and ρ's, root-signs, and the like. Newton's law went with the rest of it; for, as Wilbur Wright wrote in effect to Gelett Burgess, the author, Newton made a good guess at the law of gravitation, but he was entitled to another try when he guessed at the law of the air. At first, it seemed to the Wrights as if the air acted without any law at all.

For instance: the standard for measurement of wind pressures is a foot-square plane opposed to a current of air blowing one mile an hour. Contrary to all published tables, the Wrights at first got results that must have staggered even them. Rectangular planes tested for lift produced one effect; if curved, they gave another. Surfaces of identical area varied in pressure with every difference in shape and curvature. You'd say offhand that a square plane held to the wind at an angle of forty-five degrees would exert more lift than one tilted thirty degrees. But it doesn't. Offhand, you'd say, too, that the center of pressure of a surface moving against the wind would lie in its center of gravity. It doesn't. It moves back and forth and from side to side with every change in the angle of incidence. But with exceptions. Enough exceptions to make the Wrights wonder sometimes if they had lost their wits. If they changed the curve on the area of the surface, changes apparently abnormal occurred in its center of pressure, along with variations in its lifting power.

Prick a card through its exact center and you have both the center of area and the center of gravity. When the card rests inertly on the air, you have also the center of pressure. But tilt the card up and move it forward, and the center of pressure instantly leaps away from the centers of area and gravity. At every change of angle the center of pressure also changes, with a direct effect on balance and support that makes the card dart to and fro. So it keeps up, the card swooping about till it hits the floor. To-day, if you cut a piece of cardboard into any shape and give to it almost any kind of twist, the Wrights can tell you nearly at a glance how it will act when it falls. This matter of the center of pressure and the other essential of balance kept man from vying with the birds. The problem was to make a machine in which the center of pressure and lift could be kept coincident with the center of gravity, so that the pressure center would not go wandering all over the supporting surfaces at every change of angle every time the machine tilted one way or the other.

After four years of hard study, they built in 1900 a light gliding machine. It was designed from air tables partly their own, partly Lilienthal's, and partly Langley's. Its two curved surfaces were the result of Chanute's experiments, which, in turn, had developed the cruder ideas of Wenham and Phillips, the Englishmen. Wenham was responsible for the double, superposed surfaces; Phillips for their curves. But combined with these features were others that no man had ever used before. The Wrights put a rudder in front, and they did away with the tail. The

WILBUR WRIGHT IN HIS AERODROME ACCOMPANIED BY M. FRANZ REICHEL DURING A FLIGHT THAT LASTED OVER FIFTY-FIVE MINUTES.

hind rudder of their present machine is not a tail, like the immense trailers of the French machines. Also, in that glider, they had wing-tips that could be moved at will. Movable wing-tips and a forward rudder! No man had used these ideas before.

In this machine, without motive power, the two brothers made innumerable glides—almost a thousand in all. At times, they were deeply discouraged; flight seemed utterly impracticable, and furthermore, the two adventurers were not any too well supplied with money. But urged on by Dr. Chanute, the Chicago engineer, who himself was bewildered by the results obtained, the two went ahead, and in 1903 built their first power machine. On December 17 of that year they flew it for the first time, at Kitty Hawk, North Carolina.

It flew for twelve seconds—a modest effort, as the Wrights say, nowise to be compared with the flight of birds. But it was also, as they say, the first time in the history of the world that a power-driven flyer with a man aboard had, by its own power, winged through the air on a level course and come to earth again unharmed. That same day they flew 852 feet, and then, while the machine was on the ground, a gust of wind wrecked it. So they went back to Dayton, Ohio.

But they had flown. They had done the trick. A second power-driven machine was built and tried, at each flight going a little farther. Then, in a tremendous burst of confidence, they turned her loose, and in October, 1904, the Wright machine winged through the air for a distance of twenty-four miles. Flying was a fact at last.

It was the forward rudder and the twisting wing-tips that did the business. By these forward planes, used also for steering up and down, the travel of the center of pressure is restrained from wildly wandering fore and aft. By the movable wing-tips, which may also be used for turning, equilibrium is maintained as no other device in use maintains it.

Watch a soaring hawk, or a turkey buzzard, or a gull. When it tilts suddenly, it rights itself by flexing its wing-tips. So does the Wright flyer.

"Looks rigid, doesn't it?" said Selfridge, showing me the machine. It did, indeed, look rigid. Its upper and lower main surfaces seemed to be solidly trussed together by the wooden uprights and the wire stays. "Now watch," said Selfridge, as he pulled the right-hand lever. I saw. If you will

take a strip of thin cardboard and twist its ends in opposite directions, you will see the same thing. In the machine the right-hand wing-ends inclined their rear edges downward. At the same time, the left-hand wing-tips did the opposite, the rear edges of the two turning up. Also, in this general movement, the rudder turned to the left. Selfridge pulled the lever the other way, and the operation reversed itself, the rear edges of the left wing-tips slanting downward, the right wings up, while the rudder turned to the right.

In the air, it acts this way: If the machine starts to tilt downward on the right-hand side, the lever is pulled, so that the right-hand wing-ends present their supporting surface at a greater angle to the air than the left-hand wing-ends. This wider angle lifts the right side, but, though the wing rises, its speed is retarded, because of the drag that the greater angle of incidence causes. It moves forward more slowly than the left wing; and that is where the rudder comes in. It holds back the left-side wings by steering against them. But for this, the machine would whirl around —skid, in fact, like an automobile.

If you choose, you can steer with the wing-tips, too, and with them turn a much shorter circle than with the rudder alone. The lever that moves wing-tips and rudder together is, in reality, two levers, the two set flat against each other so that they may be gripped in one hand. By throwing the machine up at an angle, and then moving the wing-tips accordingly, the flyer can be made to turn in a circle proportionate to its size. Birds wheel in circles proportionate to their spread of wing; it requires about 700 feet for the Wright flyer to circle. The small half-moon set vertically between the forward rudder's planes acts precisely in turning as does a sailboat's stem. It and the rudder together keep the machine from slewing. But if one turns too short in it, the machine will lose headway and sink. The Wrights themselves laugh at the idea of aerodromes in the city streets. These machines can not be made to turn a corner, and they are too wide, besides, from tip to tip, to fly between the buildings.

This article, thus far, has purposely avoided the mention of other flying machines. A majority of the others that have been seen to fly either have been built, with the bare exception of Langley's, on principles long ago discarded by the Wrights, or their builders have taken the Wright ideas with or without credit to the Wrights. Every French machine that has done more than a hop, skip, and a jump across a field is the direct result of a French aeronaut's having seen a photograph of the Wrights' early glider. All have the forward rudder, but all are impracticable, because they can't use the movable wing-tips, which the Wrights patented before others found out about them. Some day the helicopter, the type that raises itself by a revolving screw, may be perfected. But it hasn't been yet. No one has built a helicopter that can raise more than its own weight from the ground. As for the orthopters, the flapping wing flyers, there are countless types of them buzzing in inventors' heads. But a single successful one has still to flap its way outside the inventor's hat.

Is flying an accomplished fact? I asked this question of Dr. Octave Chanute, Dr. Alexander Graham Bell, A. M. Herring, Dr. A. F. Zahm, Major George O. Squier, and Lieutenant Lahm of the Signal Corps; and of F. W. Baldwin and J. A. D. McCurdy, of the Aerial Experiment Association. The answer of each was:

"Yes; absolutely so!"

I believed them when I saw Wright's flyer. So then I asked the question: What is required to perfect it? The answer from each was this:

"Automatic balance."

The Wrights have flown safely in a twenty-five-mile wind. Farman and Delagrange, the Wrights' nearest competitors in point of distance covered, dare not attempt to fly in any but the lightest airs. This is because they rely for balance on acrobatics and the dihedral set of their wings. In few words, their wings, if looked at from in front or from behind, form a V, a plan long ago discarded by the Wrights. Theoretically, this provides automatic balance. In practice, it keeps the machine oscillating and, in a wind, overturns it. The Wrights, instead, make their machine as inert as possible—in fact, it really arches so that its wings turn downward instead of upward. But this apparent instability makes it respond at once to the slightest touch of the righting lever. To obtain automatic balance—balance that requires no aid from the operator—will require some mechanical device that will act instantly at every change in the horizontal.

To-day, the gyroscope is the only known mechanical contrivance that will exert leverage without a fulcrum fixed to the earth. It also tends to rotate in a fixed plane and, if placed in an aerodrome, would respond instantly to any change from the horizontal. To apply this to the flying machine, therefore, requires only some mechanical movement that will enable it to work the wing-tips automatically. The Wrights are working on an automatic controller, but whether it is a gyroscope or not remains to be seen.

Herring, however, has applied the principle to his machine, and in an ingenious way. Everything about it that revolves exerts a gyroscopic action—the propeller wheels, for instance. Herring says that he uses this to balance himself, though he still won't tell how. But even without such a device, flying is here. The Wrights' control is so great that, theoretically, they can go up a couple of thousand feet and loop the loop in midair.

But commercially, what of flying? Well, owners of railroad and steamship stocks and bonds may here set their minds at rest. The aerodrome will not do away with trains and steamships. The outlook, at the moment—though it doesn't do to forecast too much—is that the flying machine will be confined to sport, use in war, exploration, and carrying special messages. As you increase the present type of aerodrome in size, its weight increases as the cube of the dimension, while its supporting surfaces increase only as the square. In other words, the size is limited. In Bell's tetrahedral-cell machine, now building, the weight and the supporting surface increase at the same ratio. But Dr. Bell's machine is yet untried, and as he himself says: "The future of the aerodrome is still unseen." Herring, however, already speaks of large flyers capable of carrying fifty passengers. It is all an unsettled question yet. In a letter to Mr. Burgess, written from Le Mans, Orville Wright says:

"No flying machine will ever fly from New York to Paris. That seems to me to be impossible. What limits the flight is the motor. No known motor can run at the requisite speed for four days without stopping, and you can't be sure of finding the proper winds for soaring. . . . But the history of civilization has usually shown that every new invention has brought in its train new needs it can satisfy; and so what the flying machine will eventually be used for is probably what we can least predict at the present."

In connection with the question of its military utility, Dr. Bell said to me:

"The aerodrome has, at a stroke, rendered antiquated all present methods of warfare. A large percentage of fortifications are put out of business, and, in my mind, it is an era as critical as that of the Monitor and the Merrimac, the first two ironclads."

I asked Lieutenant Lahm what he thought about the aerodrome in war.

"For scouting purposes, it cannot be equaled. Used offensively against dirigible balloons, it has a strategic advantage in its greater speed. There is no reason why it cannot be used in bombarding a position with explosives."

In this connection, it may be said that the Wrights have built a machine that lifts more than sixty pounds per horse power. The one tried at Fort Myer lifted fifty pounds per horse power and could have carried two passengers as well as the operator. On this basis, it could carry, allowing for two persons in the machine, about 150 pounds of explosive. You can figure out the moral and physical effect of a bomb like that dropped from the sky inside a fortification.

No guns have yet been perfected that could grapple with this terror of the sky. They can't be pointed high enough, and if they could, there is no means of training them on a dot in the blue going forty—fifty—sixty—perhaps eighty miles an hour. And what protection could there be against anything that could hide in a cloud and hurl its thunderbolts unseen?

But what Chanute said appealed most of all to me.

"The end of war is coming. Things like this tend to make the nations' slaughter so dire and complete that, in the end, man will become appalled. The flying machine is a far step forward to the day of universal peace."

I watched him while he spoke, and there was something so earnest and compelling in his face that I, too, believed. You saw in it not the vision of the flying angel of death, but instead, of one that swept across the sky bearing a flaming torch of peace.

19.
Winning the
First International
Balloon Race
(1907)

WINNING THE FIRST INTERNATIONAL BALLOON RACE

THE STORY OF HOW AN AMERICAN OFFICER, ALMOST A NOVICE, DEFEATED THE MOST EXPERIENCED AËRONAUTS OF EUROPE AND BROUGHT THE GORDON BENNETT CUP TO THIS COUNTRY

BY

CLEVELAND MOFFETT

AUTHOR OF "THE WONDERS OF RADIUM," ETC.

ROBABLY the greatest sporting event the world has ever known—certainly the greatest the modern world has known—was the long-distance balloon race for the Gordon Bennett annual challenge cup, which started in Paris on Sunday afternoon, September 30, 1906, and finished in England some twenty-four hours later. The contest stands out surpassingly, for several reasons, among all boat races, horse races, prize-fights, bull-fights, and the like. It was a struggle for victory in a noble and spectacular sport; it required skill and courage; it involved the risk of several lives; and it was widely international, the sixteen competing balloons, with their respective champions, being sent by seven great countries: England, three balloons, France three, Germany three, Spain three, America two, Italy one, and Belgium one.

Never, I suppose, in any city, has so vast a crowd assembled for mere pleasure as on this day packed the Place de la Concorde, the Champs-Élysées, and all the neighboring region. All Paris was in the streets and on the house-tops. Some thousands paid half a franc or two francs or five francs for a privileged view, while two hundred thousand got what view they could, and paid nothing. This is one feature of a balloon race—that any one who likes may see the beginning of it.

Filling the Balloons with a Million Cubic Feet of Gas

Four o'clock was the time set for the departure of the first balloon; but already, early in the morning, a great concourse had assembled to follow the details of preparation. With tireless interest, thousands watched the process of inflation as, one after another, the huge spheres filled out their widths of fifty or sixty feet and rose proudly above tree-tops and house-tops, sixteen great struggling creatures heaving at their bonds. Twelve of them were practically of the maximum size allowed under the rules, that is, they held 79,700 cubic feet of gas or a little less; but Santos-Dumont's "Two Americas" was somewhat smaller, with 76,000 cubic feet, and Lieutenant Lahm's "United States" (it was the old "Eros" fixed over) contained 73,500 cubic feet, while Vonwiller, the Italian, had a silk balloon (the others were cotton) with 65,350 cubic feet, and the German, Scherle, had the smallest balloon in the race, with only 53,000 cubic feet. It may be noted that the larger a balloon is, the more ballast it can carry and the longer flight it ought to make; also, that no hydrogen was used in this race, all the balloons being filled with ordinary illuminating gas, brought to the grounds by special pipes. Of this gas more than a million cubic feet were required.

Despite the enormous interest in this contest, there was virtually no betting on it — partly because of the newness and strangeness of the event and its evident uncertainties, partly because the crowd, being French, was overwhelmingly in sympathy with the French pilots. Nor was this entirely a matter of national pride. France was the mother-country of ballooning, and at this time French aëronauts undoubtedly led the world in experience and skill. Count Henry de La Vaulx, one of the three French contestants, was holder of the world's long-distance record, twelve hundred miles into Russia, and of the world's duration record, forty-one hours in the air without descending. The second French contestant, Count Castillon de Saint-Victor, had sailed the skies from Paris to Sweden and won prizes — four of them first prizes — in ten balloon races. The third, Jacques Balsan, had made a long-distance flight of over eight hundred miles, and held the French record for altitude, some twenty-eight thousand feet, or over five miles. Here, certainly, was a trio to be feared, and unbiased opinion looked among them for the winner, de La Vaulx being the general favorite.

Santos-Dumont's Dirigible Balloon

There was much curiosity touching a strange contrivance fitted up under Santos-Dumont's balloon, a six-horse-power motor arranged to drive two horizontal propellers, the idea being that these would enable the aëronaut to manoeuver his balloon without loss of ballast. This was the only approach to a steerable balloon in the race, the others being simply intended to sail with the wind. I should explain that Santos-Dumont, although a Brazilian, had entered for the Aëro Club of America, owing to the fact that Brazil had no Aëro Club of its own, and that only one contestant (instead of the possible three) had entered for the United States. That one was Lieutenant Frank P. Lahm of the Sixth U. S. Cavalry, a new-comer in ballooning, with only fourteen ascents to his credit, eight of which had been crowded into a few weeks of hurried preparation. No one knew much about Lahm, or took him very seriously; yet he was the only representative of the United States, and that, as we shall presently see, by the merest accident.

As the hours advanced, anxious eyes studied the clouds, and there was an ominous shaking of heads, for the wind was straight to the west, which meant the open sea. Every few minutes trial balloons were sent up, fantastic figures of animals and men to amuse the people; but they all drifted west, where the danger lay, and many prophesied that it would be a poor race, as the pilots would certainly descend when they reached the edge of the Atlantic.

During the last hours bands played vigorously, and thousands of pigeons were set loose and went fluttering away, while the crowd applauded. One pigeon alighted on Santos-Dumont's balloon, and the Brazilian, taking this as a good omen, got a photographer to snap the picture.

The Start

At four o'clock the first cry of "Lâchez tout!" ("Let everything go!") was heard, and sharp on the minute, by a marvel of good management, Vonwiller's beautiful silk balloon, the "Elfe," rose slowly from its moorings near the little pond, while a great shout from the multitude drowned the crash of music. The Italian bowed and smiled over the side of the basket and then turned to his stathoscope as the car, rising higher, took the breeze and moved swiftly over the Place de la Concorde, sailing away to the west.

Five minutes later another balloon started, a heavy-looking sphere with a bright yellow covering of smooth, velvety finish, quite different from the more delicate French balloons. It was the "Düsseldorf," piloted by Captain Hugo von Abercron, one of the German champions, who had nearly seventy air trips to his credit.

Again after five minutes came a roar of cheers and applause, a tremendous ovation, as de La Vaulx's "Walhalla" swept upward majestically, the French champion, confident and happy, waving his thanks to a frantic multitude of his fellow-countrymen.

Next rose Lieutenant Herrera, the hope of Spain, amid shouts of "Ay! Ay! Ay!"— a daredevil pilot, it was said, who had swept over the Mediterranean from Barcelona to Salces, and had all the desperate courage of his lamented comrade, Fernandez Duro, hero of the sensational flight over the Pyrenees.

Then came Rolls, the Englishman, with the "Britannia," an old-fashioned pear-shaped balloon, the kind you see in story-books; and after him the intrepid Santos-Dumont, amid continued cheering and a great whirring of his queer "descensional" propellers; and so on, at exact five-minute intervals, until all the balloons had gone.

The twelfth was the "United States," carrying Lieutenant Lahm, a quiet-mannered, clean-shaven young American with a businesslike air and a keen, observant eye; and somehow, as one watched him, one felt that he had gone into this race to stay. He swept away to the sound of friendly shouting, and, as he floated past the Eiffel Tower and on over the Longchamps race-course, hundreds of loyal Americans looked after him and wished him luck.

The last balloon to leave (the starting positions were determined by lot) was the "Zephyr," piloted by Professor Huntington of the chair of meteorology in King's College, London. The sun sank as he disappeared in the direction of St.-Cloud, and, almost immediately, a full

THE TUILERIES GARDEN, LOOKING TOWARD THE RUE DE RIVOLI
(VON ABERCRON IN THE CENTRAL FOREGROUND ABOUT TO START OFF)

moon rose and spread its gentle radiance over a mild and beautiful night.

Lahm's Predicament

Each of the sixteen pilots had an assistant with him, so that there were two men in each basket, the sixteen aids being amateurs, for the most part, although several were professionals or semi-professionals. In Lahm's case this matter of an assistant very nearly caused serious trouble, for at the last moment a Frenchman who was to have accompanied him withdrew, leaving the American in grave embarrassment. Most fortunately, Major Henry B. Hersey of the Rough Riders, an associate of Walter Wellman, and just back from their first arctic balloon expedition, happened to be on the grounds. Learning of Lahm's predicament, he volunteered on the spot to fill the emergency. Major Hersey was not only an American with the best kind of grit in him, but he was an expert in all matters pertaining to wind-currents, having for years been connected with the meteorological service in Washington. If Lieutenant Lahm had searched Europe over, he could not have found a better man.

"Will you really go with me?" asked the lieutenant, scarcely believing his good fortune.

"Sure I'll go," answered Hersey, "if you'll let me run across to the Continental Hotel and get my overcoat."

And, with so much preparation, he stepped into the basket and calmly started on the greatest balloon race the world has thus far known.

And now, as the balloons drift away in their long flights, let us go back a moment and note the singular chance that brought into the contest this young army officer, the only American

Lieutenant Lahm and Major Hersey in the "United States" waiting for their turn to start off

n the race, upon whose efforts so much de-
ended. Who was Lahm? What was he doing
way from his regiment? How came he to
now anything about ballooning?

Chance Entry of the "United States"

Frank P. Lahm, a young man of twenty-eight,
was an aëronaut by inheritance. It was his
father, Frank S. Lahm, who had taken him on his
first ascension and taught him most of what he
knew. Indeed, it was the elder Lahm who, being
a resident of Paris and a veteran balloonist,

famous cavalry school at Saumur. His duties
there were not to begin until early in October, at
least a week after the race. It seemed provi-
dential. Here was a strong young fellow able
to take his father's place and try for the cup.
What he lacked in experience could be made up,
it was hoped, by his father's teaching. There
were two months still for preparation, and they
must make the most of them — the very most.

Lahm Begins Training

They did. It is doubtful if so much of prac-

A section of the crowd in the Place de la Concorde (in front of the Tuileries Garden)
while the balloons were starting

with far more skill and experience than the son
possessed, had originally entered for this race.
Unfortunately, Mr. Lahm was in poor health,
and had only entered so that *some one* might
represent the United States. As a matter
of fact, at that time he and his son were the
only two Americans who could enter, under
the rules of the Aëro Federation; that is, they
were the only two who had made enough ascensions to qualify as balloon pilots. This, then,
was the situation a few weeks before the race —
the elder Lahm not equal to the strain of a long
balloon journey, the son unable to leave his
regiment in America, and nobody else available.
Then, suddenly, in July, 1906, the lieutenant
was ordered to France for a year's work in the

tical aëronautics was ever crowded into so short
a time. For weeks, in Paris, this father and
son talked ballooning, dreamed ballooning,
lived ballooning. Not only did young Lahm
make eight preparatory balloon journeys, but
he made them in the light of his father's shrewd
instruction, going over the details of each attempt point by point, studying his barometric
charts, learning many difficult tricks of ballast-
handling, profiting always by mistakes, and in
each ascension coming nearer to the great art
of keeping a balloon in equilibrium, not too
high, not too low, so that its flight may be in a
straight line, with the least possible number of
wasteful up and down zigzags. That skill *must*
be possessed by the pilot who expects to win

races, and the result proved that the elder Lahm was wise to dwell upon it.

Some men, it appears, are born aëronauts. They have no agitating nerves; they keep cool in trying emergencies; and they seem to possess

utter blackness. At one o'clock the next morning they were nearly two miles above the earth, soaked to the skin, and utterly out of their bearings. The elder Lahm admits that this was one of the rare occasions when he was "badly

When it came the turn of Santos-Dumont, he set his descensional propellers whirring, to the crowd's roar of "Santos hugs the earth!"

a delicate sense of balance by which they know intuitively how much sand to throw over to hold a balloon steady — whether a small handful or a large one, or two handfuls, or a whole scoopful, or even two scoopfuls. This instinct of balance in the air is one of the most precious qualifications of a pilot, and it soon developed that young Lahm possessed it in a high degree.

As to his coolness, the father had proof of it the very first time he took his son up in a balloon — which was some years earlier. They had left Paris about half-past nine one night, and soon rose into a drenching rain-storm and

rattled"; but the son, beginner that he was, remained perfectly calm, quite indifferent, apparently, to danger and discomfort. Furthermore, Lahm had the physical endurance that a man *must* get who spends hours every day in the saddle with break-neck jumps over fences and ditches as part of his regular routine.

A Race to an Unknown Country

Such was Lieutenant Frank P. Lahm, pilot of the "United States," one of the youngest contestants in the race; by now eagerly studying the map of northwestern France with a small electric lamp, and from time to time glancing down at the moving panorama of Normandy as the west wind drove them toward the Atlantic. The race was fairly on. Sixteen balloons, a mile or two apart, were speeding down the Seine valley, and the hearts of thirty-two brave fellows aboard were full of hopes and zealous purposes. This, indeed, was a struggle worth making. There was glory in it, for the eyes of the world were on them; there was the Gordon Bennett cup — valued at twenty-five hundred dollars — to be won; there was also the Gaulois cup for the most successful French aëronaut and the Gould cup for the most successful British contestant; there was a money prize of twenty-five hundred dollars offered by Mr. Bennett to the winner; and there was a share in the Tuileries gate receipts. All this for the pilot who should drive his balloon over the greatest distance from the starting-point. And there, straight ahead, was the beating sea!

That is the great trouble with a balloon race: one may know the date months in advance, and make great preparations, without any idea in which direction the wind will take him. Thus here were thirty-two men starting on a long and dangerous journey, and not knowing, up to the very hour of departure, whether it would end in the sun-kissed vineyards of Italy or the frozen fields of Russia, in the forests of Norway or the bleak seas of Albion. Lahm, for instance, carried a heavy overcoat which he never used, and German money that he could not spend.

Gambling on the Wind

As they flew along, the lieutenant kept ever in mind his father's caution to hold the balloon low and straight; he tried for this with all his skill, being aided, of course, by the night; for it is the sun that chiefly disturbs a balloon's equilibrium. Night, however, means darkness, and darkness means that a balloonist may lose his bearings; but here, again, the lieutenant's low position was an advantage, for as they passed over the lights of town or village, their hundred-yard guide-rope sometimes sweeping the house-tops, they were within easy hailing distance, and would shout down questions through a speaking-trumpet: What town? What department? and then listen for the answers. The only difficulty was that France abounds in places with names that sound very much alike, especially to a hurrying aëronaut!

For two or three hours after the start, the Americans sailed on with four other balloons quite near them, the "Britannia" easily recognizable by the shape, and the one of German make by its color; but as the night advanced these companion air-ships dropped from view,

one by one, and shortly after nine they found themselves alone. Four hours from Paris — two hours from the sea! All well with the "United States," and the wind straight to the west.

Lahm and Hersey had their own theory about this wind which apparently was sweeping them to destruction: they believed that it would change. The last weather telegrams received before the start had reported a low-pressure area over Ireland. Such areas usually move from west to east, and the wind usually blows toward such an area. In other words, the present wind would *probably* turn to the north as soon as this low-pressure area had reached England. It was a matter of hours. There was some uncertainty, but it was a good gamble that if they let this wind carry them freely out over the sea, it would presently, at the meteorological or aëronautical moment, veer to the north and take them safely to the shores of England.

But if this did not happen? If probabilities were at fault and the wind did not behave in its accustomed manner? Then what? Would they perish in the Atlantic? That was a possibility they did not discuss; they had decided to take the chance, and they proposed to race this undersized, second-hand balloon for all she was worth. But there was one precaution that Lahm took: as fast as a bag of ballast was emptied, he tied in its mouth a wooden hoop brought along for the purpose, and so made a number of cone-anchors, to be dragged in the sea, if the worst should come, and perhaps retard their progress until a vessel could rescue them. He had these cone-anchors ready, but he hoped not to use them; he was confident the wind would change.

But would it change? No one who has not traveled in a balloon can realize the difficulty experienced by an aëronaut in determining the direction of the wind that carries him. From the very fact that he goes with it, he feels no wind at all, and can discover which way he is moving only by noting his line of progress over points on the earth and then tracing this line on the map. And if the earth is shut off by fog or darkness, then he has no means of knowing anything about the wind; he is literally lost in the skies.

In the present case, however there was no such uncertainty. The night was clear and a full moon was shining; Lahm and Hersey knew that the wind was blowing them west or (this was later) a little north of west, and they knew exactly where they were — rapidly nearing the Atlantic Ocean, rapidly nearing the practical demonstration of their pretty wind-turning theory. There already on the right was the Havre lighthouse flashing its warning. They were well to the south of the Seine, with the greatest width of the English Channel before them, more than a hundred miles of sea, even if they sailed straight over it. But with the present wind they would cross in a long slant of three or four hundred miles, and barely graze Land's End at the other side, after hanging over the water for fifteen or twenty hours. Or perhaps they would not graze Land's End at all, but *just miss it*. That could not happen, however, if the wind changed. If the wind changed — there was the dramatic point in the situation.

Over the Channel by Night

Such was the state of affairs an hour or so before midnight. Twelve of the sixteen balloons had by this time reached the sea; twelve pilots had faced the delicate question, To cross or not to cross? and had made up their minds as to whether a sound body with modest achievement was better than glory with the chance of a long sleep under the waves. Five decided for a sound body, and prudently descended within sight of the sea; these five were Von Abercron, the German; Butler, the Englishman; Salamanca and Herrera, both Spaniards; and Castillon de Saint-Victor, the Frenchman.

And seven decided for glory; seven deliberately launched their frail air-ships over the English Channel — which is a very remarkab[le] showing, as appears from the fact that, in t[he] whole previous history of aëronautics, th[e] treacherous waterway had been crossed fro[m] the Continent to England only six times.

had been crossed frequently the other way, f[or] the Continent is a big mark that cannot well b[e] missed; but to aim a gas bubble at a sma[ll] island out in the ocean, and then land it the[re] that is quite another matter. And these seve[n] knew it! Let us, then, note their name[s] Vonwiller, the Italian; Kindelan, the Spaniar[d] Lahm, the American; de La Vaulx and Balsa[n] Frenchmen; Rolls and Huntington, Englis[h] men. Brave fellows, all of them!

As to the four balloons that did not reach t[he] sea, these were overtaken by various misha[ps] (Santos-Dumont by an accident to his motor) and were obliged to descend at different poin[ts] inland, no one of them having covered a hun[dred] dred miles.

So now we have nine of the sixteen balloo[ns] definitely out of the race and seven aloft ov[er] the English Channel. And least aloft of th[e] seven was the "United States"; for, still min[d] ful of his father's warning, Lahm had kept h[im] in low, straight flight (among the self-registerin[g] barometric records there was none to compa[re] with his in this respect), and at seventee[n] minutes past eleven, when the two America[ns] swept silently over the edge of the land, the[ir] guide-rope just trailed the cliffs of Normand[y]

Frank D. Lahm at the right (father of Lieutenant Lahm), who coached his son for the cup rac[e] Walter Wellman in center; and Major Hersey at the left, who assisted Lieutenant Lahm in the ra[ce]

Lieutenant Frank P. Lahm, winner of the Gordon Bennett cup. Lieutenant Lahm is in the center of the picture — the one holding the paper

and dropped within a few yards of the water. No other balloon took the sea as low as this, and several took it hundreds of yards higher; in fact, the records show that the French champion, de La Vaulx, crossed at the height of half a mile or more.

Lahm's Brilliant Manoeuver

This question of the height at crossing had a vital bearing on the winning of the race, for, as careful observations showed, the wind was already changing, veering from north of west to west of north, following the low-pressure area that now lay over England to the northwest of them, that would soon be to the north of them, *and then to the northeast.* In a flash of inspiration Hersey, as a meteorologist, saw that their difficulty might come, not from being carried too far west, but from not being able to get far enough west. He knew, and the lieutenant knew, that, in any event, this change in the wind's direction would come first in the upper currents and last in the lower currents of the air, so that a balloon close to the sea, like Lahm's, might be sailing northwest, while another half a mile up, where the turning movement was farther advanced, might be

sailing north, and a third a mile up might be sailing northeast. Consequently, Lahm's low course to the west, so far from being an act of folly or bravado, turned out now to have been the cleverest possible manoeuver in practical aëronautics. By means of it the Americans had gained a position of unquestionable advantage; they were flying close to the sea at the extreme west of the line; they were curving more and more to the north, and would presently strike England full in the middle of her southern coast, and be swept straight on over the land, while their opponents, battling vainly with higher currents, would be carried to the east and halted by the sea.

All this added to the general cheerfulness aboard the "United States," and presently Lahm and his companion settled themselves as best they could on bags of ballast, and turned their attention to sandwiches, chicken, eggs, fruit, and coffee that had been brought along. Ah, that midnight supper in the skies! Did anything ever taste so good? Except for the lack of cigars, which are contraband articles in balloons, they were perfectly comfortable and free from anxiety. The night was deliciously mild; they did not even need light overcoats.

And there beneath them was a placid sea with the full moon shining on it. Once a little vessel slipped past far down on the waters and disappeared in the shadows. That was all they saw on the way across — that little phantom vessel, and the sea, and the moon!

So hours passed, and there was nothing to do but glance over the side now and then to see that the guide-rope swung clear of the water, and, if they settled too much, to sprinkle out sand. From time to time they studied the ripples on the sea and got their direction from the compass; and each observation showed that the anticipated turning movement (like that of the hands of a clock) was going on satisfactorily. Already the wind was blowing nearly north, so that, whatever happened, they at least were coming safe to land.

Four Left in the Contest

Which, in due course, they did, the sudden gleam of a revolving light far ahead flashing them England's welcome. They caught sight of this at about half-past two in the morning, and, as they drew nearer, saw that it came from a light-ship. So the Channel was safely passed! They had crossed a hundred miles or more of open sea, and, within an hour, were sailing above the islands of Great Britain, looking down on the lights of a city lying to the left, quite a large city, apparently, which they finally identified as Chichester in the county of Sussex. No other balloon of the seven reached England as far to the west as this, although three of the rival pilots, Vonwiller, Kindelan, and Balsan, did nearly as well. But de La Vaulx, sailing hundreds of yards higher than Lahm, crossed to Hastings, some seventy miles east of Chichester, and the two Englishmen, Rolls and Huntington, did about the same. This left these three practically no chance of victory against a wind now blowing directly to the northeast, as Hersey had foreseen; the North Sea would surely bar their advance.

So, when England was reached, only four of the sixteen contestants were really in the race: a Frenchman, a Spaniard, an Italian, and an American. And almost immediately the Spaniard, Kindelan, dropped out, descending near Chichester as day was breaking. A few miles farther on, the Frenchman, Balsan, descended, under the mistaken impression that he was being carried back to the sea. This left Lahm and Vonwiller to fight for first place, and, as they flew along, Lahm had the position of advantage. He was somewhat nearer the ground and considerably to the west. The Italian, on the other hand, had a silk balloon. At this time, of course, they were miles apart, and neither had the slightest idea what had befallen the other balloons since the previous evening.

Imaginary Oceans

For hours after they reached land the Americans saw virtually nothing of England, by reason of mist and fog. The sun itself was hidden, and of the earth they had only occasional glimpses, their guide-rope disappearing, for the most part, into a sea of clouds which more than once had the semblance of a real sea. No wonder the Frenchman was deceived into descending.

But Lahm was fortified against the terrors of imaginary oceans; he had faced them in one of his preparatory flights, and he sailed on now, serenely confident that they were over dry land. From time to time tall trees lifted black branches through the clouds to reassure him; and presently the mist parted, and they learned from astonished farmers down below (by the handy speaking-trumpet method) that they were sailing over the fertile fields of Berkshire. Through the fog they had crossed the counties of Sussex and Hampshire, making swift progress.

Eight o'clock in the morning, and the "United States" was still flying bravely to the north, three hundred miles from Paris. No sleep aboard yet, but everybody happy! So they sailed on through the morning hours until the sun came out and warmed the gas, so that it expanded and made them rise. Not the most cunning aëronaut can resist this call of the sun, and presently, from the height of three thousand feet, they looked down upon Warwick Castle and Stratford-on-Avon. Then on to the north they went, passing west of Rugby and Birmingham, and, again yielding to the sun, sailed on at the height of a mile or more toward Manchester and Leeds. They were making a great triumphal survey of King Edward's realm, sweeping it from south to north.

And Scotland? Why not Scotland, too? But that was not to be, for after midday the sun became so hot that they were lifted nearly two miles, and at that height suffered the fate of de La Vaulx and Huntington; that is, they were caught in northeasterly currents that hurried them toward the North Sea. In vain they tried to get back to the more favorable lower wind. It was too late. Already the blue sea lay before them, flashing dangerous beyond the barren moors. There was no time to lose. They had done their best, and now they must descend. Quick with the valve-cord! Down, down, thousands of feet in a minute, until the guide-rope trails the ground. Out with the anchor! It strikes a stone wall and slips off. Then it

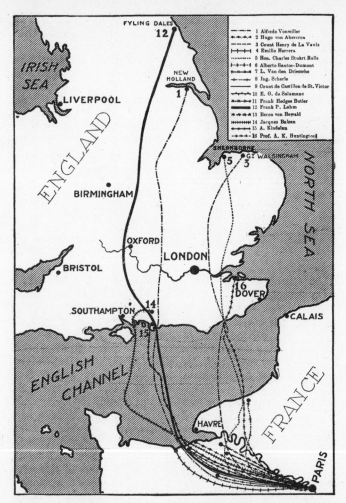

Map showing the ground covered by the sixteen contestants in the race of September 30, 1906 (reconstructed from log-books). The numbers at the landing-points refer to the list of names in the upper right-hand corner and also indicate the order of departure from Paris. (They show that Lahm and Vonwiller, classed first and second, did not trace very much the same course by merely drifting together in the same winds — Vonwiller starting first and Lahm starting twelfth. Eleven champions intervened between them, and went off in quite different arcs.)

strikes again and holds. The basket sags to earth. A pull on the "rip-cord," then a harder pull, and a great gap opens in the top of the balloon and its life goes out. The "United States" sinks heaving to the ground. Her race is run.

The "United States" Wins by Thirty-three Miles

But the "United States" had done enough, and she and her pilot could rest on their laurels, for they were thirty-three good miles beyond the point where Vonwiller had descended. They were easy winners of the race, with four hundred and ten miles to their credit and over twenty-two hours in the air. Vonwiller, it appears, the second prize-winner, came down as he approached the wide mouth of the Humber, which he mistook for the open sea. Had he crossed this, as he might easily have done, and continued his flight until really stopped by the North Sea, he would have come near to Lahm's record, but could probably not have equaled it, owing to the unfavorable slant of the coast-line.

It is of interest to note the distances covered by the seven who crossed the Channel and the points of their descent. Lahm landed at Fyling Dales, fifteen miles north of Scarborough — four hundred and ten miles; Vonwiller at New Holland — three hundred and sixty-eight miles; Rolls at Shernbourne, Norfolk — two hundred and eighty-seven miles; de La Vaulx at Great

Walsingham, Norfolk — two hundred and eighty-six miles; Balsan at Singleton — one hundred and ninety-nine miles; Kindelan at Rumboldswyke — one hundred and ninety-six miles; Huntington at Milton, Kent — one hundred and ninety miles. These distances are all estimated in straight lines from Paris; but obviously the balloons really covered longer distances, since they moved in curved lines.

I pass over the exciting scenes in London and Paris that followed this brilliant first winning of the Gordon Bennett cup, and add a word about the winner. I have had some interesting talks with him these last weeks, and with his father,

first at their home in Paris, and then at Saint-Germain, where the elder Lahm had gone with his son.

We discussed aëronautics in a great historic garden with moated walls and cool avenues of *tilleuls*, and I had from Lieutenant Lahm many of the facts set down in this narrative.

"Did you think he would win the cup?" I asked the father.

"If any one had asked me before the race," he said, "whether Frank had a chance to win, I should have answered, 'How *can* he win against such men?' but — away down in my heart I knew he had a chance."

20.
Ballooning
by Moonlight
(1907)

THE CENTURY MAGAZINE

MAY, 1907

BALLOONING BY MOONLIGHT

NARRATIVE OF A WOMAN'S TRIP OVER
THE APENNINES

BY COUNTESS GRACE DI CAMPELLO DELLA SPINA

SPORT for the gods! Who else flies over a sleeping world, through space, and knows the joy of motion without movement, without sound, without effort?

Our Roman Aëro Club is only three years old, and was instituted by no less a personage than Her Majesty Queen Margherita of Italy. It had its inspiration from the Military Balloon Brigade—the Brigata Specialisti—of the Royal Engineers, a very up-to-date corps, who were the first to make and patent aluminum-painted balloons. Now nearly every day in spring these lovely silver spheres float off over the Campagna, looking like the dome of St. Peter's let loose.

Soon after I had become a member of the club, I made my first trip, taking an enchanting flight, sometimes rising over 6000 feet, and then sinking swiftly to earth, to taste the thrilling joy of rapid travel on the guide-rope across the most fragrant and beautiful land I know. The strange sense of being disembodied, of flight without movement, of rapid travel, of motionless suspension in mid-heaven, of solemn silence, without oppression, makes a new environment for the heart of man.

My second journey, taken with my husband by moonlight, at the end of our honeymoon, confirmed a hundredfold the delightful impressions of the first voyage, and added much to them. It was with a pleasant sense of being an "old hand" that I set about preparing for this journey with which this article is to deal.

As every pound lessens the soaring quality of the balloon, the traveler has to select his outfit with care. It is wise to have a short coat with plenty of pockets, and buttoning close round the throat when necessary; and the simplest and most practical tailor-made suit of light wool should be worn. Light shoes, like those used for tennis or yachting, are necessary, with a strong pair of boots in reserve in case of landing in a mountainous district or having a long tramp at the end of one's journey. An umbrella is a desirable adjunct,—for the sun bites hard in the South,—and a motor-veil for wind and warmth. A long, light Shetland scarf such as one uses in the Alps in bad weather is useful in case of sleet and cold.

A small *nécessaire*, a "first aid," a change of underwear, a light volume of a favorite author, a map, and a guidebook, should be taken. These should be wrapped in a light waterproof cover; for in a cross-country journey one may meet with a variety of weather, and the rain that pours down in the sphere of a balloon is as drenching as a water-spout.

Excepting a small flask of brandy in case of faintness, no alcoholic drink should be carried. Smoking, matches, and spirit-lamps are, of course, absolutely prohibited, as the smallest flame might cause an explosion of the gas that inflates the balloon. The tube hangs loose and open just above the car, and small quantities of gas constantly escape from it.

Food that is nourishing, but light and easily eaten, is best. French prunes, raisins, and chocolate are a good stand-by, with cold tea, coffee, and mineral water. Bread should be very well baked. Jam and sugar are as useful as in mountaineering, sugar being one of the best of foods for exhausting expeditions. If we had been crossing the Alps instead of the Apennines, a rope, an ice-ax, and warmer wraps would have had to be taken.

We carried a barograph, which has a prepared paper stretched on a cylinder, on which a fine steel point, moved by clock-work, traces the track of the balloon. By this a good pilot can calculate to a nicety what use to make of the ballast and gas at his disposal; for the waste of three or four sand-bags may endanger life or spoil a good expedition. We had, also, a statoscope, with hydraulic indicator, which warns the aëronaut if he is ascending or descending. The motion of a balloon is often so nearly imperceptible that it may sink thousands of feet without one's noticing it. The third instrument taken was a chronometer, used with the statoscope to estimate the velocity of ascent and descent. Lastly, we carried an aneroid barometer with high scaling, able to indicate the greatest heights above sea-level to which the balloon may soar till the life-giving limit is past.

We had no anchor, for, like the Germans, we used only a tearing-cord, which rips open a small portion of the silk cover at the zenith of the balloon. When practicable, the balloon is towed down by peasants hauling at the guide-rope, which hangs from the car. The tearing-cord is most useful when a rapid landing is needed.

At 9:30 P.M., on the 15th of June, we drove to the club ground near the Tiber, where the "Fides I," of 1250 cubic meters, was gently swaying in the night breeze. Our pilot, Professor Demetrio Helbig, hurried us over our good-byes and into the car. After a few alarming manœuvers we found our equilibrium, and at the word of command the cord of the balloon's gas-tube was untied, we were let loose, and soared majestically over the brilliantly lighted city.

A full-orbed moon was just appearing in a mist of golden glory above the Alban Hills, its mellow light weaving a magic spell over all, and softening the beautiful outlines of range after range of Alban and Sabine Hills, and the snow-clad Apennines beyond. In the clear atmosphere all Rome's palaces, churches, and ruins were perfectly distinct and clearly illumined by myriads of electric lights, which stretched like gigantic diamond chains along the curving Tiber and over the many bridges.

Although it was my husband's first ascent, as soon as we were afloat, all nervousness disappeared in the enthusiasm excited by the wonderful sight beneath him. Our pilot gave him the log to keep, and explained the instrument, read by two electric lamps.

Our course was northeast, with a steady breeze from the southwest. The valley of the Tiber devoured seven and a half bags of ballast; for, as the river lies in its bed like a ribbon folded backward and forward on a table, every time we crossed a fold, the current of air carried us down. Consequently we had to throw out ballast to keep our level in the air-current we wished to follow about 700 feet above the sea.

We traveled parallel with the Via Flaminia, the highroad to Florence, and as we passed the taverns, the people laughed, cheered, and called out ironically: "Buon viaggio, signori!" ("A good journey, gentlemen!")

At Prima Porta we passed to the right of the Villa Livia. This villa belonged to the model wife of the young Augustus, and here was found the famous statue of him now in the Vatican. It is seven miles out of Rome, but, according to the legend, the builder chose the site not only for its lovely view, but because a white hen—

not a dove—with an olive twig in its beak settled on her lap. Here she kept the beautiful likeness of her lord and master that is still to-day one of the masterpieces of the world.

Passing Castelnuovo about 10:45, we saw on the left Monte Soracte, whose lovely outline figures often in Poussin's

Presently, to our wonder and delight, there appeared on the white wall of vapor opposite, and a little lower than our car, a perfect reflection of our balloon, rigging, car, and occupants, as clearly defined as in a magic lantern. All around the great shadow balloon was a radiant lunar rainbow. Straight below it was

From a photograph

"FIDES I" ON THE ROMAN CAMPAGNA

pictures, and made a bee-line for Terni. A few minutes later, while still in the valley of the Tiber, we entered a bank of clouds and saw a marvelous sight. Clouds had formed rapidly in a vast basin like the crater of a huge volcano, and through a rift in them we saw, 1900 feet below us, a curve of the river, like a broad silver band, reflecting the moon, which shone with extraordinary refulgence. Nothing could be seen above the rim of our cloud circle but two or three dark-blue points of the Sabine Hills in the southeast.

another bright little circular rainbow. For a few seconds the shadow picture seemed immovable; then the scene dissolved as swiftly as it came, and we were borne away on the freshened current of the southwest wind.

Leaving Tarano on the right, we began the ascent of Monte San Pancrazio. The balloon was now at an altitude of 3000 feet. At an exhilarating pace of forty kilometers an hour it passed as straight as an arrow between Monte San Pancrazio and the lower Monte Cardone.

The balloon having dropped rapidly down the other side (as it always does after crossing a mountain), we found ourselves, to our joy, within sight of the lights of Terni, the birthplace of Tacitus. To make such an excellent "traverse" of a rocky ridge with no other exertion than that of shoveling out a few spoonfuls of sand was a delightful and novel sensation. There was nothing of the well-known and hated "grind" with which we poor mountaineers are only too familiar, but a noiseless passing with swift and easy motion, like that of a being from another world.

Before nearing the ridge, we had hailed some shepherds sitting round their fires a thousand feet below. "What 's the name of the mountain on the left?" we called. Their answer took a long time to reach us, but came at last perfectly rounded and distinct: "Mon-te Car-do-ne, Signor-1."

At 1:45 A.M. we were hanging over Terni as over an abyss. The great cascades of Marmore have a fall of 650 feet, and are among the finest in Europe. The roar of the rushing water and the noise of vast machinery ascending on the quiet night air had a terrifying effect.

The water-power is used for government steel works, etc. The town is lighted with powerful electric lights, and this, with the glare from the furnaces and from the great obelisk-like chimneys, illume the dense clouds of spray and the fine cliffs covered with rich vegetation, making the buildings and handsome viaducts shine as white as marble.

To prevent being drawn into the strong current from the cascades, we here rose to a height of 4600 feet, which was our greatest altitude; for we usually traveled on as low a level as possible, to see the country and to save our gas and ballast.

To float away out of sight and sound of this Dantesque scene, and to see instead the peaceful Lake of Piediluco, as pretty as a miniature Como, shimmering in the moonlight, was a great relief. Beyond, to our right, lay Rieti, with its twinkling lights.

Crossing Monte Somma, we dropped down on fine old Spoleto, passing over the convent, where the sweet-sounding bells were ringing for an early mass. As the home of the Campellos, we hailed it with interest, and could peep straight into the lovely gardens of their old palace in the Piazza Bernardino Campello, which is in the highest part of the town, near the fine fortress of La Rocca, formerly the home of the ancient dukes of Spoleto.

A little farther off we saw Campello, with its lovely and classic stream, the Clitumnus. Gushing out of a grotto, it becomes at once a broad stream of most limpid water, whose praises were sung of old by Vergil, and in our day by Carducci.

By this time it was past four, and the eastern sky showed by pale rose-colored flushings that dawn was near. The air had a sharp crispiness. Our pilot shook himself into his heavy, Russian great-coat with grunts of satisfaction.

All through the livelong night the nightingales had sung, and hour after hour we had floated over this wave of harmony. On the wings of the stiffening morning breeze we raced along in joyous flight like happy swallows in springtime.

Professor Helbig changed the tracing-paper of the barograph, and declared himself famished, for he had eaten nothing all night. Count di Campello watched the instruments while the professor took a short rest. I got out his breakfast, and gave him the only seat—a strap, hooked across an angle of the basket.

In Italy, the early morning, both before and after the great heat of summer, is one of its glories. I had been fully occupied in admiring the delicate tints till the sun shone over the Adriatic, above a great bank of dark cloud. This was not a good sign for us, and gave warning that we must bring our pleasant journey to a close.

The carrier-pigeons were cooing softly in their baskets, hanging outside the car, and we took out a pair, and wrote with pride our message of good travel on a tiny form of prepared paper, rolled it up, and sealed it with wax in a minute tube attached to the underside of the tail-feathers. The gentle creatures seemed to know it to be the signal for starting homeward, and made no struggle. We threw them into the air, and, circling gracefully for a few minutes to get their bearings, they flew off joyfully to Rome.

We now left Umbria, and crossing the central chain of the Apennines near

Drawn by André Castaigne.   Half-tone plate engraved by C. W. Chadwick

"ALL AROUND THE GREAT SHADOW BALLOON WAS A RADIANT LUNAR RAINBOW"

CREEPING OUT OF THE CAR

Monte Pennino, in the Marches, passed over a fine upland plain, and arrived at Camerino, an ancient little castellated town that boasts a university. We heard the bugle calls of the soldiers to parade, though we could not see them.

Our balloon had been rushing over hill and valley, slapping the trees with its guide-rope, and skimming over hill-tops within three or four yards of the ground. Traveling on the guide-rope is rare sport. Attached to the bottom of the car, it hangs down about 300 feet, giving stability to the balloon, and keeping it erect when traveling near the ground. It looks like a long serpent on end, its supple head slipping over the earth, making a sibilant sound. Below us, too, there was the rushing music of the wind over a beech-forest, with tree-tops bending low, and showing the silver underside of the leaves. It was all good to hear and see.

The outline of the Alps seen from the Marches is very fine; and fine, too, the view of the highest and most beautiful group of the Apennines, the Gran Sasso d'Italia, still draped in its winter snows, which now came in sight.

The great heat of the sun had expanded the gas in our balloon, and made it soar in spite of constant use of the valve. The wind, too, was rising fast; Ancona and the Adriatic were drawing alarmingly near, and our ballast was reduced to a bag and a half. There was nothing for it but to choose a good landing-place.

Our pilot selected a fine corn-field close to the railway line, and at 6:30 on Sunday morning, nine and a half hours after leaving Rome, we pulled the tearing-cord, felt a few rather alarming bumps, scraped over a fruit-tree, and tumbled amid the golden corn. The car toppled over, and we crawled out like rabbits from a warren.

The peasants, seeing us descending from

afar, ran from all sides to help pack the balloon, and claim damages for the corn.

Professor Helbig sent a man with our cards to the station-master of San Severino, three or four miles off. We begged him to send us a railway trolley or hand-car to carry us down to the station. We took a few snap-shots, and sent off the remaining pair of carrier-pigeons, which wheeled for a long time in painful uncertainty before they took wing for far-off Rome.

For some time I sat on the edge of the car, talking to the peasant women, who were most primitive, and full of rustic curiosity, calculating with much frankness the cost of my clothes, asking endless questions, and speculating aloud as to which of the gentlemen I belonged to. At first, I fear, they did not think me quite respectable, the rustic Mrs. Grundy being just as uncharitable and censorious as is that lady in more polite circles. Gadding about in a balloon, instead of minding the house! It was something to shake the head over. At last, having asked my name, they became still more overwhelming, and "Signora Contessaed" me till I was weary, and clambered off my perch to seek some cooler and quieter place in which to rest. Having nothing more to interest me, I felt intolerably tired and sleepy. At last I found a shady place under a tree, lay down, and slept till the trolley appeared.

A balloon can be squeezed most conveniently into its own car, and, laced down with a tarpaulin, is ready to travel anywhere, and soon, amid the kindly greetings and cheers of our Mardregiani friends, we started off at a tearing pace downhill.

At times we have traveled faster in the balloon, but we did not *feel* the pace or the rush of the wind. The change was so great that I felt quite dizzy when we staggered off at San Severino.

The officials were most civil, and we found a large crowd of townsfolk waiting our arrival, who escorted us in a long procession as we walked through the hot streets to the inn in the wide, old square. They remained, flattening their noses in turn against the window-panes, watching all that we did.

At San Severino there is a beautiful Madonna by Pinturicchio. Is there *any* sleepy little town in Italy without some special art treasure dating back to Etruscan, Greek, Roman, or Renaissance days? Of the special glory of San Severino, alas! I can say nothing, for I went to a nice, cool bedroom and fell fast asleep till it was time to take train for Fabriano. Here we waited for the train to Rome, where we arrived at seven A.M., on Monday—no less than twenty-four hours of railway travel to bring us back to our starting-point.

"FIDES I" IN THE CORNFIELD
AT CAMERINO

21.
On the Wings
of Today

⚙⚙⚙

Flying Men-o'-War
(1910)

"—contemptuous of death, they dare
His roads between the thunder and the sun"

Exact reproduction of a remarkable photograph taken at sundown, January 12, 1910,
by H. C. Tibbitts, at the International Aviation Meet, at Los Angeles

SUNSET

THE MAGAZINE OF THE PACIFIC AND
OF ALL THE FAR WEST

MARCH, 1910

On the Wings of To-day

An Account of the First International Aviation Meet in America,
at Los Angeles, California

By CHARLES K. FIELD

ILLUSTRATED WITH PHOTOGRAPHS BY H. C. TIBBITTS

World's Records made at Los Angeles

1. *Height—Louis Paulhan (former world's record, 3200 feet) 4165 feet*
2. *Quick Start—Glenn Curtiss (former world's record, 8 seconds) 6⅗ seconds*
3. *Short Start—Glenn Curtiss (former world's record, 115 feet) 98 feet*
4. *Accuracy—Charles F. Willard; rising from a square of twenty feet on an edge, he made a complete circle and brought his machine to a full stop on the same square*
5. *Cross-Country with passenger—Paulhan and Mme. Paulhan, 21¼ miles*
6. *Cross-Country alone—Paulhan, 45.1 miles in 1 hr., 2 min., 42⅗ sec.*

HAVE you ever dodged an air-ship? It is a very different matter from dodging the usual motor-car. Most of us have become fairly expert at that—it is only a matter of a jump to one side or the other of a street to which the automobile is confined. There is nothing of this definiteness about an air-ship. The aeroplane has all space in which to swerve as sharply as a hawk while it literally bears down upon you. There is only one way to dodge it—lie down flat upon the ground. If the air-ship does not alight at that particular spot, you have dodged it.

One fact will work in your favor—it will be much more serious for the aviator than for you if he should hit you. This is another difference, considering automobiles. Yet, to one who crossed the aviation field at Dominguez during the aviation meet at Los Angeles, the latter part of January, getting hurriedly out of the way of the bewildering air-craft that came humming at his head, it seemed that if this form of travel is to become general some system of refuge, some underground safety station must be invented for the harrassed pedestrian—assuming that the pedestrian is not a species on the way to extinction. Was it not natural to attach significance to the purchase of an aeroplane on the field by a man from Kansas? The cyclone-cellar, already in use, offers an excellent beginning for the necessary utility.

Rough Riders of
yesterday and to-day.
A Mexican deputy
sheriff in the trappings
of early California,
and Miscarol, the
French aviateur,
grooming his
Bleriot monoplane

Los Angeles had gone air-ship mad. The hotel lobbies were peopled with visitors, each of whom had some sort of air-craft at home, unpatented and guarded as the solution of the whole problem. Overheard conversations held such terms as monoplane, heliocopter, ornithopter, aeronef, almost as frequent as the word dollars. Even the big Charity Ball at the Hotel Maryland, Pasadena, was an Aviation Ball, with Paulhan, the King of the Air, always moving in the upper circles, leader of the grand march. Statements in the press of the possibilities of lofty aerial flight had drawn the eyes of the town from its thronged pavements to the smiling skies above them. One evening, about sundown, everyone on the streets had tipped his chin toward the horizon and sent his eyes searching through the sky for whatever it was that had caused his neighbor to do likewise. Successful searchers pointed out their find to slower eyes. It was a star, faintly shining high in the west and apparently flying at record speed across the sky. The effect of motion was lent by a speeding film of vapor that moved in a contrary direction. In the fever that had struck the town, it was easy to believe that what appeared to be a star was in reality the aviator from France—Paulhan, the incomparable—taking his place temporarily among the constellations.

"Have you seen Trixie?" The question came large from a megaphone at the crowded gates of the field. We had not seen her, and if she were lost in that surging mass of people, so much the worse for Trixie. "The fattest girl in the world," explained the megaphone. Joined to the newest wonder, the flying men, were the oldest of the world's wonders, housed in hasty tents along the great white way to the grandstand—Fatima, the Sultan's Delight—"Just arrived, a mother rattlesnake and five little ones." The Secrets of the Egyptian Pyramids ("tell me your birthday and I'll tell you your horrorscope"), and Cora-Etta, a version of the Siamese Twins, and now, in the light of present-day marvels, fitly termed the Human Biplane. In the line with these motley attractions, so singularly unnecessary and unrelated to the interest that had drawn the eager people to Dominguez, stretched countless lunch-counters with a varied appeal, and none of it very strong. Behind it lay a deep swale which we called Grub Gulch, its nearer slope covered with lunch débris, offering excellent forage for birds that did not feed on gasoline.

At the end of this gauntlet stood the grandstand, with fourteen sections that held each about a thousand closely-seated people. On the slightly sloping floor below those seats were the boxes, sold for the entire ten days of the meet, and at a point in front of these, the boxes for the newspaper people. Location of seats mattered little for events scheduled for the air. A wire fence ran along in front of the spectators' seats and stretched away down the gently sloping field and around the mile-and-a-half course, guarded by deputy sheriffs, some of whom were elaborate with riatas and mountings of silver and carved leather, descended from "the splendid idle forties."

For at least a quarter of the distance the fence was lined with people, six and more deep. They were a patient lot, these audiences, for there are long waits between the acts at an aviation meet—the god of the gas machine demands assiduous worship and this the people seemed to have learned. But, indeed, the landscape that lay before them might well have held them. From the spectators' vantage-ground an open prairie, spread with the soft green of California's January, sloped very gently toward the distant city. Half-way across it were three large circus-tents, respectively the headquarters of Glenn H. Curtiss, with Hamilton and Willard; Paulhan, with Miscarol and Masson and Renan; and the local aviators with their varied engines of the air. It was of these last that some wag said: "The local aviators were early on the ground —and never left it." Back of the tents the field sloped sharply toward broad, newly-plowed fields; then to east and north spread a panorama of blended orchards and bungalow roofs and eucalyptus groves, beyond these the pinkish-red mass of the city, and behind all, the violet wall of the Sierra Madre, with Baldy lifting his snowy shoulders above it. The soft air of a spring day wrapped the beautiful expanse of country. On the way to the field the cars had passed through bungalow villages whose streets, lined with fruit trees, told the story of an orchard's metamorphosis. On the porches of these bungalows sunbonneted women sat sewing in the January sun. Under a great bare willow in one yard some children played

on an enormous red plush sofa. The grandstand at the field was gay with Japanese parasols. It was the magical preliminary spring of California, a season that seems sufficiently unreal to produce such a marvel as men who fly with wings. Toward the end of the day, when all breeze died away and the best flying was done, the great vista lay dreaming in rose and lavender. Perhaps it was a dream of a comparatively recent past when the adventurous but lowly-minded padres toiled along El Camino Real and tried to bring to the slow minds of the Mission Indians some understanding of their promise of a future of winged angels and a rising into heaven.

It has never been authoritatively stated whether Pegasus was kept in a stable or in an aviary. It is equally unsettled as to which of these terms is to be applied to the housing of a flying-machine. Thus the word *hangar* (pronounced quite otherwise as *unger*), is a welcome addition to a vocabulary which was refreshed only yesterday with *garage*. The great worm-like dirigible balloons, fat and brown and pointed at head and tail, were kept down in Grub Gulch—an added reason for the name. These issued forth unexpectedly from behind the grandstand, casting their gigantic shadows on the people as they sailed over the audience and rose and dived with whatever ponderousness may be said to apply to lighter-than-air machines. Knabenshue, sailing over six hundred feet above the field on his slender snowshoe rack under the big yellow bag, the Stars and Stripes flying flat beneath him, was greeted with cheers for his daring. Beachy, less successful, but equally brave, guided his unwieldy craft along the erratic air-currents. But the crowd, though cordial, was not there for balloons. Interest centers in the heavier-

"The local aviators were early on the ground—and never left it"

than-air machines. Men have been lifted from the earth by heated air and by gas for many years—the world has been waiting for them to rise on wings.

As though obedient to this call for wings, Prof. Zerbe's multiplane came

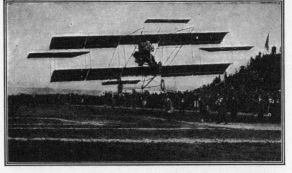

Glenn Curtiss passing before the grandstand in his biplane

on the field with many of them—a queer, lumbering affair that looked like a ship under full sail, or a flock of great white geese, or a stand for potted plants, or some fossil vertebrate out of the enormous past, according to one's point of view. There was a noble spurt along the ground, some steam, and then the great creature with a laborious sigh lay over upon its side. The audience laughed —a cruel thumbs-down laugh—careless of the eager thought that had failed to rise from the ground. Men had flown at Rheims— they must not do less at Dominguez.

The tents of the aviators, each holding several of the winged engines, looked like circus-tents in which the characteristic wagons had somehow been stripped to their slender frames. When an engine was tested the tent became a machine-shop and the side-flaps stood out straight in the draught from the whirring propeller. In the Curtiss tent the machines were khaki-colored, as though in anticipation of military service— frames of bamboo and ash, and coverings of rubberized silk. The Farman and Bleriot machines which the Frenchmen operated were grayish-white, taking the sun like silver when in swerving flight; among the other machines there was one of a dawnlike pink—seemingly born to blush unseen.

In the tent of the Frenchmen, apparently deserted, a San Francisco visitor, aflame with the desire for wings, climbed into a Bleriot cross-channel monoplane and sat there imagining the grandstand cheering far below him. This eaglet dream was shattered by a hailstorm of French expletives. A *mecanicien*, his hair and mustaches bristling with rage, fumed beside the machine. With a calm that should some day carry him through aerial difficulties the San Franciscan regarded the irate bird-

hostler in astonished hauteur; drawing aside his coat-lapel he exhibited the circular button of the Panama Exposition boosters. The *mecanicien* bowed, said *"Pardon,"* and faded away in true European reverence for authority.

Glenn Curtiss is a slender, sober-faced man—a blending of the practical engineer and the young college professor. He appears to have been born deaf and blind to the grandstand. His performance has about as much sensational atmosphere to it as that of a busy man leaving home in his auto for his office. He has an air of quiet authority, of intimate knowledge of his machine, a serious intentness upon the business in hand. He is strictly in the business of selling flying-machines, among other motor vehicles, of which business the winning of the world's speed record is but an incident on advertising account. His demonstration seems to be, not the rivalry of the eagle or the carrier-pigeon— both of whom Paulhan, the Frenchman, has put to shame—but the present-day utility of these novel equipages. And, indeed, as one watches the quiet way in which he takes trips along the air, with or without passengers, one understands why Harmon, the New Yorker, has bought one of these air-canoes, and why to-morrow may see your neighbor practicing over the golf-links with less reason for the family's fear than in the usual auto scorching. The high flying may be reserved for daring spirits until a remote day, but pleasure boating, with a motor to send the craft along the unmapped rivers of the flowing air, is a fact of the here and now.

In spite of the bird-lime spread by the Wrights' injunction, the khaki-colored biplane is drawn along on its pneumatic wheels before the grandstand. Curtiss gives a last look over the machine, climbs into the seat between the engine and the steering-wheel, the engine is cranked by its propeller, the men who have been holding the light vehicle against the force of the propeller until Curtiss gives the signal, release it and a new form of automobile, a flimsy double-kite mounted on a tricycle with an un-muffled gas-engine, is under way across the grass. Thirty thousand eyes are on those rubber-tired wheels, waiting for the miraculous moment—historical for him who has not experienced it. Suddenly something happens to these whirling wheels—they slacken their speed, yet the vehicle advances more rapidly. It is the moment of miracle. The wheels are on the tops of the grass. Then, as though an invisible incline has been spread before him, Curtiss runs up the air along a gentle slope and soon is coursing along a plane a hundred feet above the earth. It has all happened suddenly, yet how much it signifies! It is the moment for which the faith of a world grown used to material conquests has waited, apparently baffled—it is the dream of centuries come true. Instinctively, one draws an awed breath, his mind runs over a list of natural miracles almost within his own memory, he asks himself: "What is there left to conquer?"

Across the field, attenuated by distance to the lines of a gigantic insect, Curtiss is sailing through the air. On he comes, turning the pylons at the corners of the course with a motion less of the bird than of the machine. As he passes the starting line, drawn in sawdust on the black adobe of Dominguez, his hands fast to the wheel, his gaze intent upon the ground, he shuts off his engine, and with a couple of gentle swoops he alights as delicately upon the green as a gull settles upon a bay, and he becomes for a little way an automobile again. This rising in flight and alighting is really a complete demonstration—the birds have been matched for all the needs of argument.

With eyes fixed upon Curtiss at the finish, few have noticed another biplane rising from the far side of the field and following in the American's wake. It is Paulhan, the Frenchman, in a Farman machine, distinguished from the Curtiss biplane by its color and by its single elevating plane in front and its wide box tail. Paulhan flies far up

Louis Paulhan, ready to start in a Farman biplane for one of his spectacular cross-country flights

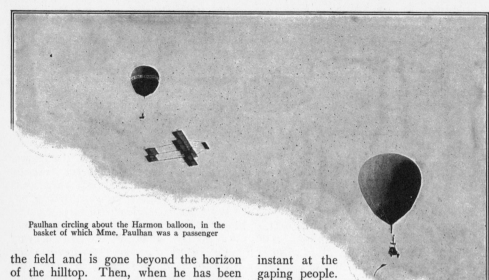

Paulhan circling about the Harmon balloon, in the basket of which Mme. Paulhan was a passenger

the field and is gone beyond the horizon of the hilltop. Then, when he has been forgotten in other movement upon the field, there comes the humming of an engine far aloft—the sound the sailors heard that memorable dawn off the Dover coast —and seemingly out of a great black cloud that hangs far above the grandstand bursts the flying creature with his parallel wings. When opposite the audience the intrepid little Frenchman waves his hand for an instant at the gaping people. Then on he goes round the course; passing in review again he waves his woolen cap and the crowd responds, cheering with the breath it has just held; round he goes again and, coming the third time, he stops his engine and coasting down the air he raises both arms to the grandstand and alights like a dove while the crowd goes mad at the performance. Ah, he is a theatrical artist, this Paulhan! He knows the value of an entrance and of cumulative gesture. And he possesses that intangible magnetism that of itself wakes an audience before performance so that the performance is a foregone triumph. He is a born player to the grandstand. Rumor has it that he was once a tight-rope walker. He has risen to a more daring and more poetic act, and he has carried to it the art of the theater and of the ring. He is an interesting little figure in his thick woolens and his sweater, with

Countess de Pennendreff   Clifford B. Harmon   Mme. Paulhan   Nat Goodwin   Paulhan   Dick Ferris

Paulhan, having alighted, greets Mme. Paulhan and the rest of the balloon party heavy-ribbed stockings. He has a face of rose and olive and the smile that won't come off, even in danger. He looks like a debonair Alpine guide, but his are the unseen mountain slopes, the uncharted glaciers of the air.

Thrilling as is Paulhan's flight, the spectator is aware that Willard, in a Curtiss biplane, has performed a marvelous feat when, after rising from a twenty-foot square of sawdust in front of the grandstand, he circles the field and comes to a stop within that starting-square as true as a bird seeks its nest. Hamilton, the third American aviator, flies his Curtiss machine to heights of seven hundred feet and more, and even when his crank-shaft breaks in mid-air, he comes to the ground with the sweep and the precision that marks these airships as cousins to the birds.

Miscarol, attendant and disciple of Paulhan, is a picturesque figure in voluminous overalls and a cap like Bleriot's. He is one of Millet's men with the hoe, turned from a dreary battle with the overworked earth to a glorious struggle with the mysterious air. After several creditable short flights, Miscarol essays to send the Bleriot monoplane skimming like a giant dragon-fly just above the green surface of the field. After flying a little distance the wings waver, they struggle in the air in evident distress, and then, after a desperate bit of bird-busting on the part of the rider, the machine falls like a wounded bird, breaking its left wing.

To the spectators at Dominguez there was far too little of the monoplane. In addition to the romance forever attaching to it because of Bleriot's flight across the

The man-bird had become a
tiny cross against the sky

English Channel, it is, to the eye, the accomplishment of man's emulation of the birds. Nothing at the Los Angeles meet was more lovely than a flight that Paulhan made toward evening, early in the week. The great valley, spread before the grandstand like a scene in a vast theater, was already bathed in the lavender of evening, but the wall of snow-covered mountains was brilliant with rosy light. Athwart this background flew the wonderful, wingéd thing of man's invention, so birdlike that man was forgotten in its flight. Turning on the line of the course the wings tipped and were turned by the setting sun into gleaming bronze.

Toward the middle of one afternoon a golden balloon that had been hanging above the valley between the field and Los Angeles, drew nearer and soon came floating gracefully over the field, drawn by a horse. While yet it hung several hundred feet above the field, Paulhan, winged with a Farman biplane, soared into the air and circling the slow-moving newcomer, gave greetings to the party in the basket, which included Mme. Paulhan, chubby, petite and vivacious in an aviation hat that was significant because of the absence of dead birds' wings, and no small factor in the theatrical element that added so keenly to the enjoyment of the Frenchman's performances. The party were the guests of Clifford Harmon, a millionaire "balloonatic" who has also bought a Curtiss biplane in which he made short flights on the aviation field. The balloon came to earth in dignity and out stepped, among others, Nat Goodwin, the actor, solemn as an owl, though his coat-sleeve bore the title "Aviator."

Both Curtiss and Paulhan took the biplane out of the class of solo performances by taking passengers for short flights, and Paulhan thrilled by flying with his pretty wife nestled close to him in those frail wings, a thousand feet above us and miles away cross-country and over the blue Pacific. Such performances cannot be written of lightly—they are the beginnings of a new era in the history of men.

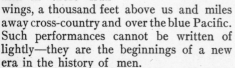

This is not a prehistoric bug; it is a Bleriot cross-channel monoplane

Stirring as were all these flights to those who thought as they watched them, there was one transcendent afternoon in that calendar of thrills. Paulhan rose lightly into the still air of late afternoon. As he climbed above the landscape the megaphone announced that "Mister Lewis Pollen" would try for altitude. Round and round the course the biplane sailed steadily, ever higher in ever widening circles. From instruments by the judges' stand an estimate of altitude was made as the bird-man climbed the sky, and as the figures mounted the excitement of the grandstand climbed with them. Now Paulhan was so high that man and engine had merged into one body beyond which the planes, lighted underneath by the setting sun, stretched like the blood-filled membranes of a bat. Icarus, in Greek legend, flew too near the sun and his wings of wax were melted to his undoing. Paulhan, choosing the sunset

hour, had flown above the sun and now climbed fearlessly toward the stars. Presently on the blackboard the world's record was written, three thousand and two hundred feet; the hoarse voice of the megaphone called to the throng of listeners: "two thousand and nine hundred feet, and still going up."

Then the world's record was passed and the instruments and the cameras lost track of the flying man, and still this new wonder of our strenuous life swept higher into the heavens. As the birdlike figure lessened in the sky until it was but a dark cross against the darkening blue, the crowd of fascinated groundlings grew silent. This man who had flown away before our eyes had become a thing apart, a creature utterly lonely, almost a mile above us in a realm where we did not belong. To the memory of many must have come the speech of Bryant to the waterfowl—in the desert and illimitable air above us, one of our own kind, yet different, was lone wandering yet not lost. It was the realization, there in that early dusk of an enchanted winter-day, of Shelley's soaring skylark that "soaring ever singest." There, lonely and cold as he was, that man-bird must irresistibly have sung aloud as he dared the condor's "roads between the thunder and the sun."

Flying home, like a droning beetle, through the dusk

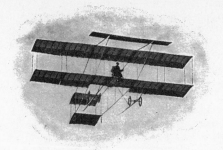

Flying Men-o'-War

By PAUL W. BECK

First Lieutenant U. S. Signal Corps. Special Observer for the War Department
at the International Aviation Meet at Los Angeles and one
of the Judges of the Contests

"THE latest report from the aerodrome flying squadron sent out from the decks of the Pacific scoutboat flotilla locates the enemy at a point one hundred miles west of San Francisco"; thus might an up-to-date newspaper begin its account of war movements should war now come.

That this is not mere fiction has just been demonstrated at Los Angeles where the speed of flight and short starting of Glenn Curtiss, the height and endurance of Louis Paulhan, and the accuracy of Charles F. Willard bring the matter home in no uncertain manner. Mr. Curtiss, in his Rheims racer, covered sixteen and eleven hundredths miles at the speed of forty-one miles an hour, and rose from the ground after a ninety-eight-foot run; Monsieur Paulhan, driving a Henry Farman biplane, rose to the height of at least four thousand one hundred and sixty-five feet, and remained in the air for two hours—lacking but one and one-half minutes, and Charles F. Willard, in the original Curtiss biplane, rose from a square twenty feet on an edge, sailed through the air for a distance of one and sixty-one hundredths miles, and, alighting, stopped on the same square. The combining of these feats, the partial modification of the deck of a scout-boat, and the United States Navy has acquired a new and important factor in warfare.

Furthermore, both Paulhan and Curtiss carried passengers—the former, two on several occasions. From which the feasibility of transporting high explosives for offensive work is clearly demonstrated. Couple this weight-carrying power with the heights attained by Paulhan, and all fortifications save those protected overhead by covering sufficient to resist the force of a hundred and fifty pounds of high explosive will become untenable. The two principal factors opposed to the offensive success of aerodromes are: The difficulty of accurate direction of objects dropped from such great heights and the accuracy of hostile fire. Both of these factors are largely unknown, but both are readily solvable. It is the duty of the Signal Corps of the Army to compute the tables and work out all other details pertaining to the former, while the Coast Artillery Corps and the Ordnance Department are united in designing weapons whose sole object is to afford means for ridding the sky of these, to them, dangerous pests.

The Signal Corps problem is almost purely mathematical and is based on the law of falling bodies as combined with forward movement. For example, if an aeroplane is equipped with aneroid barometer and recording anemometer, the height and speed may be known with great accuracy at any instant. Knowing these facts, a reference to previously computed tables will show the exact distance from the objective to some spot on the ground over which the aeroplane must be at the instant of releasing the explosive. The principal difficulty lies in locating this exact spot and in knowing just when the aeroplane is over it. The difficulty of locating the spot obviously increases as the height, while the difficulty of exact release of the projectile increases as the speed.

On Wednesday, January 19, 1910, at Los Angeles, the writer, accompanying Louis Paulhan in his Farman biplane, dropped three small bags containing dirt from a height approximating two hundred and fifty feet, at a speed estimated at forty miles an hour. Any one of these bags would have hit within a gun-pit or the one adjacent had the machine been flying down a line of twelve-inch or ten-inch pits. In this experiment no count should be taken of lateral deviation since, owing to the presence

thousand and two thousand feet, great accuracy should be readily acquired in dropping projectiles, and the difficulty of hitting an aeroplane at such elevation should be great.

The computation of tables may be greatly simplified and the difficulties of instant drop greatly overcome if angular distances are used instead of linear. This is probably the line along which progress will be made. Unless some now unforeseen obstacle should prevent, we may see the

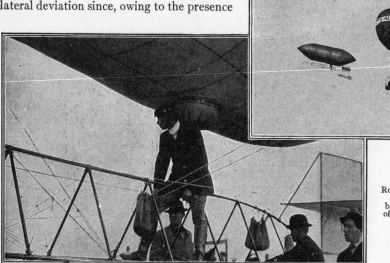

Roy Knabenshue ready to rise with his dirigible balloon. Also a glimpse of him three hundred feet up, circling a captive balloon

of wires in the machine and the danger of catching in the propeller had the bags been dropped directly in front of the aviator, it was necessary to steer the craft to the right of the target. In actual practice some mechanical means for dropping projectiles straight down from a point beneath the aviator would be devised and the machine would be directed exactly over the target.

It is clear that the height from which this experiment was made is insufficient for practical use during daylight as it would present a most vulnerable target for rifle fire. The difficulty of night success lies in the invisibility of the target. However, a multiplication of the number of machines making simultaneous attack would result, even in daylight, in serious embarrassment in the gun-pits. At heights between a

Signal Corps utilizing sextants in conjunction with such tables. For example of this method, suppose a machine to be flying at the rate of forty-five miles an hour at a height of approximately two hundred and fifty feet. From the law of falling bodies an object will drop to the ground from this elevation in about four seconds. In about the same time the machine will move forward about two hundred and fifty feet. The angle of fall will, therefore, be about forty-five degrees. By setting the sextant or slope-board to read forty-five degrees and waiting until the target is in prolongation of the line of sight, the projectile can be dropped with great accuracy.

However futile may be conjectures as to the ultimate outcome of the offensive and defensive measures in relation to aero-

Charles K. Hamilton
at the wheel of a
Curtiss biplane

standpoint, they have their value, and are worthy, therefore, of notice and comment. More particularly are they valuable for obtaining information of the location of moving bodies of the enemy or of their fortifications, and the general characteristics of the terrane over which operations are being made. Cameras and telephones are used freely in connection with these vehicles, and they have a wide and valuable field of action. Much has already been written and said of the actual and probable value of these aircraft in their relation to warfare, hence it is not the intention of this brief resumé to dwell at length on them. These lighter-than-air (gas or hot-air-lifted) vehicles are either dirigible or non-dirigible. The dirigible types are subdivided into rigid and semirigid. The rigid type have internal bracings which keep the gas-bags distended even when not inflated with gas, and, in addition, they are strongly braced to the nacelle or framework on which the engine, propeller and rudders are mounted, and on which the passenger or passengers ride. The

Glenn H. Curtiss, holder of the world's speed record. His passenger is Lieut. Paul W. Beck

dromes, there is one fact patent to all thinking persons: The time has come when the Army and Navy of the United States *must* study the subject thoroughly if the nation is to retain its prestige among the powers of the world. Man's mastery of the air, while not yet absolute, has reached that point where it ceases to be a fad and becomes a solid, persisting fact.

Like all sciences, this one has its nomenclature and classifications. To a correct understanding of the subject it is necessary to prefix at least part of this nomenclature and a general outline of the classifications. In general, all vehicles that fly may be grouped under the name "vehicles of the air." The two primary subdivisions of these vehicles give us: (1) lighter-than-air and (2) heavier-than-air types. Those lighter-than-air may be considered not as a solution but as an evasion of the problem of aerial navigation, yet, from a military

Charles F. Willard at the rudder of the biplane in
which he made a sensational landing

A Bleriot monoplane
in flight

semi-rigid type lacks the internal bracing. Non-dirigibles are either free or captive, the best shapes being approximations of globular. A free balloon becomes captive by being anchored to one spot by a rope, wire or cord. Thus tied and located at a position out of range of hostile fire, it becomes valuable as a high observation tower.

Dirigible balloons have been brought to a state of perfection that admits of almost perfect control as to direction and elevation, and they have attained a speed approximating twenty-five miles an hour. One of the Zeppelin dirigibles has carried twenty-five passengers. Germany, France and Spain are among the European powers having regularly organized balloon corps. In the United States the work is carried on as a branch of the Signal Corps since the uses appear to pertain more to the gaining and transmission of information than to any other branch of warfare.

Of the heavier-than-air flying-machines there are four general types based on the method of elevation and propulsion. These are: (1) heliocopters, (2) ornithopters, (3) feathering paddlers, (4) aeroplanes.

It has long been recognized that the problem of heavier-than-air machines is embraced in the solutions of rising from the ground and control after rising. The question of propulsion, once serious, has been simplified by the perfecting of gas-engines in motor-boat, motocycle and automobile manufacture.

Heliocopters are based on the lifting-power of a propeller rotated rapidly on a vertical axis. The questions of ultimate angle of tip, control of direction and propulsion have

not yet been solved, nor has a successful man-carrying heliocopter yet been constructed. One apparent danger to this type is the resulting fall should power be temporarily shut off from the lifting-propeller while in the air.

Ornithopters present the first, logical solution of the question of flight, being based upon the commonest known natural flight phenomenon—that of the flapping-flight of birds. However, paradoxical as it may seem, mankind has not yet been successful in solving this problem.

Feathering paddlers depend upon the lifting-power of a curved, horizontal surface moved rapidly downward and returned to the top position while lying edgewise to the horizontal plane. A number of such surfaces follow each other somewhat on the principle of a chain of dredge-buckets. There are no successful paddlers as yet.

Aeroplanes (more properly aerocurves) are the only successful heavier-than-air machines at the present writing. They depend upon the principles of soaring-bird flight, and for purposes of differentiation are divided into: (1) monoplanes, (2) biplanes, and (3) multiplanes. As these names imply, monoplanes have but one wing-surface; biplanes have two superposed wing-surfaces, and multiplanes have more than two superposed wing-surfaces. There have been no really successful multiplanes as yet. From which it is seen that a real description of successful heavier-than-air machines is complete in a discussion of the monoplane and biplane types.

Accepting, then, as we must, the fact monoplanes and biplanes cover the best in all present development of air-craft, there are a number of interesting points with regard to the two types which are of general interest and regarding which the general public has great difficulty in obtaining information.

In elucidating some of these points one of the most important is the question of ultimate size and utility. In regard to this it is safe to state that there is speedily reached a maximum size, and that, unless some new method of producing power with relatively lighter engines is discovered, there will be no air-craft analogous to railway trains or steamships. This is made clear when it is remembered that two superposed planes of equal areas increase the lifting and sustaining-power of a single plane by but one-fifth; that all areas (wing-spreads) increase as the product of two dimensions —length and breadth; while all solids (engines) increase as the product of three dimensions—length, breadth and thickness. Just where these three factors will cause a stoppage of increasing size has not been worked out.

Courtlandt Bishop, President of the Aero Club of America

However, the loss from a commercial standpoint through relatively small carrying units will be more than compensated for in the increased individual initiative of those who fly in the air, for where there are but few to transport the question of route, speed and stopping points is left more freely to those carried, and there is a resultant advantage in personal pleasure.

From this it might be concluded that aeroplanes are to be vehicles for the wealthy only, yet such a conclusion is not necessarily correct, for the initial cost of construction is not great, owing to the cheapness of materials used and to the constantly decreasing cost of engines. Maintenance cost should be light as the small power needed for propulsion and lack of resistant road-surfaces will undoubtedly present decided advantages over land vehicles. Furthermore, anyone possessing the necessary data can construct an aeroplane, thus avoiding the high cost of expensive factories.

The question of physical hazard in using an aeroplane has a deterrent effect upon many who might otherwise take up the active use of these machines. There have been but five fatal accidents in the history of aeroplane flights since power has been placed in the machines. Not one of these is traceable to faulty principles of construction or control. In each case the accident has been the result of some part breaking or becoming unfastened. In other words, the danger lies not in the principles involved but in man's carelessness, recklessness or inability to foresee possible dangers from defects of material. Breaks in the steering-gear of automobiles are analogous to propeller breaks in flying-machines, and they have been conducive to many more fatalities. At present aeroplanes are in the exploiting stage, and owing to their size, it is necessary that they be readily taken to pieces for transporting. In assembling there are numerous wires and nuts and bolts, many pieces of wood, bamboo and metal. Each one of these must be absolutely flawless to insure safety. When this fact is fully understood, and owners of flying-machines put them in permanent commission, locking or burring all nuts, soldering all wire joints, microscopically examining all propellers and other woodwork, and, similarly, testing out every detail of the apparatus, then the safety of aerial flight will become equal to or greater than that of any other method of transportation. This must of necessity follow since the wear and tear on machinery is subjected to less strain than when traversing through either the water or on the land, and since there are no bearing parts in contact with resistance other than that of air.

A question ever present in the minds of all who contemplate the possibility of aerial flight is that of the result should power be shut off while in the air. In the monoplanes and biplanes that have been successful, this question has been answered many times by accidental and intentional stoppages. Just so long as there is sufficient clear space beneath to admit of a landing within an area of flight comprehended within that distance of flight remaining as a result of previously acquired momentum, the aviator and his vehicle are perfectly safe. In other words, control as to direction and equilibrium is not lost merely because power is shut off. The ability to soar great distances *is* lost.

Looking down upon the beautiful birdlike Bleriot monoplane as it flew above the audience
Photographed by A. C. Pillsbury from a captive balloon

22.
The Greyhounds
of the Air
(1912)

THE WRECK OF THE WAR-AIRSHIP ZEPPELIN II, WHICH
BROKE FROM DEFECTIVE MOORINGS AND DRIFTED AWAY,
UNMANNED. THE STRENGTH OF THE FRAMEWORK IS SHOWN
BY ITS RESISTANCE TO SO SHATTERING A SMASH-UP.

Photo by the Trans-Atlantic Company.   *THE GREYHOUNDS OF THE AIR.*

VOL. XXVII
NO. 3

Everybody's Magazine

SEPTEMBER
1912

The Greyhounds of the Air

by

T. R. MacMechen

and

Carl Dienstbach

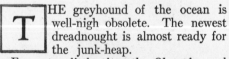

THE greyhound of the ocean is well-nigh obsolete. The newest dreadnought is almost ready for the junk-heap.

For yet a little time the *Olympics* and the *Mauretanias* will continue their boastful voyages, and perhaps for another decade nations will waste their treasures upon floating fortresses. But the end is near.

To-morrow those who wish to hasten across the Atlantic will take an airship. For them the crossing will be one of hours. The slower steamship will continue to serve those who do not consider time a vital factor.

In the past, Great Britain, regarding herself as the mistress of the seas, has enjoyed a dream of complacent confidence. But supremacy is now in the air; and the next great war will demonstrate that the master of the air is master of the earth.

This is not theory. The vision of Jules Verne, the dream of H. G. Wells, and the fantasy of Tennyson have been realized. Demonstration and proof are ready. The largest of all the wonderful Zeppelin air-

Photo by Trans-Atlantic Co.

**LOOKING UP THE
EIFFEL TOWER.**

Photo by Trans-Atlantic Co.

**ZEPPELIN III,
DESCENDING.**

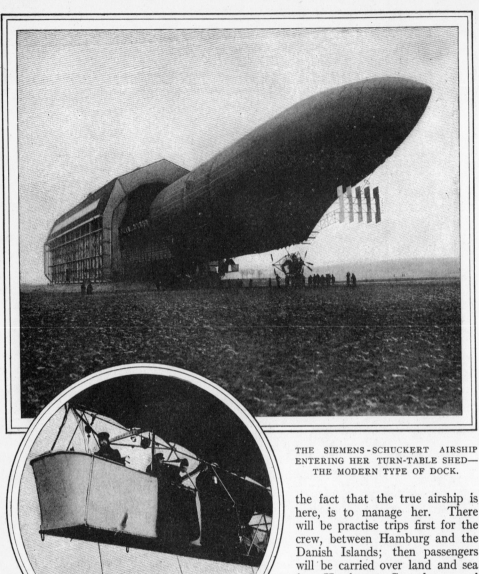

THE SIEMENS-SCHUCKERT AIRSHIP
ENTERING HER TURN-TABLE SHED—
THE MODERN TYPE OF DOCK.

THE MIDDLE PASSENGER-"GONDOLA." THIS AIRSHIP
HAS JUST BEEN BOUGHT BY THE GERMAN GOVERNMENT.

the fact that the true airship is here, is to manage her. There will be practise trips first for the crew, between Hamburg and the Danish Islands; then passengers will be carried over land and sea from Hamburg to Copenhagen, and later, as far as Christiania. Then—but airship history is making too fast for detailed prediction.

Even while this article is being written, two flights have been accomplished that are the first steps in demonstrating the practicability of the airship at sea. The Viktoria Luise, one of the big Zeppelins that have been plying between German cities, made an eight-hour over-sea trip of three hundred and fifty miles. Carrying four naval officers, eleven passengers, and her crew of ten, she flew from Hamburg out over the North

ships is about to be operated over the North Sea—the first commercial navigation of the air above the ocean. The Hansa, Count Zeppelin's fourteenth airship, has been chosen for this epoch-making service. The Hamburg-American line, first to recognize

THE WAR AIRSHIP ZEPPELIN III EF-
FECTING A LANDING ON LAKE
CONSTANCE.

COUNT ZEPPELIN; THE GERMAN AIRSHIP COMMISSIONER;
AND CHIEF OF THE GERMAN AERONAUT BATTALIONS.

Sea, and circled the Island of Nord-
erney—successfully finishing the
first extensive over-ocean voyage
ever made by an airship. And
without requiring further proof of a
Zeppelin's value for sea-fighting, the
German admiralty is having built
a colossal airship that, with a speed
of fifty-five miles an hour, can scout
far out over sea and pursue hostile naval fleets.

A few days later the Viktoria
Luise again made an over-sea flight,
flying for forty miles directly above
the steamship *Amerika*. She demonstrated that an airship, by lowering
mains, can take gas from steel decanters
carried on a liner, and can lift fuel as well.
This means an enormous gain in the air-
ship's time of staying aloft.

As a result of these flights, America is
drawn perceptibly closer to Europe. Venturesome persons are indeed planning
flights across the Atlantic for the near future. A German dirigible has been constructed whose owners contemplate a trans-
atlantic voyage. The fate of the unfor-

tunate Melvin Vaniman shows the risk these men are willing to take. But the disaster that came to Vaniman July 2, 1912, when his dirigible, the Akron, burst in mid-air off Atlantic City, killing its inventor and four others, has little bearing on the development of the airship. His craft was a mistake, and in his methods he violated principles the soundness of which have been thoroughly demonstrated.

There is good reason for believing that the accident to the Akron followed an attempt to inflate the air ballonets inside the big gas-bag, by which means Vaniman erroneously believed he could compress the gas and prevent it from expanding under the influence of the sun or the rarefied atmosphere of a higher altitude. This strain burst the envelope. The disaster was all the more deplorable because it was unnecessary.

In America, attention, unfortunately, has been centered on the spectacular aeroplane, practically to the exclusion of the airship, or it has been directed to such

Dumont, and Captain Baldwin. It is time that a rational study should be made of what is being done in the air.

The Zeppelin airship is more than a dirigible balloon. It is as true a ship as any that floats on the ocean. It has a strong, rigid

Photograph by Trans-Atlantic Company

THE GERMAN ARMY AIRSHIP SCHUETTE-LANZ ENTERING HER DOCK.   THE D
THE *TITANIC*, STRUCK THE GROUND

mistaken experiments as those conducted by Vaniman, and, before him, by Walter Wellman, or to flights of toy-like dirigibles by Roy Knabenshue, Frank Goodale, Santos-

hull, with a deck on top and a deck suspended below. It has separated compartments for gas that perform exactly the same function as the air-tight compartments inside an ocean liner, and is so constructed that an injury which might absolutely destroy an ordinary dirigible would have upon it little effect. Sustained by displacing more than its own weight of air and by its speed, floating free like a submarine within its use of airships—leagues ahead, too, as we shall see, of her European neighbors. Two years of regular flight, connecting Frankfort, Düsseldorf, Baden-Baden, and Hamburg, have made travel by the highways of the air a matter of everyday.

FORE THE TITANIC DISASTER, THIS AIRSHIP, SIXTEEN MILES FASTER THAN LL SPEED, WITHOUT SERIOUS DAMAGE.

During the greater part of this year the Viktoria Luise, with a capacity of twenty-eight passengers, has made daily round trips between Frankfort and Düsseldorf, in three hours. This ship is now making excursions out of Hamburg to various points on the North Sea, and she will soon be running between Berlin and Bremen, maintaining a passenger service in connection with the transatlantic steamships, which will save time for those who do not care to travel by the slower railroad. The Schwaben last year made excursions out of Baden-Baden to points of interest for one hundred and fifty miles around, in addition to maintaining a weekly service to Frankfort. This ship recently replaced the Viktoria Luise between Frankfort and Düsseldorf.

own element, it undergoes little strain, even in tempests.

It is a commonplace that Germany is leagues ahead of us in the construction and And besides this passenger service, the Zeppelin airships are now a recognized branch of the German mail service.

It was the Schwaben that was wrecked

the other day while lying at anchor. And perhaps this is the place for a word of explanation about the accidents that have befallen the Zeppelins, and their bearing on the safety of airship travel.

In 1907, at Echterdingen, the Zeppelin IV, while on the ground, was set afire by a charge of electricity that had collected in her metallic frame during a flight that had just ended. Instruments now detect these charges before they become dangerous, and a fabric has just been made for covering the balloons that will obviate frictional electricity.

In 1910, the war airship Zeppelin II broke from defective moorings and, drifting away unmanned, was wrecked. Since then adequate anchors have made it possible to moor any Zeppelin in the open if necessary.

In the fall of 1910, the first of the Zeppelin passenger airships, Deutschland I, was wrecked in the Teutoburg Forest, because her business manager had sent her aloft with nine hours' of fuel instead of a normal supply of thirty hours. She could not outlast a storm she encountered. That mistake will never be repeated.

That same fall, the Zeppelin VI was accidentally set on fire through the carelessness of her cleaners while she lay in her shed. Of course, this was not a wreck.

In the spring of 1911, the Deutschland II was wrecked because she was anchored too near her shed at Düsseldorf.

More recently the Schwaben was wrecked while on the ground before the same shed at Düsseldorf. Of all Zeppelin sheds this is the only one that has not been provided with modern docking appliances and the only one that does not have double doors at each end. Improvements have been ordered, and another source of danger will soon be removed.

All of these accidents have been the result of mishandling, and can not be attributed to any defect of constructive principles. Not one can be charged against the Zeppelin strictly as an airship. It is worthy of special note, too, that, in all these disasters, no Zeppelin has ever lost a life among either crews or passengers. Indeed, in Germany the airship is regarded as a vehicle of greater safety than the ocean steamship.

Does it pay to maintain one of these great aerial vessels, with its expert commander and its crew of ten? In America, where all this aerial achievement seems like a dream, we are accustomed to rely on figures. So does the German Air Navigation Company, which operates these passenger ships.

Last year the Schwaben made 125 trips, carrying a total of 2,846 passengers, including the German Crown Prince and the German Chancellor. It earned $140,000, or $1,120 for each trip of about one hundred and fifty miles. On its longer trips from Düsseldorf to Berlin, from Berlin to Gotha, and from Frankfort to Düsseldorf, this ship limited its number of passengers to ten, charging a correspondingly higher fare. After paying all expenses, the Schwaben earned for its owners $83,000. Its construction cost was $125,000, and it would have been good for about seven more years of active service, as shown by the war Zeppelin I, which has been in active service since 1906. The Schwaben's service this year, in five months, earned the entire cost of the Zeppelin Company's operation for a whole year, including the financial loss caused by the wreck of the Deutschland. Up to the time it was wrecked the Schwaben had made 363 trips, on which it covered 28,000 miles and carried 6,045 passengers. Four-fifths of the loss was covered by insurance.

As for the Hansa, Count Zeppelin estimates that, charging a fare not higher than $12.50 for its over-sea trips, it can still earn a profit of $25,000, estimated on a service of one hundred days.

Two years of successful flight between the largest German cities have made it possible to obtain abundant capital for the building and equipping of new ships, which soon will be in regular and commercial operation, connecting all the larger German cities one with another, and including Copenhagen.

Within the last twelve months five Zeppelin airships have been built and put into service. Each one has been larger and more powerful than its immediate predecessor. Four others are now in process of construction, and twelve more will be started in the immediate future. These twelve are to be war-craft and are to be paid for by popular subscription.

The performances in 1911 and 1912 of the Schwaben, Viktoria Luise, and the war Zeppelins II and III, have demonstrated that the larger a Zeppelin is built, the

Photo by Paul Thompson, N. Y.

THE VIKTORIA LUISE, 511 FEET LONG, ABOVE THE YACHTS AT THE RECENT KIEL RACES.

stronger it is; the greater its carrying capacity; the greater its radius of activity, and, above everything else, the greater its speed.

Speed is the thing. Speed means safety, because the faster an airship flies, the more easily is it controlled and the greater assurance is there of dodging or outrunning a storm. See how these factors work together in some of the recent Zeppelins.

In May of last year, Count Zeppelin built his eleventh airship—the Schwaben—larger and more powerful than any of his former ships. It immediately demonstrated its worth by attaining a speed double that of the ordinary ocean greyhound—a speed that not only held it on a true course in an arrow-like flight, regardless of prevailing winds, but created an interior ventilation of its hull that prevented the sustaining gas from unduly expanding, even on the hottest days. In actual flights a Zeppelin gains sustaining power because the loss of weight resulting from the consumption of fuel

more than counterbalances any loss of gas.

But another factor gives the ship additional lifting power: It is not generally understood that a Zeppelin is really heavier than air when it starts on a trip. Its gas-chambers are only inflated to about three-quarters of their capacity, to allow for the full expansion of the gas after the ship has been driven up to its level of travel by the dynamic action of its engines and propellers. The flat top and under-surface of the hull, acting as an aeroplane, give the airship a further lifting force of one and a half to two tons, nearly half the weight of the ship's cargo, and at the same time maintain its level flight.

In this way, the Schwaben last year made a flight of one hundred and twenty-five miles, from Berlin to Gotha, encountering a heavy gale for the greater part of the distance, and arrived at its destination carrying more than a ton of wet snow on its hull.

More recently Count Zeppelin on the war

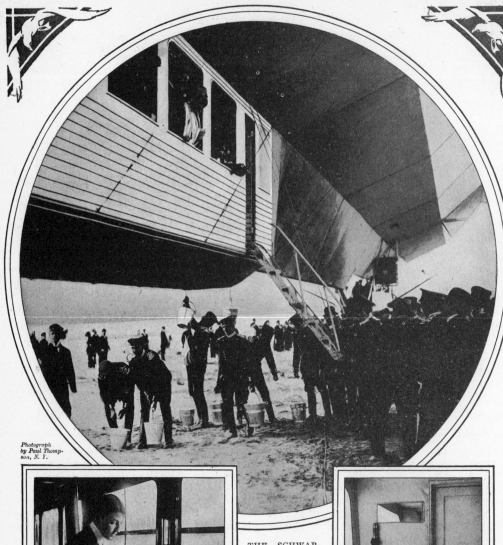

Photograph
by Paul Thomp-
son, N. Y.

IN THE SCHWABEN'S DINER—AN AIRSHIP
PULLMAN.

THE SCHWAB-
EN'S PASSEN-
GERS DISEM-
BARKING AT
POTSDAM.

airship Zep-
pelin III—to
keep his
schedule for
the return
trip from
Hamburg to

THE LAVATORY OF THE
SCHWABEN.

Friedrichshafen, a distance of four hundred and eighty miles—ran through the same
storm that strewed the path of the Berlin-
Vienna aeroplane race with the wrecks of
eight machines. He was somewhat delayed,

THE AIRSHIP PORT AT POTS-DAM.

THE SCHWABEN, LANDING. VIEW OF THE PROW.

but the airship was in no way damaged.

Count Zeppelin's twelfth ship, the Viktoria Luise, 511 feet long, with engines greater than those of the Schwaben, has a speed of forty-four and one-half miles an hour, and easily stems a thirty-six-mile wind. The Hansa, with a length of 537 feet, travels at the

Photographs by Paul Thompson, N. Y.

SCHWABEN—STERN VIEW, SHOWING STEERING PLANES.

rate of forty-six miles an hour and easily overcomes all winds that prevail over Germany. Much larger airships will develop double and triple the speed of the fastest ship on the water; they will do this driven by engines of less than two per cent. of the power of a steamer. The Hansa has three separate engines which, combined, have only 480 horse-power—less than that of three racing automobiles. The passenger airship Potsdam, now in process of construction at Friedrichshafen, still larger than the Hansa, will have even greater power and, with a speed of fifty-five miles an hour, will be able to run against winds approaching a tempest in strength.

Nothing but its size limits the distance a Zeppelin can cover, and the limit of practical size is nowhere in sight. Count Zeppelin, whose conservatism is marked, has recently said that an airship which will carry one hundred passengers is now in reach. And he announces that his ships can travel from Berlin to St. Petersburg in less than a day and a half, or to Moscow or Constantinople, with average weather, in thirty hours—which is less than the present railroad time.

The great speed and dirigibility of the Zeppelin are made possible by its motors, which are the invention of Karl Maybach, a young engineer whose fame has just begun to penetrate beyond the borders of Germany. Three of these motors, each weighing half a ton, are placed in each ship.

Maybach noted that nature had supplied man with a duplicate set of sensitive organs —two eyes, two nostrils, and two ears— and he built his engine in the same manner. In the Maybach motor two carbureters prepare the explosive mixture, and there are two spark-plugs in each•cylinder to fire it, and two magnetos to supply electric current. Then two valves introduce the driving-gas into each cylinder, and there are two exhaust valves. The engine will not stop running if any one of these parts gets out of order, for its duplicate will continue doing the work for both.

One of the best features of the Maybach motor is its automatic system of pumping fuel. A slight accident to one of the earlier dirigibles—not a Zeppelin—caused the ship to take such a position in the air that the flow of fuel was interrupted. The pumps introduced by Mr. Maybach work so that it makes no difference what is the position of the airship. In fact, for the purpose of demonstration, a Zeppelin was pointed almost vertically in the air, and while in that position its motors continued to work perfectly.

These motors make it possible to control a five-hundred-foot Zeppelin as easily as an automobile. Even the crippling of one of the propellers has no other effect than retarding speed, as a single propeller is sufficient to keep the craft upon a straight course.

In flight, a Zeppelin chooses its course and air position according to the winds that blow. If an adverse current of air aloft is too strong, the ship is kept close to the ground; or it may be sent to an altitude of eight thousand feet or even higher, if the winds make that desirable. This enables it to dodge a storm which might work disaster to an ordinary dirigible. And the fact that it carries fuel sufficient for a flight of seventy hours gives it another margin of safety. Two small rudders at the stern steady the ship and overcome the effect of violent gusts and eddies of wind. The ship's motion is very gentle; there is none of the vibration felt on an ocean liner, because the airship's engines are working against elastic, yielding air.

The hull of a Zeppelin is built of reinforced aluminum in what has been referred to as "napkin-ring" sections—sections of a standard size of twenty-six feet. The Hansa is 537 feet long; the next Zeppelin, larger by one section, will have a length of 563 feet. Each of these rings contains a drum-shaped gas cell, and each is strong enough in itself to support the ordinary weight of a man. The rings are joined together by strakes and ribs braced inside and all bolted together in one long hull. This frame is tremendously strengthened by the outward pressure of the gas. When completed, its top can support a weight of two and one-half tons of guns and ammunition.

It is not making too large a claim to say that this rigid airship, in its best form, is stronger and more stable than is the ordinary ocean-going steamship. There is a strikingly dramatic instance in proof of the point:

When the *Titanic* struck an iceberg, her steel plates were sheared like cardboard, and, sinking head on, her so-called safety compartments burst under the strain. The day before the terrible *Titanic* disaster the German army's airship Schuette-Lanz—Zeppelin type—sixteen miles faster than the *Titanic*—as the result of a mishap to its rudder while it was being driven to the earth, struck the ground at full speed. Yet, with forward engines disabled, the Schuette-Lanz rose, drifted across the Rhine, and

the present-day ocean-going steamships. They land on four motor-trucks held between the guide-rails of a wide track, sweeping in two curves. This makes it possible to land against any wind.

The ship is first driven down at full speed. Then its engines are stopped, and it glides under its own momentum until

THE FRENCH MILITARY DIRIGIBLE, ADJUTANT REAU, WHICH, BY A THEORETICAL ATTACK,
PROVED TO FRANCE THE MENACE OF WAR AIRSHIPS.

finally was brought to earth without further damage or any loss of life. It withstood the terrific collision because its gas cells remained intact. However, had one-third of them been ruptured, the ship still would have righted itself. A Zeppelin will not sink if several of its gas chambers burst or are perforated in war, because this loss of buoyancy is made up by the aeroplane lift of its hull, while being driven at full speed.

It is popularly believed that the landing of a Zeppelin is a dangerous maneuver. On the contrary, all modern Zeppelins are docked with greater ease than is any one of

the sustaining power of its gas checks the descent. A second before the ship glides over its cradle landing, cables are cast off. The stern is secured to the trucks on the windward side. Winches draw the great bulk down, while the bow is brought around against the wind and fastened to the trucks. The lee side is then made fast. No sudden side-wind can budge the ship. After everything is made taut, motors drive the vessel into the shed. It is taken out for a flight in the same manner, always leaving from the track that points into the wind.

Six hundred landings in the past two

years without an accident are a demonstration of safety that has been accepted by the German public as sufficient.

Two years ago the Zeppelin Company announced that it would begin air traffic between Germany and England.

But England looked upon this intended traffic as a warlike menace. In protest she built an imitation of Count Zeppelin's ships; and though her engineers, through lack of experience, made errors which resulted in the ship's breaking in the middle, the English objections to the Zeppelin service became so apparent that Germany thought it advisable for the present to abandon the flights.

France is equally alert to the potential menace of the German airships. Within the past six months, the supremacy of the Zeppelins has been acknowledged on the floor of the French Senate. General Cherfils, the renowned French military writer, has also admitted that the French style of dirigible balloons can not possibly compete with the Zeppelin, and has even pronounced all aeroplanes powerless against the German airship.

The French, on the theory that the more colossal craft were too unwieldy to be easily handled and too large to be fast, have built smaller dirigibles of short endurance which can do only one thing well at a time. These dirigibles attain a very high altitude, an advantage if it is desired to launch bombs upon a near-by enemy; but this advantage is counterbalanced by the fact that their capacity for further flight is reduced practically to zero.

Now it has been discovered that the Zeppelins have won by reversing the French idea. The Zeppelin carries engines sufficiently powerful to drive it almost twice as fast as any French dirigible has been able to travel, and, in fact, has reached a speed equal to that of the best of the French war aeroplanes, which of necessity are the larger and slower type of biplane. This high speed enables a Zeppelin not only to cover great distances in a short time, but also to attain a height of a mile in less than five minutes after it leaves the earth—which is about one-fourth the time that is required for a war aeroplane to reach the same height.

It was the Italian commander's official reports of the war in Tripoli that cured France of her delusion as to the relative values of aeroplanes and airships:

Two baby Italian dirigibles cruised day after day a mile above the ground, surveying every Turkish post within twenty miles of the Italian camp. While these small airships were at work, swift aeroplanes were also in service, but they did well if they explored one camp in a flight and got safely back to headquarters. In fact, except for scouting in fair weather, their successes in bomb-throwing were not worth mentioning. On the other hand, the airships reported constantly by wireless to the troops and to the war-ships. They played the game true to aerial tactics. When the enemy opened fire upon them and they discovered that they were within possible reach of the bullets, they simply took a higher altitude, from which they deliberately continued their observations. Later, the same dirigibles returned to the Italian camps, where they took on a supply of bombs. Then they cruised leisurely about over the Turkish camps, from time to time dropping a bomb.

On May second, at daybreak, the dirigibles, flying at a height of more than a mile, first reconnoitered the enemy's camps at Aziza and at Suani Ben Aden. Then a sudden attack was made. The ships cast loose twenty bombs, each of which did considerable damage. One bomb destroyed an entire square of huts, and it was afterward learned that the loss of life from this one explosion was one hundred and thirty-six. The infantry and artillery attempted to return the fire, but were absolutely unable to reach the airships. The Turks, however, soon learned their costly error, and scattered their troops as soon as a dirigible appeared overhead. Italy has since built four dirigibles, each of the size of the largest German Parseval air-cruisers, and has armed their cars with machine-guns and sent them to the front. With these she has been operating against the Turks with such effect as all the world now knows.

These little Italian ships, which served as an object-lesson to France, were merely the ordinary dirigible variety. No wonder France openly shudders at the thought of a fleet of mammoth Zeppelins hovering over Paris!

Converted for war purposes—all the commercial Zeppelins are so constructed that with slight alteration they may be converted into war machines—the Viktoria Luise mounts one and three-quarters tons of military equipment. The cabin is made to give place to guns and fighting men. Every possible ounce of weight is saved, the result being that, carrying this heavy equipment, the ship can float thirty hours, and in that period may cover 1140 miles. If stripped for a longer trip, it can remain afloat fifty hours and cover 1900 miles. This would carry it over the entire French territory, or permit it to range freely over the British Isles.

The Hansa, which is a larger ship, carries two tons of armament, and avails itself of an even greater radius than that of the Viktoria Luise. Either one of these two ships, prepared for war, carries one hundred and fifty rounds of special high-explosive shells, each weighing four and one-eighth pounds, and two of the big, long-range guns of fifty pounds apiece, which, with their ammunition, are mounted on top of the hull. In addition each carries, in the long gallery under the hull, ten machine-rifles, weighing fourteen pounds apiece—these being intended to repel any possible attack made by aeroplanes. This armament is practically two-thirds of the carrying capacity of the airship.

From one of these airships little or no ammunition is wasted. The aim is nearly absolute, and at a distance of from three to six miles the possible destruction is tremendous. The pilot of the ship maintains an exact distance from the target by steering the ship at a certain elevation and maintaining a pivotal point. Gunners, with the heaviest weapons pivoted so that they may be aimed in any direction, sight as if from a mountainside, and are able to note exactly where each shell strikes. Fired down at a slant of not less than forty-five degrees, the shell is propelled not only by the charge of powder behind it but by the power of gravity, which multiplies as the shell's flight continues. A modern half-pound shell fired from an altitude of one mile penetrates two inches of steel almost as easily as an ordinary rifle-bullet at short range penetrates an inch of pine board. And a recent official report shows that the heavier guns may be fired from a Zeppelin floating at an altitude of a mile and a half with such perfect accuracy that they will destroy the strongest battleship afloat.

A Zeppelin's secondary battery of lighter machine-guns consists of even more deadly aerial weapons. They slay with an absurdly small bullet. One of these guns, discharging as it does five hundred shots a minute, might well put an army to rout, while the fast airship upon which it is mounted would be beyond any land weapon's reach.

There are three Zeppelins that are purely war craft—numbered, not named. Add the convertible passenger ships and the twelve army Zeppelins soon to be constructed, and the big naval airships, with their successors, and you grasp the tremendous advantage Germany has over her neighbors. With their deadly perfect guns; with a speed superior to that of war aeroplanes; with the power to travel by night as well as by day, and unhindered by fog; to remain afloat three days or even longer; to travel wide distances over land and sea; with the very thin armor just devised—the Zeppelins are truly the greatest of modern weapons—and naturally the terror of the French and English war parties.

France has recently offered herself proof of her own peril in case of hostilities. Her own greatest dirigible, the Adjutant Reau, made a theoretical night attack upon the city of Verdun, near the German border line. Maintaining a position of perfect safety, it floated about over the city, unseen. It would have been possible for it to wreck the five defending fortresses without receiving a shot in reply. Notice of its attack had been given, and the searchlights of all the fortresses swept the sky—in vain. The airship passed on, still invisible.

And the Adjutant Reau is nothing but a gas-bag, which could not sustain an attack from one of the smallest of the deadly Zeppelins! The demonstration that even such an airship as that could destroy a city helpless to defend itself, and the comparison with a Zeppelin's power, have made the French realize how thoroughly they have permitted their ancient enemy to outwit them in the matter of a navy of the air.

An official trial of the Zeppelin II—Count Zeppelin's new war cruiser—a short time after the demonstration by the Adjutant Reau, proves this again, from the German side. The war Zeppelin met all military tests by running the French border in fourteen and one-half hours. It maintained a speed of forty-seven and a quarter miles an hour, and had little difficulty in outracing a French war aeroplane that attempted to keep pace with it. During eight hours of its flight this ship remained at the prescribed battle height of one mile—long enough to have done deadly execution.

Following this demonstration, and without landing, the air cruiser went through a dense fog to Baden-Baden and cruised over that city, unknown to its inhabitants, for five and one-half hours more.

So much for the Zeppelin as the last word in swift continental travel and as a weapon so terrible that it may be a powerful factor in furthering world peace. Let us go back to the airship's possibilities as a successor to the ocean liner.

The flights of the Hansa over the North Sea are in a sense a preparation for more important voyages to come. Next year, the Zeppelin Polar Airship Expedition will proceed with its scheduled flights with two airships over the ice fields of the far North, where it will not only cover distances equal to that between Europe and America but will alight and anchor on the ice. There the preliminary polar expedition sent out in 1911 found ideal conditions for the final demonstration of the Zeppelin as an ocean-going airship.

Aerial navigation that will bring Europe and America within three days of each other waits, chiefly, not upon a suitable ship, not upon new steering or propelling apparatus, but on more and better weather reports!

The governments of the world are making ready for the future navigation of the air on a magnificent scale by joining their efforts to obtain more accurate meteorological information. Weather observation stations are being multiplied. Weather service is being extended to take in reports from ships at sea, which will give the chief forecasting stations complete knowledge of the weather situation over the entire world.

In Germany at the present time the direction and force of the winds may be predicted three hours in advance without frequent mistake. All German weather stations are provided with pilot balloons and theodolites, by means of which the speed and direction of winds at all altitudes are ascertained. This information is telegraphed to the chief aerological station at Lindenberg, where a general report is prepared and sent out to all wireless stations, including the two hundred established by the Air Navigation Company, for communication with their ships. Airships equipped with wireless go aloft without fear of meeting unexpected storms in the upper air. By means of the wireless, too, they are enabled to establish their exact positions regardless of darkness or fog.

So with an accurate knowledge of the upper-air currents above the ocean, successful flight across the Atlantic will depend only upon the building of a proper craft; and that is a detail which may be left to Count Zeppelin.

Already, engineers are giving us a glimpse of that very ship. At Kiel an airship is nearing completion that furnishes a definite idea of the thousand-foot ocean-crossing vessel. It is in the form of a perfectly smooth torpedo, weighing twenty-nine tons. Five hundred feet long it will be—as long as many an ocean liner. Its strong steel frame will be braced, ship-like, from the inside; and its seven and one-quarter tons of passengers, crews, motors, and supplies, all will be carried inside the hull below the gas chambers. A draught of seventy-three feet will give head-room for comfortable passenger quarters far from the engine-rooms. Companionways will lead to the outside of the hull, so that on the voyage the men can make any necessary repairs to rudder or propellers. And the ship will be perfectly dirigible—so that it can be turned in its own length.

But we can not divorce the dirigible, as pleasure and commercial craft, from its grim and deadly uses. For this very ship can in a few days be converted to a war craft. Ehrhardt, the ordnance man of Düsseldorf, is building two powerful long-range guns to be mounted upon the upper deck of this leviathan of the air. With engines of nine hundred horse-power to drive it at a speed of sixty miles an hour; with a fuel capacity sufficient to keep it afloat from eighty to one hundred hours, it could range over two thousand miles of territory, dealing out death and destruction, with perfect safety from the attack of any craft, any weapon now in existence, save another such Zeppelin as itself.

This is the kind of ship that some day—some day soon, when the vagaries of the Atlantic air currents have been reduced to a science—will hover over New York, bringing America and Europe closer together by air than they have yet been drawn by water.

23.
The Dirigible Balloon of M. Santos-Dumont (1901)

THE DIRIGIBLE BALLOON OF M. SANTOS-DUMONT.

BY STERLING HEILIG.

This article is published with the knowledge and consent of M. Santos-Dumont. Because he is resolved not to be drawn into a local controversy, and, more particularly, because he considers himself to be still in the experimental period, M. Santos-Dumont refuses to write any article, popular or technical, or to give diagrams of the inventions with which he is constantly experimenting, and which are, therefore, subject to continual changes. In the following interview, however, the writer, who has been a great deal with him during the past four years, was permitted by M. Santos-Dumont to take down questions and answers in shorthand.—S. H.

M. ALBERTO SANTOS-DUMONT, a young Brazilian resident in Paris, after four years of invention, construction, and constant experiment, has been navigating a cigar-shaped balloon with a sixteen horse-power petroleum motor under it, capable of making way against any wind that is less than forty kilometers (twenty-five miles) an hour. What this means may be imagined when it is remembered that a wind of fifty kilometers an hour is called a storm.

At the outset, a word should be allowed the inventor concerning two very different factors of his success—inventing and managing a dirigible balloon. Indeed, the factors are three,—inventing, constructing, and managing,—as inventors on paper are likely to discover before they find themselves navigating the air. M. Santos-Dumont has occupied four years with invention and construction. Now he is learning to manage the perfected air-ship.

"Suppose you buy a new bicycle or automobile," he says. "You will have a perfect machine to your hand; but it does not necessarily mean that you will go spinning with it over the highways. You may be so unpractised that you fall off the bicycle or blow up the automobile. The machine is all right, but you must learn to run it. That is what I am doing with my air-ship."

This is what the crowds of Parisians who have been following M. Santos-Dumont's aërial evolutions take but imperfectly into account; and the readers of the daily papers in far-off lands, who hear of his trials and narrow escapes only by way of garbled and hurriedly written cable despatches, are still less likely to appreciate it. Everything about the navigation of the air is new; newest of all is the art—practised only by this daring youth—of diving and mounting obliquely in the air by means of his propeller force. In the complicated and novel task of putting an air-ship through its best paces, much must necessarily be at the mercy of chance details. Thus a trial trip whose start and finish were witnessed by scarcely twenty-five persons was much more satisfactory than the succeeding day's official trial before the Technical Committee of the Deutsch Prize Foundation and a brilliant *tout-Paris* assemblage.

On this occasion (the morning of July 13, 1901) M. Santos-Dumont sped straight through the air above western Paris to the Eiffel Tower, turned round it, and returned to his starting-point, a distance of eleven kilometers (nearly seven miles), in thirty-nine minutes, and this in spite of a new petroleum motor that was discovered to be working imperfectly shortly after starting. The day before, while going over the same course, he found that his right-hand rudder-guide had become loose. This happened near the Eiffel Tower. Without sacrificing a cubic inch of gas, he descended to the ground by means of his shifting-weights; that is to say, he pointed the nose of his cigar-shaped balloon obliquely downward and navigated to the surface of the earth by means of his propeller. There he procured a ladder and repaired his rudder-guide. Then he mounted into the air and resumed his course without sacrificing a pound of ballast; that is to say, he pointed the balloon's nose obliquely upward by means of the shifting-weights, and so navigated on high again by the force of his propeller.

To those who know anything about dirigible balloons, these evolutions, simple as they appear, constitute M. Santos-Dumont's greatest triumph. They have never been accomplished by any other aëronaut. The ease and precision with which he executes them have called forth the special admiration of competent authorities. Thus M. Armengaud *jeune*, the engineer, who, with the late M. Hureau de Villeneuve, was one of the founders of the Société de Navigation Aérienne, and was for a long time its vice-president, owns frankly: "I can say that what most strikes me is the ease with which M. Santos-Dumont, by inclining his aërostat at will, is able to dive or rise so readily in the air, and thus bring himself on a level with the more favorable layers of the atmosphere by crossing through contrary currents."

How M. Santos-Dumont made his sensational trips between St. Cloud and the Eiffel Tower, to show Paris what he could do, and incidentally to win the Deutsch Prize of one hundred thousand francs for the first dirigible balloon or flying-machine that should make the round trip in half an hour, is a matter of common knowledge. At the first official trial he missed winning the prize by only nine minutes. At the second he covered the distance from St. Cloud to the Eiffel Tower in eight minutes fifty seconds, turned the tower in forty seconds more, and in twelve minutes from his start was over the Bois de Boulogne on his return, with eighteen minutes to spare for the short distance remaining, when an accident, which might have been tragic, brought him to the ground with a wrecked air-ship.

The fact that M. Santos-Dumont really navigates the air is in itself the all-sufficient explanation of the universal chorus of wonderment that has gone up in response to the news of his performances. In Paris they have also excited recriminations from friends of the official military balloonists of the Chalais-Meudon Park, reaching to denial of the new air-ship's novelty of invention and superiority of action. These military balloonists have been for many years the supposed possessors of the secret of dirigible ballooning. In a spirit of emulation more admirable than their first movement of detraction, they now announce the rapid construction of a steerable balloon of their own, expected to offer "great resistance to the wind" and to be "capable of facing any weather." In this way the young inventor will have to his honor not only his own performances, but the renewed efforts to which they shall have excited others. As for himself, he is occupied with his new balloon, the "Santos-Dumont No. 6," his perfected model embodying all that he has learned from experimenting with the five which preceded it.

THE YEARS OF PREPARATION.

THIS young Brazilian inventor works for the love of the thing, not for lucre. He has never felt moved to apply for a single patent. He is a son of the "Coffee King" of Brazil, the proprietor of the Santos-Dumont plantations of São Paulo, the friend of the former Emperor Dom Pedro, and the benefactor and adviser of whole populations. Santos-Dumont, the father, although a Brazilian by birth and nationality, was French by descent, and had his technical education at the École Centrale (Arts and Industries) in Paris. Thanks to this education, he was the first to apply scientific methods to Brazilian coffee-culture, so that his plantations became the most flourishing in the land, having four million coffee-plants, occupying nine thousand laborers, comprising towns, manufactories, docks, and steamships, and served by one hundred and forty-six miles of private railroads. It was on these railroads that the young Santos-Dumont, before he was twelve years of age, drove locomotive-engines for his pleasure, and developed the taste for mechanics and invention which saved him, coming young and rich to Paris, from a life of mere sporting leisure. Until eighteen years of age, when he completed his education at the University of Rio de Janeiro, he remained in Brazil, always returning in vacation-time to the wild back-country of the plantation, where he became a mighty hunter, killing wild pigs and small tigers by preference, and great snakes out of a sense of duty.

Arriving in Europe in 1891, he made a tourist trip and ascended Mont Blanc. A part of 1891 and 1892 he spent between London and Brighton, perfecting his English, which he now speaks as well and as often as French; but he always returned to Paris, where in 1892 he was already driving automobiles. In 1894 he made a short trip to the United States, visiting New York, Chicago, and Boston. He did not begin ballooning until 1897, in the summer of which year he made his first ascent in company with the late M. Machuron. In the same year he made twenty other ascensions, a number of them unaccompanied, and became a reliable pilot of spherical balloons. He has, indeed, an ideal figure for the sport, uniting remarkable strength, agility, and coolness to his jockey's weight of scarcely one hundred pounds. For this reason he was able to lower the volume of the "Brazil," his first spherical balloon, to the unusual minimum of one hundred and thirteen cubic meters. The little "Brazil" was always filled with hydrogen, and after each ascension he never failed to bring it back with him in his valise.

This Brazilian has neither the structure, the complexion, nor the exuberant gestures of the men of his country. He is pale, cold, and phlegmatic, even, if the word may be applied to one so active. In his moments of greatest enthusiasm and of most lively disappointment he is always the same; and he is as free from affectation as a child. He has a weakness for driving dog-cart tandems, and—something which has had a vital influence over his career as a balloonist—he has been an intrepid automobile *chauffeur* from the first.

He began with a Peugeot roadster of two and a half horse-power. He has since owned and driven half a dozen automobiles of continually increasing speed and power, his longest trip without stop being taken in 1898, between Nice and Paris, and accomplished with a six horse-power Panhard in fifty-four hours. Latterly he has abandoned petroleum in favor of electricity, in a dainty light-running American buggy manufactured in Chicago. It serves him, he says, better than the more troublesome *teuf-teuf* for his morning spin through the Bois and his afternoon errands from the balloonmaker's at Vaugirard to his apartment in the Avenue des Champs-Élysées, and from the Aéro Club's ground at St. Cloud to the Automobile Club in the Place de la Concorde. "I was once enamoured of petroleum automobiles, because of their freedom," he explains. "You can buy the essence everywhere; and so, at a moment's notice, one is at liberty to start off for Rome or St. Petersburg. But when I discovered that I did not want to go to Rome or St. Petersburg, but only to take short trips about Paris, I went in for the electric buggy.

"I got *my first idea of putting an automobile motor under a cigar-shaped balloon filled with hydrogen gas* while returning from the Paris-Amsterdam automobile race in 1897," he said when he began giving me this interview. "From the beginning everybody was against the idea. I was told that an explosive gas-engine would ignite the hydrogen in the balloon above it, and that the resulting explosion would end the experiment with my life. Lachambre, my balloon-constructor, went to work without enthusiasm. So far

from others 'convincing me that their notions were worth taking up,' as has been said, I met with nothing but discouragement."

Such a categorical statement ought to dispose of the legend of a young "Mæcenas of balloon-builders," who "does not set up himself to invent machines, only to judge of those which inventors bring to him, and of the work done by the mechanics he employs."[1] Colonel Renard's assertion that M. Santos-Dumont is not a man of science, but *un sportsman de l'aérostation qui a beaucoup de crânerie* (an aërostatic sportsman who has a great deal of swagger), is equally inexact. Sufficiently at home in mathematical mechanics to make the calculations which necessarily preceded not only the construction of his various air-ships, but their very idea, sufficiently practised and ingenious to make his own models, the young inventor owes no more to his constructors and hired mechanics than he does to his theoretical friends.

THE EVOLUTION OF THE INVENTION.

"I ORDERED my first dirigible balloon from Lachambre in the summer of 1898," M. Santos-Dumont said. "It was in the form of a cylinder terminated at each end by a cone; it was eighty-two feet long and almost six feet in diameter, with a capacity of sixty-four hundred cubic feet of gas, which gave it a lifting-power of four hundred and fifty pounds. Being of varnished Japanese silk, it weighed only sixty-six pounds. This left me some three hundred and eighty pounds for basket, motor and other machinery, ballast, and my own weight.

"There was a time when any piece of silk of seemingly good quality was accepted in balloon-construction, without subjecting it to preliminary tension; to-day each piece is experimented with, and if its dynamometric resistance does not attain the number of kilograms necessary to offset the maximum force of gas dilatation, it is pitilessly rejected. It is the same for all ropes and cords; they are tried with the dynamometer up to the greatest strain that may ever come to be put on them."

This minute painstaking in the construction of his air-ships has served M. Santos-Dumont to good purpose more than once— most of all in the accident of August 6, 1901, when nothing but a long and slender "keel" of thin pine scantlings and piano-

[1] London "Truth," July 18, 1901.

wire, resting its extremities on the roofs of two houses, interposed between him and a fall of eight flights to the ground.

"While the balloon envelop was being minutely pieced together," continued M. Santos-Dumont, "I succeeded in getting the rest of the air-ship completed. Hanging beneath the cigar-shaped balloon, it consisted simply of a light basket containing motor, propeller, ballast, and myself. The motor was one of the De Dion-Bouton tricycles, of an early type, with one cylinder, and giving about one and a half horse-power. You know how they work? Reduced to their greatest simplicity, you may say that there is gasolene in a receptacle. Air passing through it comes out mixed with gasolene gas, ready to explode. You give a whirl to a crank, and the thing begins working automatically. The piston goes down, sucking combined gas and air into the cylinder. Then the piston comes back and compresses it. Then it goes down again, striking an electric spark. There is an immediate explosion; and the piston goes up again, discharging the used-up gas. Thus there was one explosion for every two turns of the piston. In order to get the most power out of the least weight, I joined two of these cylinders end to end, and realized a three and a half horse-power motor."

"I have heard that joining end to end spoken of as a most ingenious invention," I said.

"I was rather proud of it at the time; but it heated too rapidly, and I abandoned the idea in subsequent constructions. The motor, being fixed at the back of the basket, acted directly on the screw-propeller placed below it, but projecting a few feet out. Basket and machinery weighed one hundred and forty pounds, while I weighed one hundred pounds. This left one hundred and forty pounds for ballast and my primitive shifting-weights; for I saw from the beginning that if I would navigate the air seriously *I must be able to dive and mount without expending gas and ballast.* Otherwise the very life of my little air-ship would be oozing away with every evolution. A rope hung down from the fore part of the cigar-shaped balloon and another from the after part. I had in the basket with me a rather heavy bag of ballast. When I wished to point the balloon's nose upward, I had only to pull in the after rope and attach the bag of ballast to it. When I wished to point it downward, I had only to pull in the forward rope and attach the bag to it. In either case the center of gravity was changed, and the horizontal

cigar-shaped balloon inclined as desired. The device worked well from the first day, and has since become one of the essential features of my air-ship.

"My 'Santos-Dumont No. 1,' as I called it, foreseeing that it was going to be the first of a series of constructions, was torn at the start, getting caught in a tree at the Jardin d'Acclimatation. It was from this pleasure-ground in the Bois that I made my first ascents, because it had a gas-plant to serve its own captive balloon. During the second trial, which was successful, the little air-pump on which I depended to keep the balloon taut refused to work. Condensation and dilatation are the two enemies of ballooning, the former causing the gas in the balloon to shrink and the latter to expand too rapidly. Caused by changes in temperature and atmospheric pressure, they continually react upon each other in the ordinary spherical balloon, necessitating continual losses of ballast and gas.

"Suppose you are in equilibrium at five hundred meters height. All at once a little cloud, almost imperceptible, masks the sun for a few seconds. The temperature of the gas in your balloon cools down a little; and if, at the very moment, you do not throw out enough ballast to correspond to the ascensional force lost by the condensation of the gas, you will begin descending. Imagine that you have thrown out the ballast—just enough, for if you throw too much, you will become too light and go too high. The little cloud ceases to mask the sun. Your gas heats up again to its first temperature and regains its old lifting-power. But, having less to lift by the amount of ballast thrown out, it now shoots higher into the air, and the gas in the balloon dilates still more, and either escapes through the safety-valve or has to be deliberately sacrificed to prevent the balloon going too high. Then, the balloon having overshot its equilibrium and lost too much gas, it begins descending,—to condense its gas again,—when more ballast must be sacrificed, and the trouble recommences. These *montagnes-russes* (or 'shoot-the-chutes') vagaries of spherical ballooning must be avoided to the utmost with my air-ship.

"Thanks to my shifting-weights, I was never obliged to sacrifice gas or ballast to combat them; but condensation and dilatation are, on the other hand, peculiarly dangerous to a cigar-shaped balloon, which absolutely must keep its form. I had, therefore, placed *a little compensating air-balloon inside the other*. It was connected with the air-pump by a tube, so that when the cigar-shaped balloon began to shrink, I could swell it out again by pumping in atmospheric air. *Hélas!* the air-pump refused to work at the critical moment. The balloon began to double on itself as it grew flabby; and soon I was falling at the rate of sixteen feet per second. The air-ship fell thirteen hundred feet to the ground, and it would have ended fatally for me had I not called out to some people who had spontaneously caught hold of my guide-rope to pull hard in the direction opposite to that of the wind. By this manœuver I diminished the final speed of the fall and the worst part of the shock."

All his friends remember this sensational trip in the autumn of 1898. The air-ship rose above us in the Jardin d'Acclimatation. For a while we could hear the motor spitting and the propeller churning the air. Then, when he had reached his equilibrium, we could still observe Santos manipulating the machinery and the ropes. Around and around he manœuvered in great circles and figure 8's, showing that he had perfect control of his direction. Then, according to the program, he started in a straight line for the west. As the air-ship grew smaller in the distance, those who had opera-glasses began crying that it was "doubling up." We saw it coming down rapidly, growing larger and larger. Women screamed. Men called hoarsely to one another. Those who had bicycles or automobiles hastened to the spot where he must be dashed to the ground. Yet within an hour M. Santos-Dumont was among his friends again, unhurt, laughing nervously, and explaining all about the unlucky air-pump.

"I made a third trial with No. 1, this time with a long rope, like a captive balloon," he continued, "but I saw that I should have to build another. I built it, but never made a proper ascension in it. It was the same type as No. 1, but larger. After a few trials with the rope, I definitely abandoned this long and slender balloon model, so seductive from certain points of view, but so dangerous from others.

"My No. 3, which was completed in the summer of 1899, was a shorter and very much thicker balloon, sixty-six feet long and eleven and a half feet in its greatest diameter. Its gas capacity was seventeen thousand six hundred cubic feet, which gave it three times the lifting-power of No. 1, and twice that of No. 2. On the other hand, I had decided to fill it with common illuminat-

ing-gas, whose lifting-power is not nearly so great as that of hydrogen. The hydrogen-plant at the Jardin d'Acclimatation was badly served. It had cost me vexatious delays and no end of trouble. With illuminating-gas I should be more free. In this model I also suppressed the compensating air-balloon. I had gone through a bad experience with its air-pump already; and the changed form of the new balloon, so much shorter and thicker, would help to do away with the danger of doubling up. For the rest, I wanted to try the stiffening qualities of a thirty-foot bamboo pole fixed lengthwise to the suspension-cords above my head and directly beneath the balloon.

"*This was my first keel*. It supported basket and guide-ropes, and it brought the shifting-weights into play still more effectually.

"Being filled with ordinary illuminating-gas, the new balloon (No. 3) lifted basket, machinery, my own weight, and two hundred and thirty pounds of ballast—ballast which I might now reserve for great emergencies.

"On November 13, 1899, I started from Lachambre's atelier in Vaugirard with the No. 3 on the most successful trip I had yet made. From Vaugirard I went directly to the Champ de Mars, over which I practised describing figure 8's. The air-ship obeyed the rudder beautifully. After circling round the Eiffel Tower a number of times, I made a straight course to the Parc des Princes at Auteuil; then, making a hook, I navigated to the manœuver-grounds of Bagatelle, where I landed. At this time, remember, neither I nor the Aéro Club had a balloon-park to start from or return to. To go back to Lachambre's at Vaugirard, surrounded as it is by houses, presented too many dangers.

"Considerations like these made it desirable to have a plant of my own. The Aéro Club had now acquired some land on the newly opened Côteaux de Longchamps at St. Cloud; and I decided to become my own master by building on it a great shed, high enough to contain my air-ship with the balloon fully inflated, and furnished with a modern hydrogen-gas generator. Even here I had to contend with the conceit and prejudice of the Paris artisans, who had already given me so much trouble at the Jardin d'Acclimatation. It was declared that the high sliding-doors of my shed could not be made to slide. I had to insist. 'Follow my directions,' I said, 'and do not concern yourselves with their practicability. I will answer for the sliding.'

"I made other successful trips in the 'Santos-Dumont No. 3,' the last time losing my rudder and landing, luckily, on the plain at Ivry. I did not repair it. The balloon was too clumsy and the motor was too weak. I now had my own 'stable' and gas-plant; and, anxious to profit by past experience, I gave Lachambre the order for my No. 4."

"That was the air-ship of the Exposition year and the International Congress of Aëronauts, was it not?"

"Yes, the one with the bicycle-saddle."

This is also the model with which the foreign public has been made most familiar, because most of the newspapers came out with old cuts and photographs of it during M. Santos-Dumont's sensational trips, with a quite different keel, in July, 1901. In No. 4 the thirty-foot bamboo pole became part of a real keel, no longer hanging above the navigator's head, but amplified by vertical and horizontal cross-pieces and a system of tightly stretched cords. It sustained motor, petroleum-reservoir, propeller, and navigator in a spider-web frame without a basket. It was a daring innovation. The navigator himself must sit on a simple bicycle-saddle in the midst of the spider-web, where the absence of the traditional balloon-basket seemed to leave him astride a pole in the midst of a confusion of ropes, tubes, and machinery.

It was more than a bicycle-saddle, however; it was a whole bicycle-frame, around which the inventor had united cords and other means for the controlling of the shifting-weights, the striking of the motor's electric spark, the opening and shutting of the balloon's valves, the turning of the water-ballast's spigots, and all the other functions of the air-ship. The rudder, for example, was controlled by the handle-bars; and the propeller was started, as in a petroleum tricycle, by working the pedals. Even the bicycle's wheels were put to use for moving the air-ship about on the ground. They were, of course, detachable.

"My balloon No. 4," the inventor went on to explain, "was, both in form and capacity, a compromise between No. 3 and its predecessors. With a gas-capacity of fourteen thousand eight hundred cubic feet, it was ninety-five feet long and nine feet in its greatest diameter, but no longer a cylinder terminated by two cones. It was, rather, elliptical in form, and while not a return to the slender straightness of No. 1, it had so little of No. 3's podgy compactness that I thought it prudent to put the compensating

air-balloon inside it again, this time fed by a rotary ventilator of aluminium. Being smaller than No. 3, it would have less lifting-power; but this I made up by going back to hydrogen gas.

"A new seven horse-power two-cylinder motor, made for me by Bouchet, turned the propeller at the rate of one hundred revolutions per minute, furnishing a traction effort of sixty-six pounds. It made a great improvement in my speed, and for two weeks during the summer of 1900 I enjoyed, almost daily, what seemed to me then ideal trips. On September 19 I made a kind of official trial in presence of the International Congress of Aëronauts, and received the felicitations of its members, among whom came later Professor Langley of the Smithsonian Institution.

"By this time I felt that I had gained enough experience to justify materially increasing my motive power, and a new type of sixteen horse-power motor with *refroidissement à ailettes* (i.e., without water-jacket) having just been created, I set about adapting it to the air-ship. It had four cylinders instead of two. This increased the weight to be lifted to such an extent that I must either construct a new balloon or enlarge the old one. I tried the latter course. Cutting the balloon in half, I had a piece put in, as you put a new leaf in an extension-table; and the length was thus brought to one hundred and nine feet. I then found that my balloon-shed was too short by ten feet.

"In prevision of a 'Santos-Dumont No. 5,' I added thirteen feet to the shed. Motor, balloon, and shed were transformed in fifteen days. It was wasted pains, for no sooner had I got the enlarged balloon filled with hydrogen than the autumn rains set in. After two weeks of the worst possible weather, I let out the hydrogen and began experimenting with the motor and propeller from a fixed point. This was not lost time; for bringing the speed up to one hundred and forty turns per minute, I realized one hundred and twenty-one pounds of traction. In truth, the motor turned the propeller with such force that I contracted pneumonia in the current of air, and found myself laid up for the winter."

"Then you went to Monte Carlo?"

"Yes. I cured myself automobiling in the mistral. At the same time I found a broad-minded carpenter at Nice who, for a consideration, allowed me to work out a new idea in his atelier. The idea took the form of my present keel, a long triangular-sectioned pine framework, of great lightness and rigidity, sixty feet in length and weighing only ninety pounds. Its joints were in aluminium, and its rigidity was reinforced by tightly drawn piano-wires. Into this keel, twenty feet from the stern, I fixed the new sixteen horse-power four-cylinder motor, connecting it with the propeller by a long hollow steel shaft. My own place was in a very light basket, twenty-three feet from the front or stem.

"In one way this was a disadvantage, for I had now to command the motor at a distance by means of cords. I could not put it in movement en route, although I could stop it. For this reason *I longed for the bicycle-frame's pedals of No.* 3; and I am still studying a device to replace them. In all other respects, however, the new keel was a great improvement, distributing the weight and lending great tautness to the balloon above it.

"The interior air-balloon I now retained definitely, it being fed by an aluminium ventilator. Both balloon and air-balloon were furnished with valves whose springs, of unequal force, were so arranged that in case of an excess of pressure the air, and not the gas, would first escape. Valves, motor, fuel-reservoir, rudder, and all other functions of the air-ship were connected with my little basket by means of ropes and pulleys. I will not deny that it required coolness and experience to handle them. Still, at the worst, I could always climb out and along the framework of the keel to the spot needing attention.[1]

"You know what the end of my No. 5 was. In the early morning of August 8, having called together the Technical Committee of the Deutsch Foundation, I navigated from St. Cloud to the Eiffel Tower in eight minutes and fifty seconds, turned round the tower in forty seconds more, and was just reaching the Bois on the home stretch, with eighteen minutes to the good, when the catastrophe happened. The balloon had already begun losing gas before I reached the tower.

"Had I not been making a kind of official trial, I should have returned to the shed to examine the balloon. Going round the tower it was manifestly deflated; but I had made

such good speed that I risked continuing. I had not been four minutes on the home stretch, however, when the balloon began swinging like an elephant's trunk, it was so flabby. I felt myself falling, and was about to switch the motor-power to the air-pump to stiffen it out again, and so come to earth as gently as possible, when the aft ropes, losing their rigidity, caught in the propeller. I stopped the propeller instantly. The rapidly emptying balloon now obeyed nothing but the vagrant winds. I came down, without much of a shock, between the roofs of the Trocadéro hotels, the balloon ripping up with the noise of an explosion. The new keel saved my life. Its two extremities rested on the two roofs, one lower than the other; and there I hung, sustained by the keel, until I could be pulled up to the higher roof by means of a rope."

"Do you know the cause of the accident?" I asked.

"I am not certain of it yet," he answered, "though I suspect the automatic valves, whose reacting on each other is a very delicate affair. Or it may have been the interior air-balloon that refused to fill out properly. Yesterday Lachambre's man came to me for the plans of the air-balloon for my No. 6. From something he said I gathered that the air-balloon of No. 5, not having been given time for its varnish to dry before being adjusted, might have stuck together or to the side of the outer balloon. Next time we shall be more careful, although with so many things to think of, and all new, it is scarcely human not to overlook something."

"In what will No. 6 differ from its predecessors?" I asked.

"It will be longer, thicker, and consequently of considerably greater gas-capacity than No. 5, and more closely ellipsoidal in form. In it I shall try to take advantage of all past experience, even the most unpleasant—which is not always the least valuable."

"So far you have done everything alone," I said. "Shall you be prepared to take up a passenger in No. 6?"

"I want more weight-carrying power in order to take up more petroleum and a passenger—that is to say, an aid. There is a great deal of work, really too much for one man, and up in the air, whatever must be

[1] "The balloon made a curve and began to come back to the Parc. It was the prettiest sight imaginable to see the steadiness with which it followed its course . . . until it was exactly overhead, when M. Santos-Dumont stopped the propeller and began his preparations for descending. Something, however, had gone wrong. This was evident, for at a certain moment the fearless aëronaut was seen to clamber out of the little car on to the framework supporting the motor. A shudder ran through the crowd of onlookers at the sight; and it was with a sentiment of relief that he was seen to climb into the car again and start the propeller once more."—Paris edition of the New York "Herald," August 5, 1901.

DRAWN BY ANDRÉ CASTAIGNE.   HALF-TONE PLATE ENGRAVED BY GEORGE M. LEWIS.

VIEWING THE BALLOON FROM THE EIFFEL TOWER.

done must be done promptly. But I shall not want a nervous passenger, a fearful passenger, or even a useless passenger. Also I want more motive power for my propeller; for when I have obtained a more complete mastery of the air-ship I shall wish to begin the great battle with the wind. But, as a model, I consider my Nos. 5 and 6 already perfect. The rudder, which was the last part to persist in giving trouble, now works beautifully."

RESULTS AND PROSPECTS.

"BEFORE we get any further," was my next question, "what do you consider you have accomplished?"

"Everything I set out to accomplish. I have gone up dozens of times and, in the presence of half Paris, I have followed the route laid down in advance and returned to my starting-point. I was nine minutes late in my first trial for the Deutsch Prize.[1] Put

FROM A PHOTOGRAPH BY P. RAFFAELE.

ASCENDING FROM THE LONGCHAMPS RACE-TRACK, JULY 12–13, 1901.

On the occasion of the first trial, M. Santos-Dumont, after a few evolutions to gain control of his machine, proceeded from the grounds of the Aéro Club to the near-by race-track of Longchamps. There, before mounting in the upper air for a long flight, he tried his paces around the track. He went around the circular course a number of times, and on each occasion descended and alighted exactly in front of the grand stand. In this picture he is seen just after mounting again, the stem of the balloon being still pointed upward.—S. H.

[1] M. Henry Deutsch (de la Meurthe), a wealthy petroleum-refiner and pillar of the Aéro Club, has offered a prize of one hundred thousand francs for the first dirigible balloon or air-ship that, between May 1 and October 1 of 1900, 1901, 1902, 1903, and 1904, shall rise from the Parc d'Aérostation of the Aéro Club at St. Cloud, and without touching ground and by its own self-contained means describe a closed curve in such a way that the axis of the Eiffel Tower shall be within the interior of the circuit, and return to the point of

departure in the maximum time of half an hour. A special committee of prominent Aéro Club members, sometimes called the Technical Committee, was named to formulate M. Deutsch's conditions and judge of their fulfilment. By reason of certain of these conditions, trying for the prize is a more formidable undertaking than would appear at first glance. The course from the Aéro Club's grounds to the Eiffel Tower and back is eleven kilometers; and these eleven kilometers plus the turning round the tower must be accomplished in

FROM A PHOTOGRAPH BY V. GRIBAYÉDOFF.

M. SANTOS-DUMONT DESCENDING TO HIS BALLOON-SHED, JULY 12-13, 1901.

this down to the poor work of a motor which had, nevertheless, worked well the day before—petroleum motors are like the ladies, capricious, and nobody knows what to do with them. But look at the Paris-Berlin automobile race," he continued with animation; and here M. Santos-Dumont gave what is almost a complete general answer to all the criticisms made concerning his experiments. "Of the one hundred and seventy automobiles registered for it, only one hundred and nine completed the first day's run, and of these only twenty-six got to Berlin. The others broke down or stopped on the way. And of the twenty-six arriving, how many do you imagine made the trip without a serious accident? It is perfectly natural, and people think nothing of it. But if I break down while up in the air, I cannot stop for repairs—I must go on."

"Many people will ask why you select favorable days when you have an air-ship capable of making way against any wind less than forty kilometers an hour."

"I am waiting until practice shall make me a better navigator. Do you think I want to break the air-ship often?" he inquired— "never mind what it has cost me, or the value of the Deutsch Prize, or my labors, my disappointments and hopes, and the pleasure the balloon gives me every time I take it into the air? Suppose I am obliged to land in Paris; how many of those great chimney-pots might I not bring down on people's heads before I came to ground, say, in a public square? I cannot get a company to insure me against the damage I might do on a squally day. Then there is danger in bringing the inflated balloon out of its shed on a windy day. The

thirty minutes, no matter what the force of contrary winds may be. This means, in a perfect calm, a necessary speed of thirty kilometers an hour for the straight stretches. Then the Technical Committee must be informed twenty-four hours in advance of each intended trial; and when it has met together at St. Cloud there is a kind of moral pressure to go on, no matter how the weather may have changed or in what condition the balloon or its machinery may be found to be. Yet a previous day's preliminary spin may easily derange so uncertain an engine as the present-day petroleum mo-

tor. When M. Santos-Dumont last spring won the four thousand francs annual Prize of Encouragement of the Aéro Club, he handed the money back to the club for the foundation of a Santos-Dumont Prize clogged by no such vexatious conditions. The Santos-Dumont Prize is to go to the first dirigible balloon or flying-machine (other than the founder's) that shall navigate the air from the Aéro Club's grounds to the Eiffel Tower, turn round it, and return to the Aéro Club's grounds, in no matter what time and under the observation of no matter what witnesses.—S. H.

THE RESCUE OF M. SANTOS-DUMONT, AUGUST 6, 1901.

grounds are small and encumbered, nothing like the grounds of a balloon club of the future, when clear, wide, elevated terraces will be considered essential to the aërial navigator's safety and convenience." [1]

"I expect the great contest now will be the battle with the air," I said. "I have seen you go against it."

"One scarcely goes 'against' the wind in a balloon," replied M. Santos-Dumont. "You are in the wind itself; you are part of it, and so you do not feel it blowing against you. The old adage, "Il n'y a pas de vent en ballon," is not completely true, because a streamer attached even to a spherical balloon will sometimes flutter, while if there were no wind at all, it would point to the ground; but the saying is true enough for practical purposes. The navigation of the air, for me, is like the navigation of a river," he went on. "It is not like the navigation of the ocean; and to talk about 'tacking' is a mistake. With my propeller pushing me at the rate of, say, thirty miles an hour, I am in the position of a river-steamboat captain whose propeller is driving him up or down the river at the rate of thirty miles an hour. Suppose the current to be ten miles an hour. When he goes up-stream he will accomplish thirty less ten, or twenty miles an hour with respect to the land. When he goes down-stream he will accomplish thirty plus ten, or forty miles an hour with respect to the shore. It is the same in the air, a question of plus or minus. Like any river-steamboat captain, I would prefer to go with the current or navigate the calm, say, of a lake; but when the time comes that I must navigate 'up-stream' I will do it. I have done it."

At the Chalais-Meudon Military Balloon Park they have gathered statistics of the wind over Paris. In every instance its force was measured by means of a registering anemometer situated on the plateau of Châtillon, at the summit of a mast ninety-two feet high. Thus it has been found that the winds vary from five and a half miles to one hundred miles an hour; but as a wind of a hundred miles an hour has been noted only once in eleven thousand six hundred and forty-nine hours of observation, analysis of the data has shown that a dirigible balloon possessing a speed of its own of forty-five kilometers (twenty-eight miles) an hour will be able to navigate the air above Paris eight hundred and fifteen times out of a thousand, and make almost six miles an hour straight ahead in the wind seven hundred and eight times out of a thousand. The military balloonists, therefore, conclude that: "The conquest of the air will be practically accomplished on the day when there shall be constructed a dirigible balloon having a speed of forty-five kilometers an hour and able to sustain this speed all day."

"What was your speed with No. 5?" I asked of M. Santos-Dumont.

"Forty kilometers an hour," he replied, without expressing an opinion of the above figures which I cited; "and my No. 6 will be still more powerful."

"M. Henry Deutsch is building a sixty horse-power air-ship modeled on your own," I suggested. "He ought to get great speed out of it. What do you think of it?"

"Yes, it ought to furnish great speed," he answered; "but I think it too much for any one to begin with. Such a balloon will be sixty yards long, where mine, after four years of growth based on experience, is still only thirty-five yards long. In every way it will be hard for a beginner to manage. I am afraid M. Deutsch will not be able to get any one to drive it. So far every professional chauffeur has refused to go up with him. 'To think that they are willing to risk their necks daily on the highways,' he exclaims, 'and yet they are afraid to go a few hundred feet into the air!'"

"But shall you never build a sixty horse-power dirigible balloon yourself?"

"Why not? And why not one of six hundred horse-power? My experience demonstrates that the thing itself is practicable; then why not go on improving in mere size and strength?"

---

[1] The grounds of the Aéro Club are peculiarly encumbered by the gigantic skeleton of M. Henry Deutsch's own balloon-shed, designed to "stable" the great air-ship he is having built on the exact lines of the "Santos-Dumont No. 5." Rising as it does directly opposite the sliding-doors of M. Santos-Dumont's shed, and at scarcely two balloon-lengths' distance, it constitutes a veritable peril to the latter's air-ship on any but the calmest days.

Once in the air, with its propeller working, the balloon is far safer than on the surface in the midst of such encumbrances.—S. H.

NOTE TO THE PICTURE ON THE OPPOSITE PAGE.

M. Santos-Dumont is seen sitting on a window-sill, to which he climbed, unaided, from his basket. A rope has been lowered to him from the roof above, but M. Santos-Dumont, who is being supported against the barred window by a pole held by a person on the inside of the building, surveys the wreck for a few minutes before allowing himself to be pulled up to the roof.—S. H.

24.
First Meet of the Man-Birds in America (1910)

FIRST MEET OF THE MAN-BIRDS IN AMERICA

by Samuel Travers Clover

Photographs Taken Expressly for THE OUTING MAGAZINE

AMERICA'S first "aviation meet" held at Los Angeles, California, January 10th–20th, is now a matter of history. So also are the records for altitude, fast and slow flying, sustained flight, and passenger carrying. Nearly five hundred thousand people, in the aggregate, saw the contests and the repeated visits of many of them testified to the deep interest in aerial sports. It must be borne in mind that the Los Angeles meeting was the first to be held in America and following, as it did within a comparatively short time, the successful Rheims affair, the American public, up and down the coast, was hungry to put to ocular proof the much-discussed flying machines.

Photographed expressly for THE OUTING MAGAZINE by Ralph S. Hawkins.

CURTISS IN BIPLANE JUST AFTER LEAVING THE GROUND.

Photographed expressly for THE OUTING MAGAZINE by Ralph S. Hawkins.

CURTISS IN BIPLANE PREPARING TO ALIGHT.

Photographed expressly for THE OUTING MAGAZINE by Ralph S. Hawkins.

LOUIS PAULHAN, THE SOLE FRENCH REPRESENTATIVE, WAS THE DRAMATIC CENTER
OF THE WEEK.

That many Easterners, particularly from New York, traveled across the continent to watch the tests of monoplanes, biplanes, and dirigibles is additional evidence of the widespread interest in this effort to conquer the air highways.

Within six miles of the Pacific Ocean and fourteen miles southwest of Los Angeles, on the famous old Dominguez rancho—a notable holding in pre-Gringo days—was the site chosen for the exhibits. On the west line of a vast field, devoid of trees or shrubbery, the immense grand stand was erected, giving to its fifteen thousand occupants an unobstructed view of the aviation maneuvers. Strung around the inclosure on three sides, many ranks deep, on foot, in carriages, and in automobiles, was a daily attendance at least as large again as the crowd filling the grand stand and boxes.

Not even the Scotch mist at the close of the first week of the meet could dampen the enthusiasm with which the daring flights of Paulhan, the whizzing rush of Glenn Curtiss, the clever head work of the young New Yorker, Willard, the pertinacious efforts of Hamilton to rival the feats of the Frenchman, and the soaring aloft of Knabenshue and Beachey in their dirigibles were witnessed. Quite as inspiring as the operations of these machines was the typical California multitude, pleased as children with new toys and itching to examine at close range the wonderful inventions that sailed so easily and so smoothly before them.

They saw the oncoming aeroplane, swift as a bird in full flight and appearing every whit as graceful, under perfect control of the aviator, riding the air at any desired height and with far more safety, apparently, than the automobile hugging terra firma, several hundred feet below the extended canvas wings. It was a sight calculated to make the blood flow faster, even in the

Photographed expressly for THE OUTING MAGAZINE by Ralph S. Hawkins.

PAULHAN IN THE BLERIOT MONOPLANE WHICH DID NOT COME UP TO EXPECTATIONS
AT LOS ANGELES.

veins of the most sluggish. Never deviating from a chosen course, answering instantly to the direction of the steersman, this new creature of the air seemed endowed with life, so responsive was it to the slightest indicated wish of the controlling power. With each succeeding day's exhibit of man's ingenuity and his ability to cleave the atmosphere unscathed, the clamor on the part of nonaviators to share the flights of the manbirds grew louder.

Louis Paulhan, in his Farman biplane, was easily the idol of the people at this first of all American meets. Of medium height, blue-eyed, and fairer of skin than the average typical Frenchman; still in the twenties and weighing less than one hundred and forty pounds, he approaches his machine with a whimsical smile, climbs lightly into his seat, and without the slightest demonstration whirs aloft, followed by the applause of tens of thousands of admirers.

Naturally, all other of his achieve-ments gave way to the remarkable exhibition of Wednesday, January 12, when, without any preliminary notice whatever, the young Frenchman began circling the field in the attempt to break the world's record for altitude. As his biplane mounted higher and higher, the attention of the fifty thousand spectators, now concentrated upon the rapidly receding object above, grew almost painful in its intensity. Even with powerful binoculars the machine, at its highest flight, appeared scarcely larger than a soap box and the figure of the man was entirely lost to view.

That he had attained his object and exceeded the height credited to Latham of 3,600 feet, was not doubted by a soul present. This belief soon became a certainty when the experts engaged in establishing the vertical distance of the aviator from earth by triangulation announced that he had passed the 4,000-foot level. Paulhan carried aloft with him an aneroid barometer, but this was

Photographed expressly for THE OUTING MAGAZINE by Ralph S. Hawkins.

PAULHAN CLIMBS LIGHTLY INTO HIS SEAT, AND WITHOUT THE SLIGHTEST DEMON-
STRATION WHIRS ALOFT.

not depended upon for the official marking.

A series of observations was taken by
experts as the Frenchman ascended, the
last one being secured just before he
tipped the front planes to descend. The
field man held the glasses on him and
signaled the operators at the two transit
instruments to clamp. In taking Paulhan's altitude three triangles had to be
solved, one of them a scalene, the other
two right triangles. The use of the
second transit instrument was necessary
because of the moving object being off
the base line.

As the aviator swam nearer into view
on his downward flight the excitement
of the onlookers increased. Women
gave vent to hysterical laughs that
changed into sobs and in the eyes of many
men were tears of excitement. It was
a relief when the band dashed into the
"Marseillaise," in which thousands of
voices blended. Five minutes later Paulhan glided to the earth in midfield and

was immediately surrounded by a score
of excited men.

Richard Ferris, the general manager
and originator of the meet, Cortlandt
Field Bishop, president of the Aero
Club of America and chairman of the
judges' committee, Edward Cleary,
manager of the Paulhan interests, and
Col. W. M. Garland of the executive
committee, at once hoisted the record-
breaker to their shoulders, but before
they could rush him across the field
to the grand stand, Madam Paulhan
reached his side and, stooping toward
her, the happy Frenchman planted a
very emphatic kiss on his wife's upturned
lips.

This was the signal for still more
cheering from the field, which swelled
into a great roar as Paulhan faced the
sea of faces from the improvised throne
to which he had been hoisted. Hand-
kerchiefs and parasols waved all along
the crowded grand stand and the field
echoed with the shouts of applause. It

CURTISS'S FLIGHTS VIED WITH PAULHAN'S MORE SPECTACULAR FEATS IN AROUSING
POPULAR ENTHUSIASM.

was the perihelion of Paulhan's popularity; a generous and deserved tribute to the 4,165 feet of air-climbing that was given as the result of the mathematical observations. The aneroid instrument carried by Paulhan announced 4,600 feet, but the records of the transit instruments were accepted as the official figures.

This memorable flight was accomplished under ideal conditions. There was the barest perceptible breeze, the sky was unflecked by a single cloud, and the sun shone as it can shine only in southern California in January. Overcoats were unnecessary, even in riding to the aviation camp in an automobile; the thousands of women present were gayly clad, their vari-colored costumes lighting up the grand stand and boxes picturesquely. The hour at which Paulhan began his flight was 4 P.M., when the air is quietest and most favorable in this region for essaying difficult feats of flying.

The altitude was accomplished in forty-five minutes. Five minutes and forty-six seconds sufficed for the descent, making the total time elapsed fifty minutes and forty-six seconds. The day was known as San Diego Day, several thousand visitors from the southernmost California city being on the grounds, and as a memorial of the event the San Diegans presented the flying Frenchman with a handsome silver trophy. From the aviation committee Paulhan received the purse of $3,000 offered for highest altitude reached, his record not being outdone during the meet.

Next to Paulhan's star achievement must be placed the fast time made by Glenn Curtiss, in the Curtiss monoplane, over the 16.11-mile course, against time, Thursday, January 13th. Curtiss flew the ten laps required in 24 minutes, 54.3 seconds. Although the grand prize-winner for speed at Rheims ably sustained his reputation in this respect on the Los Angeles field, he was closely

Posed expressly for THE OUTING MAGAZINE. Photographed by Ralph S. Hawkins.

M. LOUIS PAULHAN IN FARMAN BIPLANE, BEFORE MAKING HIS WORLD-RECORD CROSS-COUNTRY FLIGHT.

Posed expressly for THE OUTING MAGAZINE. *Photographed by Ralph S. Hawkins.*

GLENN CURTISS IN CURTISS BIPLANE THAT BROKE THE WORLD'S RECORDS FOR SPEED AND QUICK ASCENT.

pushed by Paulhan, who in his Farman machine finished the total circuit in 24 minutes, 59.3 seconds, or only five seconds behind the Rheims winner—a narrow defeat on a course covering nearly sixteen and a half miles.

Curtiss is the antithesis of Paulhan in temperament. He is cold and reserved, almost to moroseness, and as cautious and calculating as the Frenchman is spectacular and volatile. But while he failed to win the popular applause in anything like the degree achieved by Paulhan, the American at all times had the hearty respect of the people, who cheered him to the echo when the judges announced their findings and declared him the winner. In addition to this feat Curtiss broke the world's record for quick rising from a standing start, making it in ninety-eight feet. He also set a new record for quick rise, after starting his engine, accomplishing it in 6.25 seconds.

Curtiss has given deep study to aerial navigation and is inclined to serious reflection. He exchanges few words with anybody and responds in monosyllables to all questioning. Undoubtedly, he has a remarkable type of flying machine, whatever may be the justice of the Wright contentions, but his engine appears to give him trouble. His eight-cylinder motor refused to work to his entire satisfaction; in the speed test he lost fully ten seconds on one lap through adverse conditions.

. Paulhan, on the other hand, carried an engine that was the envy of every aviator on the Dominguez field. It was never out of order, is of Paris special make, seventy horse power, and weighs 1,100 pounds. Apparently, Paulhan's confidence in his engine is no small part of the secret of his ability to mount higher than any other aviator dare go, to perform in the air with his machine feats that no other flier cares to attempt, and to make sustained flights that far exceed in duration those of his competitors.

Of the American aviators little Charles F. Willard, of the New York Aero Club, operating a Curtiss biplane, was the most popular at Los Angeles. He is as slender as a jockey and not over five feet six inches in height. Despite his youth—he cannot be more than twenty-four—he is an experienced aeronaut, plucky and determined, with a cool head and a winning way. That he is as skillful as he is daring was demonstrated by the handy manner in which he won the $250 purse offered by the aviation committee for starting and stopping his aeroplane in a twenty-foot square, in a one-lap round. It was a masterly display of control and won generous applause for the aviator.

Willard rose from the square precisely as required, circled the mile and a half course at full speed and alighted at the starting point so handily that the judges could find one wheel only a microscopic fraction of an inch over one of the lines of the square. This insignificant lapse was very properly ignored in making the award and the youngster gleefully bore off his well-earned prize. Willard has no extravagant notions concerning the practical utility of flying machines, but he argues that if the automobile, which ten years ago was still in an experimental stage, can be brought to the point of perfection it has attained within a decade, there may be as bright a future for the flying machine; not as a freight carrier, but certainly for passenger purposes.

Charles K. Hamilton, who flew the Curtiss biplane purchased by Clifford Harmon of New York, is an odd-looking genius, with cavernous eyes and rather gaunt cheeks, his scant frame appearing to fit loosely within the dark suit he affects. But his eyes glint from beneath their overhanging arches when he takes his seat on the biplane, and if he had not been handicapped by an unsatisfactory engine he would have contested for altitude with Paulhan. Hamilton has deep faith in the Curtiss type of machine, unbounded ambition, and the courage of his convictions. Handicapped as he was by his engine, he made many successful flights and demonstrated his ability to handle his machine in a masterful manner when he covered the ten-lap course of 16.11 miles in 30 minutes and 34 seconds. Considering that Curtiss had a sixty horse power engine as against a twenty-five horse power in

Photographed expressly for THE OUTING MAGAZINE by Ralph S. Hawkins.

PAULHAN CARRYING A PASSENGER; IN THE DISTANCE IS HAMILTON, IN CURTISS BIPLANE, WHOM PAULHAN HAS JUST PASSED.

the Hamilton machine, this was a highly creditable showing.

Of the dirigible airships the one operated by Roy Knabenshue rose to the greatest height, with an altitude of 1,656 feet to its credit. Knabenshue is an adept at balancing, and having a better engine than was in the airship commanded by L. Beachey was able to perform feats not attainable by the latter. Where Beachey was unable to make progress against head winds Knabenshue readily demonstrated his ability to cope with them and circled in the upper currents with apparent ease. Beachey, however, seems to have a thorough understanding of the control of the dirigible airship.

In a test of speed over a one-lap course Saturday, January 15th, Beachey sailed the distance in 5 minutes, 21 seconds, beating Knabenshue by 14 seconds. The day before, however, the latter made the distance in 5.10. As demonstrating the value of the dirigible in war times, Knabenshue, from a height of eighty feet, dropped two bombs into a twenty-foot square. What the gunners below would do to the huge cigar-shaped objects only eighty feet away may be easily imagined.

Dirigibles were numerous and there was hardly an hour when one was not in the air. Lieut. Paul W. Beck, in charge of the U. S. Signal Corps at the Presidio, San Francisco, had a government dirigible on the field toward the close of the meet. Of the special balloons operated at Huntington Park, distant three miles from Dominguez field, and affiliated with the main exhibit, the "New York," owned by Clifford B. Harmon was in constant service. Five other airships rose daily from the park, the "Dick Ferris," piloted by a brother of Roy Knabenshue, the "City of Los Angeles," in charge of George B. Harrison, the "City of Oakland," with J. C. Mars in command, the Company A, Signal Corps balloon, operated

Photographed expressly for THE OUTING MAGAZINE by Ralph S. Hawkins.

CURTISS (LOWER FIGURE) PASSING PAULHAN ON THE LAST DAY OF MEET, WHEN
CURTISS WAS OUT FOR THE SPEED RECORD AND PAULHAN FOR ENDURANCE.

by members of the aeronautical squad, and the "Peoria," controlled by Frank J. Kanne.

The latter, with a basketful of passengers, had the startling experience of the meet in an effort to follow Clifford Harmon of the "New York." Striking a contrary wind, the "Peoria" deviated from the course and was carried several miles out to sea, to the consternation of the residents of the beach towns near Los Angeles. Happily, a call for the Venice life-saving crew was not needed as the wind suddenly shifted and an in-shore current bore the voyagers safely to land, where a quick descent followed.

But the feature of the meet was the aeroplane, and the king of the aviators in popular esteem was Paulhan. There were half a dozen assistant aviators and mechanicians in the Paulhan entourage and they all had the profoundest adoration for their chief, whom they seemed to regard as a sort of demigod.

"Ah, *mon Dieu!*" one said, "he is, in the air, what we are on the ground, perfectly at home! He can do anything with his machine, go to any height he please. He is a wizard!" Which opinion, it must be admitted, was shared pretty generally by countless others who sat for days entranced and fascinated by the Frenchman's daring and skill.

To see him mount skyward, with an insouciance that nothing short of a double-somersault downward with broken planes could daunt is to compel one's admiration. Once, after circling the field and disappearing, he suddenly emerged to view from behind a black cloud that had crept in from the ocean. It was a startling and dramatic reappearance. It seemed as though the daring fellow had come to earth inside the cloud and had just stepped out of the framework.

Another time, just before sunset, when the western sky was dotted with fleecy specks, Paulhan's machine was silhouetted against a white cloud whose edges

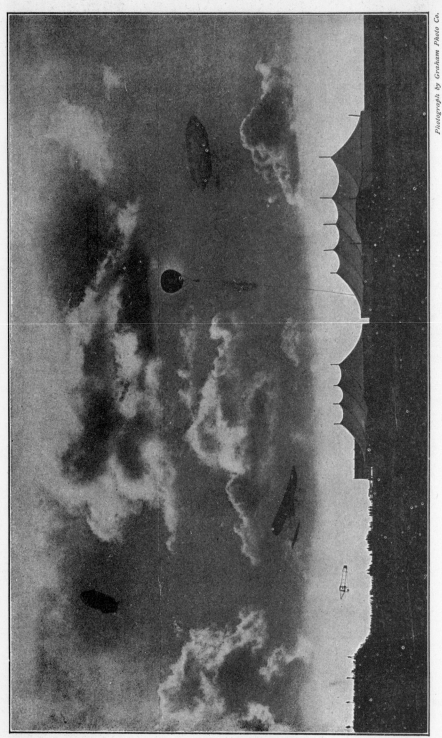

Photograph by Graham Photo Co.

A SKYFUL OF MAN-BIRDS.

L. Beachy in Dirigible. L. Paulhan in Monoplane. Captive Balloon. G. Curtiss in Biplane. Roy Knabenshue in Dirigible.

were tipped with the rosy glow of the setting sun. He seemed to ride in the center of the flaky mass and the effect was almost uncanny. Of course, both these spectacles were unintended by the Frenchman, although he was continually on the alert for the surprising and the dramatic.

One afternoon Paulhan ascended in full view of the grand stand, circled the course once, rose to a higher plane, and suddenly headed for the ocean. He was gone thirty minutes, no one knew whither. It developed later that the restless Frenchman, seeing the shipping in the harbor from his lofty perch, had taken a notion to fly across to San Pedro, hover above the warship that chanced to be in port, fly over the new fortification site recently acquired by the Federal Government at Point Firmin, acknowledge the salute of whistles and bells from the factories and ships along the harbor by dipping his front planes, unconcernedly whirring back to his starting point. It was a dramatic performance, the full significance of which was not appreciated by the people who had missed him until they read of his mad flight in the local papers next day.

A Race in the Air

Still another entertaining feat was his contest with Hamilton who was attempting to beat the speed record for ten laps. The American had circled the course three times when Paulhan rose in the air with his Farman and, like a falcon released from its bonds, sped headlong after the Curtiss machine. Around the course they raced with the huge crowd yelling its delight in a frenzied fashion. Each aviator was doing his best, apparently, but suddenly Paulhan called upon his powerful "Gnome" engine for its capacity work and opening wide the throttle raced ahead of his opponent.

Two laps later the Frenchman again overtook Hamilton. As the northwest pylon was reached near the grand stand Paulhan, who was immediately above the American, suddenly deflected his front planes and with the rapidity of lightning dove underneath the Curtiss

machine and landed in the squared space in front of the judge's stand, while the concourse fairly howled its approval. Hamilton, a trifle disconcerted, flew wildly for a minute but quickly recovered and continued his course. Paulhan's action may have been unprofessional, but to all intents and purposes it was a real racing contest and the only one witnessed. Needless to say, the spectators were vastly entertained by the sensational swoop of their favorite.

Only two monoplanes were exhibited. They were of the Bleriot type, but Paulhan succeeded in making only one sustained flight in this flimsy craft, whose appearance in midair is not unlike that of a huge dragon fly. Saturday afternoon, January 15th, Miscarol, of Paulhan's staff, had taken one of the monoplanes out on the back stretch of the field to test the propeller. It worked all right for a time, until the aviator attempted to increase the speed, having attained a sufficient height. But the machine refused to run true and veering suddenly tipped downward to the ground, with which the left wing of the man-made bird came in violent contact.

Miscarol was thrown forward, striking his head on one of the truss rods and receiving a painful bruise. The damage to the machine was more serious as the propeller blade was cracked, the left plane bent almost double, the underframe buckled and broken, and a fore wheel jerked off its axle. The engine, fortunately, was uninjured, but the monoplane was put out of commission for the remainder of the meet.

Los Angeles had three local amateur aviators who came to grief on the first day's tryout. Edgar Smith was making repairs on a Langley monoplane of his own construction when the revolving propeller, which he had started, struck him a terrific blow on the back of the head, rendering him unconscious. Attendants rushed him to the emergency hospital and next day he was well enough to be removed to his rooms, with the probabilities in favor of his recovery.

Professor Zerbe, in a multiplane resembling a huge flowerpot, attempted to rise from the course but was unsuccessful. The machine lumbered along until it struck a small hummock, when it toppled over, breaking a rear plane, but not seriously injuring the operator. The hopes of the inventor, however, were blighted for the season.

Another local aspirant in the person of J. H. Klassen had similar ill success with his monoplane which refused to fly at the crucial moment, due to a defective engine. It was a sad trio of home-grown geniuses and their mishaps proved a source of genuine disappointment to their friends.

From a financial viewpoint as well as from the artistic and practical sides the first American aviation meet was an unqualified success. Apparently all the subscribers will receive back the amount of their subscriptions, with a balance in the treasury. The climatic conditions could hardly have been more perfect, but under foot the ground was anything but ideal, the "dobe" proving most trying to the delicate machines gliding over the course. The aviators were satisfied, the crowds were delighted, and Los Angeles wants everybody to come again.

25.
Over Sea
by Air-Ship
(1910)

From a photograph by Hans Fohr

PARSEVAL III (222 HORSE-POWER) AND ZEPPELIN III (300 HORSE-POWER) IN FLIGHT
ABOVE THE CITY HALL, FRANKFORT-ON-THE-MAIN

OVER SEA BY AIR-SHIP

SURPRISING PROGRESS OF GERMAN PLANS FOR A TRANSATLANTIC SERVICE

BY T. R. MacMECHEN AND CARL DIENSTBACH

Authors of "The Aërial Battleship," "Fighting in the Air," "The Dirigible of To-day"

BEHIND all its thought and effort to conquer new spheres of activity, there is in the German Empire a determined purpose to achieve complete mastery of the air. Each test of successive air-ships has marked a step nearer the goal. In the spring of 1909, the war air-ship Zeppelin I, returning to Friedrichshafen, flew to its destination on a 40-mile wind. The air-ship's speed was 70 miles an hour. It will be news to many that since that time, all air currents in Germany have been charted for navigation. During October, bulletins were sent and received a distance over three hundred miles by wire-less telegraphy on the Zeppelin III, while in flight. To-day, the telegraphic range equals an ocean liner's. From a system of wireless stations, hourly advices of the winds are available by all imperial air-ships. Captains even now exchange the "latest wind," independent of bulletins from stations. On this information, they go with the wind in one fourth the time lost in running against the current. This means that within the coming year, air-ships with passengers and mail may cross the ocean in one and a half to two days. This probability marks the supremacy of Germany's position in the contest for commercial supremacy, for Emperor, press, and people are united on the creation of large air-ships for international traffic.

Germany's technologists have completely overcome a skepticism equal to that which greeted Mother Shipton's prediction that iron and steel would float. It is now known that aërial space will support great weights; clouds carry for long distances enormous loads of rain and snow, before depositing their cargoes. Germany has proved that the ship in air and the ship in water are in many respects identical; an increase in size and in power of the machinery has with each resulted in an increase of speed and endurance. Within two years, the air-ship's speed has grown from 32 to 38 miles an hour. The largest German air-ships glide against the air from a quarter to a half-hour after their engines have been stopped, exactly as an ocean vessel moves forward after its speed has been checked. Stronger hulls have made air-ships more airworthy; with tougher gas-chambers, they leak only thirty to forty pounds of gas in twenty-four hours, instead of a hundred, as a year ago. As auxiliary power all air-ships now carry four instead of two engines; and they have space for more passengers; moreover, the crucial problem of controlling the supporting gas has been worked out.

PIONEER ATLANTIC EXPEDITIONS

PIONEERING expeditions by Dr. Gans-Fabrice, lately president of the Frankfort Aëronautical Exposition, and by Joseph Brucker of Berlin, are preparing to start in May, 1910, to cross the ocean on the trade-wind in small dirigibles of six thousand and seven thousand cubic meters, with only moderate power. They are in the interest of rival air-ship enterprises, the chief purpose being to record the wind on the entire route, and to collect data for navigation on a larger scale. Both expeditions will start from Teneriffe, with the Antilles as their destination. They are expected to drift slowly with the wind, the engines being used merely to keep the air-ships in the course. Dr. Gans-Fabrice's device of two gas-envelops, between which the air circulates for the purpose of saving the gas, is a makeshift of the principle developed in the new German ships for preventing expansion of the

gas by the sun, and by overflowing. The actual overflow will be so slight that small pumps can be used to condense it.

ABSOLUTE CONTROL OF FLOATING POWER

A PROCESS has been invented by Professor Schuette, of the University of Dantzig, which is expected to enable two new ships, one of which is virtually finished, to fly three to five thousand miles, to float for seven days, and to carry cargoes of five to seven tons, at a height of two to three miles above the earth's gusts. Zeppelin air-ships have twice carried four to five tons over nine hundred miles, in one and one half days, with imperfect control of the gas. The new air-ships will not weaken their potential support by discharging gas. As it expands beyond the capacity of the sustaining chambers, automatic pumps will transfer the excess into reservoirs; and when the air-ship's instruments indicate a shrinkage, hydrogen will be rapidly restored to the chambers. Engines of four hundred and fifty to five hundred and forty combined horse-power, will drive the ships at estimated speeds of thirty-seven to forty-three miles an hour. For some time the German war air-ship, Gross III, has been traveling thirty-eight miles an hour, with less than its three hundred horse-power. These are some of the expected improvements that Professor Hergesell (meteorological adviser of Count Zeppelin), on his recent trip to America, said would permit ships to remain in the air a week.

THE ADVANTAGE OF USING THE AIR CURRENTS

YET Germany's greatest achievement is not the technical perfection of the air-going craft; she has learned how to use the air currents, as the birds do, in traveling. This is a science; the ship is only its instrument. Air-ships will double and treble their speed by acting in harmony with the forces of Nature, the primal speed-maker. There is a working force only lately reckoned with, even by builders of air craft,—and that is the wind. Air-ships will use the trade-wind to reach this continent because it always blows one way. That is as simple a proposition as that a low-powered steamer should use the

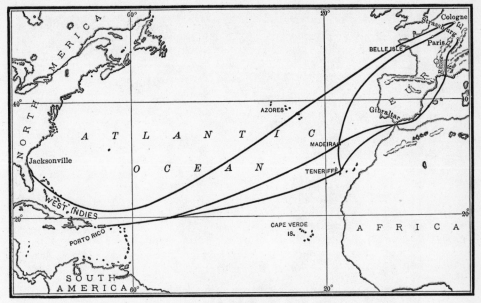

MAP OF TRADE-WIND ROUTES BY AIR-SHIP FROM GERMANY
TO THE WEST INDIES AND FLORIDA

Gulf Stream. Air-traffic, to compete with rail or water, must maintain as sure a schedule of travel. Germany has already mapped her air-ship routes to and from America.

SURVEYING THE AIR-SHIP ROUTES

In December of 1909, Professor Hergesell balloon-sounded the American terminus in the trade region, from the German training cruiser *Victoria Luise*. He found that the wind blows twenty-seven miles an hour daily, at sea-level, during that season. Professor Hergesell's previous soundings in 1903, extended over the entire trade region of the North Atlantic. His recent report to the German Admiralty makes it certain that the trade-wind can be used even in winter, as far north as the Azores, the fortieth degree of latitude, for voyages to the West Indies. From Cologne, by way of Belle Isle, France, is the route that is being considered as the shortest by the German government and the popular Air-navy League, the entire distance to the Florida coast being thirty-seven hundred miles. Two other routes have been considered as even more trustworthy, one from Cologne, by way of Belle Isle, France, across the Bay of Biscay, around the Spanish Peninsula, to Madeira or Teneriffe,

nineteen hundred and twenty-one hundred miles respectively; the other from Strassburg, southward, skirting the eastern slope of the Vosges Mountains, crossing France along the western slope of the Jura Range, and at Marseilles passing out over the Mediterranean, thence around the Peninsula and through the Strait of Gibraltar, to Madeira or Teneriffe, nineteen hundred miles. Both routes lengthen the voyage to America, to forty-eight hundred miles; but all are within the range of the new ships.

OVER SEA ON THE TRADE-WINDS

At forty miles an hour, air-ships can cross the Atlantic on the trade-wind in less than two days. Driven thirty-five miles on the twenty-seven-mile wind, they should make the trip in fifty hours. If blowing eighteen miles in summer, the faster craft should come over in fifty-two hours. Even on a ten-mile current, the slower air-ship should arrive on the western side in two and three-quarter days. An air-ship flying forty miles an hour should go from Germany to the Madeiras in a little over forty hours, without the help of the wind. The Azores would be reached in about the same time; but on the trade-wind, the remaining eighteen

From a photograph by Arthur Hoffschild

GANGWAY OF ZEPPELIN III

This air-ship has accommodations for twenty-seven passengers. The lady is the daughter of Count Zeppelin and the person following is Councilor-of-Commerce Lanz, President of the German Air-navy League

hundred miles to Porto Rico, the first terminus of the transoceanic route, might be covered in one day. This means traveling from Cologne to America in two and three quarter days. Allowing liberally for a stop at the Madeiras to replenish fuel, the longer voyage of forty-eight hundred miles would take less than four days. Though the trade-wind is deflected southward, calculation shows that fact to be negligible, owing to the ship's high speed and its southern course. The air-ship is expected to travel only fifty to one hundred feet above the waves because Professor Hergesell found the trade-wind strongest over the water.

FLYING TO EUROPE IN THIRTY-SIX HOURS

AIR-SHIPS, it is believed, will return from America to Europe in one and one half days, on the permanent upper air currents that flow in a broad stream with the planet's motion, from west to east, over the United States, the Atlantic, and Europe. Balloon and kite soundings for ten years have definitely settled that between two and three miles high—and to navigate at

that level air-ships are now being built— these currents have a uniform speed of forty-eight miles an hour, in summer; and just twice that velocity in winter. An instance of using this upper drift for over-sea travel, was the voyage of the balloon Mammoth in October of 1907. With three passengers, it drifted at a height of one and one half to over two miles, from London, across the North Sea, to Denmark, five hundred miles in nine hours, this being at the rate of fifty-five miles an hour. Skilful piloting has taken balloons from France, for eleven hundred miles, into Russia; and nearly nine hundred miles across the American continent, descending only at the brink of the ocean. Air-ships for traffic could hardly fly against this movement of the air. For economic reasons, therefore, the trade-wind and the upper planetary drift are the natural navigable wind-rivers between Europe and America.

AIR-LANES USED BY BIRDS

THOUGH Science has not found north and south winds as regular as these planetary streams, air-lanes are opened across the

From a photograph by Arthur Hoffschild

PROMENADE DECK OF ZEPPELIN III

This picture and that on the previous page were made at the International
Exhibition of air-ships held at Frankfort in 1909.

great eastward drift that do not interrupt its flow. Air-ships will fly between northern and southern continents, exactly as the little plover flies from Nova Scotia, over the midatlantic to South America, without a known stop. This trip of three thousand miles shows the bewildering speed with which the creature must travel. Telescopes sometimes reveal birds of passage crossing the sun or moon; calculations taken from instruments prove they were traveling at altitudes of one, two, or three miles, with a rapidity of two or three miles a minute. The secret of their mastery of the air currents, as found by a German scientist, gives the nautical key for dealing with all winds. It is now known that migrating birds never fly except on the swiftest winds blowing toward their destination.

CLEWS IN THE AIR

GERMAN air navigators are applying some of the clews to air currents which it is now known that birds find in the air, for their guidance in flight. They take account of "zones of discontinuity" and "upper inversions"—invisible strata, yet often visible as cloud-waves, where the order of things in the air is either gradually or abruptly reversed. These zones reveal the nature of the wind above and below the air craft, and betray the temperature, moisture, pressure and electric charging of the air. Any change in moisture or temperature means that the wind will suddenly vary its speed and shift its direction. In 1907, Friedrich Ritter discovered the two principal wind-zones, the "upper-wind," and the "under-wind," that shallow air-surf, two hundred to three hundred feet deep, along the ground, which gives the popular notion of wind. It may be blowing in any direction, but in ascending, the navigator feels it growing less, until it is reduced to a zephyr. He has entered a "zone of discontinuity" or "calm-zone," a neutral meeting-place of rising currents and the upper wind. Here storm-birds that overtake or lag behind a ship in a tempest, are flying; and in that

From a photograph

ZEPPELIN III IN FLIGHT

This picture was made when the air-ship was almost directly above the camera. The reader may
realize the situation by holding the picture horizontally overhead, and looking up at it. The picture
clearly shows the underbody of the air-ship, with forward and rear cars, and cabin space amidships.

zone the French aviator Paulhan flew in
January, 1910, steadily above the people at
Los Angeles while a high wind scurried
along the ground. German air-ships use
these zones on exploring detours, in search
of favorable winds, above or below.

THE "INVERSION" NAVIGATING LEVEL

BETWEEN thirty-two hundred feet and a
mile above the earth the air navigator
passes through a second "zone of discontinuity," where cumulus clouds gather;
but usually they are prevented from rising
higher than a mile, by the "inversion,"
consisting of compact masses of warm air
spreading out like a ceiling and floating in
the cold atmosphere. The "inversion"
stops the forming of clouds and reabsorbs
their moisture. Above it, the air is dry
and the wind is apt to be steady and
strong. There, just above the cumulus
clouds, actual experience has established
the daytime navigating level at about one
and one quarter miles. The Schuette air-
ship has been designed to lift its twenty-
four tons to that height, without casting

ballast. Dr. George von dem Borne, who
has investigated these inversions, thus describes traveling on them:

At a height of one and one half miles,
we found a misty stratum stretching from
Berlin far into the Russian Empire. Heavy,
dark clouds broke through it. Their tops of
cirrus-cloud waves, identified them as a
thunder-storm, even without the thunder rolling within them. These clouds, moving at
the balloon's speed, kept two to two and one
half miles ahead of us, the entire day. I
realized that a gigantic draft of warm air was
flooding over the sub-lying strata, and carrying us along. Such inversions, without a
gap, are frequent in summer, a little under
two miles. They form lids over immense
masses of air, permitting great quantities of
heat to accumulate below; this energy finds
an outlet in the thunder-storm. They offer
splendid chances for navigating.

STORMS OF THE UPPER REGIONS

A THUNDER-STORM'S great eddies are the
typhoons of the upper air. They involve

its entire depth. Captain Hildebrandt and Professor Miethe, while ballooning in Germany, were caught in an aërial billow, that swept them aloft; gas-bag, car, and guide-rope floated side by side like feathers. Into the trough of the wave, they plunged like a cannon-ball. If caught in such a storm the air-ship would be powerless, but the motors should enable the ship to evade a current carrying a storm. Atmosphere filled with electricity may dangerously charge an air-ship's metal parts and set it afire on contact with the ground, but provision has been made automatically to relieve such tension. A ship in the air is safe from lightning. The German method of navigation seeks to read weather offhand from the natural processes of each form of cloud. No navigator disregards their warnings. They betray what will happen next. Clouds that are changing their levels denote varying conditions. The strata float three quarters to one and a quarter miles apart. After leaving the earth, if the air-ship passes through an inversion, detected by increased warmth, or flat clouds, clear weather is ahead, for some hours at least; in that case, clouds, the trouble-makers, cannot rise to precipitate rain above, or to cause a thunderstorm. The watch on the airliner, sailing above two miles, at the freezing line, will look below, not above, for weather. If the cloud-tops rise like mushrooms, spread like an umbrella, and invade the ship's level, the navigator will expect a thunderstorm quickly. An air-ship will encounter rain or snow only at low levels, where it can counteract the weight due to wetting by filling its chambers from the gas-reserve.

WEATHER CHANGES INDICATED EACH HOUR, BY WIRELESS

THOUGH weather may be read in the sky, remote processes of air, hundreds of miles away, which fix the air-ship's course in advance, are only revealed by communica-

From a photograph by Arthur Hoffschild

ZEPPELIN III GETTING UNDER WAY

The rear car is shown, also the vapor exhaust from its one engine.
The forward car carries two engines.

tion through space, and this will be eventually achieved by a network system of wireless telegraphy. The feasibility of this is indicated by the practice of the United States Weather Bureau, which flashes storm warnings to the naval wireless station at Newport, which in turn relays news of winds and storms, flashed to distant air craft, will be serviceable only when accompanied by the exact latitude and longitude of the observation. Exact reckoning of the air-ship's location will fix its position with reference to shifting

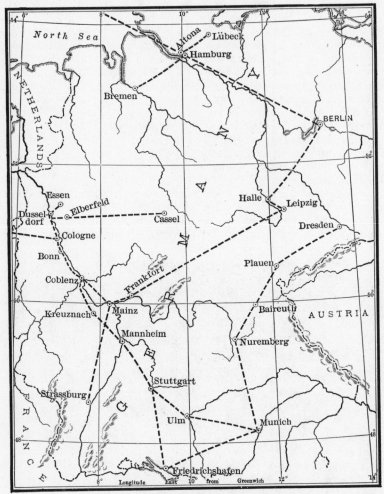

MAP OF THE "WIND-RIVERS," OR MAIN ROUTES, IN GERMANY, WHICH
HAVE BEEN SURVEYED FOR REGULAR AIR-NAVIGATION

The direction to London is a little south of due west from Berlin, while a continuation
of the line from Berlin to Hamburg will touch Edinburgh

tion at Newport, which in turn relays bulletins to the Nantucket Shoals Lightship, where they are distributed to all vessels within calling distance, and exchanged between ships, hundreds of miles at sea. Wireless relaying every hour will be indispensable to the proper navigation of airships, for the pilot must keep constantly in touch with atmospheric events. Wireless air-lanes. The greatest mastery will consist in constantly compiling a running schedule, as the result of tacking tactics. Air-ships will have to run from current to counter-current, to make time, frequently drifting back and zigzagging to pick up their wind. An air-ship will be able to make up lost time by seeking a faster current. Aërial tacking has been practised

even by skilful pilots of the ordinary rud-
derless balloon, who, changing from wind
to wind, for hundreds of miles, have landed
within a short distance of a designated
goal. But air-ships will not go up and
down in search of the wind, which will be
sought with instruments on kites. The
aërological station at Lake Constance has
a fast boat for raising kites in still air.
The faster air-ship may send kites to any
height; or the atmosphere can be probed
with a light-caliber gun, firing a shell that
explodes on time, producing a smoke-
cloud (or a ball of
fire at night), the
drifting of which rel-
ative to the air-ship's
speed and course, will
reveal the wind's di-
rection and strength.
The relative drift of
natural clouds en-
ables a pilot with a
theodolite to measure
the upper winds.
Cloud-waves at the
"zones of discontinu-
ity" often make the
wind's direction visi-
ble to the naked eye.

THE WORK OF NAV-
IGATING OFFICERS

EACH air-ship will
require two or three
navigators to take
latitude and longi-
tude at short inter-
vals and to alternate in the preparation
of wind-charts. The navigating instruments are those used at sea, but on the
non-magnetic air-ships the compass is more
exact, since the motors alone deflect it
from its natural direction. Since the
air-ship has no natural horizon, an artificial one is made by sighting an air-bub-
ble quadrant. Latitude and longitude
is quickly reckoned from tables compiled
by German astronomers. There is no
"dead reckoning" in the air, and speed
may easily be logged with wind-gages.
In sight of land, piloting is as simple as
coastwise navigation, since beacons and
landmarks are seen more distinctly from
above than from a steamer. Heavy "lea-
drift" from the wind will make steering

COUNT FERDINAND VON ZEPPELIN

ticklish in fog and night, above the clouds
and sea. Aërial lighthouses in Germany
pierce the darkness with broad vertical
beams, and there are fog-signals. Air-
harbors and wharves now display lights
and signals. Roofs are being marked with
a code of letters and figures, to identify
localities. New aëritime maps have been
prepared by an international commission,
under supervision of Lieutenant-Colonel
Moedebeck of Berlin. Air-ships "sound"
in the fog and night with a line, like
water-craft. In daylight, distance to the
"bottom" is found
by triangulation. On
Count Zeppelin's ad-
vice, the new maps
show every locality's
height above sea-
level. Lights mark
mountains and pla-
teaus, which may be
as dangerous to the
air navigator as cliffs
and shoals to the sea-
man. When Count
Zeppelin circumnav-
igated the Alps, on
his first two hun-
dred-mile voyage
through Switzerland,
it was as hazardous
as the voyage of a
low-powered steamer
hugging a rocky
shore in a strong
current. Rules of the
aërial road are fast
resembling those of
the sea. Red and green, and bow and
stern lights are used; yellow lights indicate top and bottom. Aëroplanes will
carry special lights, faster craft yielding
the right of way to slower ones. Fog-
sirens must sound while ships are steering
inside the clouds, with an understanding
by wireless as to which shall have right of
way.

PUTTING THE WINDS TO WORK

GERMANY has stopped fighting the winds
and means to put them to work. Mar-
shaling their forces means faster and
cheaper traffic. In that country aëronautics and meteorology have worked together, with the result that Germany has
not only more and better air-ships, but the

From a photograph by Felicetti

THE MOST RECENT ITALIAN MILITARY DIRIGIBLE
The distinctive feature of this balloon is the extensive use that has been made of aëroplane surfaces.

greatest number of aërological stations. Dr. Richard Assmann, head of the chief aërological station at Lindenberg, recently finished mapping the lower winds up to a mile, for air-ship navigation. It is the pilot's first working chart. These maps divide Germany into groups of "wind-weak" and "wind-strong" districts, with the average speed of each, and show the frequency and usual paths of their storms. All central Germany is "wind-weak." Most of the storms blow in the north and west near the sea. The coasts therefore form a "wind-strong" region. The frequency and strength of the wind in all directions, is shown at the rays of many small compass-dials, which the pilot reads at a glance.

AIR-HARBORS AND WIND-RIVERS

AIR-PILOTS now take their craft safely into port. It has been found that the winds of localities are shaped by hills and valleys, and resemble the marine currents, of harbors and bays. Air-ships come into Cassel on the south wind, the year round, though westerly winds prevail all over Germany. In making Strassburg harbor on the upper Rhine, the air-ships always use the north and south currents that follow the river valley. The Alps about Friedrichshafen, the Zeppelins' homeport, form a V pocket of northwest and northeast currents along the range; the air-ships enter through the middle of the V. Important air-harbors are established in naturally sheltered places, like Frankfort-on-the-Main, where regular southwest winds blow along the river plains, parallel with the Taunus Mountains, shutting off all air currents from the northwest. All air-harbors are similarly charted. The new air-ship lines have been surveyed along these natural wind-rivers all over the empire. In the winds below a mile, ships navigate more smoothly at night, because there the aërial ocean is calmer than during the day; its temperature being more even, the winds are steadier in speed and direction. Landings at the air-harbors are easiest at night. Pilots know the wind is strongest along the ground in the afternoon and weakest in the early morning until an hour or so before sunrise. During the day air-ships ascend to the higher levels. The pilot's calculations include a semi-daily tide in the lower air up to two miles, the currents swinging slightly toward the north in the afternoon and early evening; and slightly to the south from about midnight until sunrise; at the same time varying in strength. A navigating system based on such definite understanding of air currents, explains the confidence with which more than $4,000,000 of German capital has been invested in Zeppelin airships, alone.

RIVALS OF THE ZEPPELIN SHIPS

COUNT ZEPPELIN, who proved that airships have a practical future, is no longer undisputed "king of the air." His rivals have taken his pattern, and improved it until soon air-ships will be able to keep afloat for many days and in that case to cross oceans. A type of this modern ship is the first Schuette leviathan of wood and steel bracing, now nearly finished at Mannheim. It is expected to lift its twenty-four and one fifth tons one and a quarter miles, because its beam is sixty feet as compared with the forty-four feet of the Zeppelin II. This giant is four hundred and thirty-six feet long, about the length of the Zeppelin II. The car is one hundred and thirty-one feet long, with a cabin to accommodate thirty passengers. The new ship displaces nineteen thousand cubic meters, as against fifteen thousand in the Zeppelin III. It is expected to carry a cargo of five to six tons supported by ten spherical sustaining chambers, and eight ring-shape reservoir chambers connected by a secret apparatus. These eight reservoirs automatically receive all expanding gas that escapes from the sustaining chambers, thus conserving the entire supporting power. Four motors of combined five hundred and forty horse-power will drive the propellers. . Expert opinion predicts a speed of thirty-seven to forty-three miles an hour, three miles faster than the Gross

III, at this writing the fastest air craft in the world. The whole enterprise is backed by Mr. Lanz, a rich manufacturer, who is president of the German Air-navy League. A wooden-braced ship of equal equipment and size, designed by the Engineer Rettich, is well under way.

Another rival of the Zeppelin, so far only projected, has been designed by the Engineers Radinger and Wagner, and is intended to be an advance in endurance. It should float for fifty days without replenishing gas. It is planned to have a rigid hull of hollow paper tubes and steel bracing and to be thirty per cent. lighter than a Zeppelin built of aluminium, in any equal size. Drum-shape compartments are to hold the sustaining hydrogen, none of which is to be lost through expansion by the sun, as any surplus will be compressed by automatic pumps into the hollow tubes. Having six thousand meters less displacement than the Zeppelin III, it will carry a reserve of seven hundred cubic meters of gas. Thirty-two per cent. of its weight-carrying capacity will be given up to passengers, fuel, and baggage. Engines of two hundred and forty-two combined horse-power are expected to develop a speed of forty to fifty miles an hour. Larger craft of the same type would, of course, carry much heavier cargoes and have higher speed. This type of ship, soon to be placed in the construction cradle, is expected to cross the ocean easily with fifteen passengers.

NEW ZEPPELINS

THE Zeppelin IV, to be finished in May of this year, will displace twenty thousand cubic meters. One engine in the front, and two in the rear car will have, combined, three hundred and sixty horse-power. Two will drive the ship at an estimated speed of thirty-seven miles an hour. The cabin, amidships, will accommodate twenty passengers. This is the last Zeppelin of aluminium frame. The Zeppelin V, placed in the cradle during the winter, will be finished in June. It will have twenty-five thousand cubic meters (within five thousand of the size predicted by the writers a year ago). This craft is expected to carry thirty passengers. Three motors of combined four hundred and twenty horse-power are built to drive the ship forty

From a photograph

ZEPPELIN IV

The air-ship is shown rising from Lake Constance after scooping water ballast.
This ship was destroyed by lightning in 1907.

miles an hour. The hull is to be of "elektron," a new metal alloy, forty per cent. lighter than aluminium, and as strong. A Zeppelin of aluminium weighs twelve to fourteen tons without its cargo; of elektron seven to nine tons, thereby saving in its own weight four to five tons for useful load. This means that it will be able to carry at two to three miles high (as will the Schuette, Rettich, and Radinger-Wagner types), the same load that the Zeppelin III can carry only up to one mile. The latter ship would have to drop its twenty-eight passengers and some fuel to reach a height of two miles. Elektron is wrought like steel and the ship built of it has spiral fittings and bolts, with clean-cut threads, light as papier-mâché. It will be Jules Verne's dream of the air-ship come true.

AIR-SHIPS WITH WINGS

THE German air-ship has developed into a flying-machine with wonderful power of ascent. In 1909 it was discovered that the horizontal rudders,—which are flat planes fore and aft on the hull, for steering up and down,—act like aëroplanes and help lift the ship. Auxiliary motors were then mounted to assist this lifting force. The old Zeppelin I, driven thirty-one miles an hour, with rudders set at an upward angle of fifteen degrees, lifted one and a quarter tons, nearly half its cargo.

That weight is taken off the gas. The planes of the new ships should easily lift over two tons, and thus its high speed, on the principle of the aëroplane, assists in supporting an air-ship. Driven forty miles an hour it can neither rise or fall; driven seventy miles, it would still fly if inflated with ordinary air. It has been realized that slightly larger and better curved planes will support much more weight than flat planes; so it is probable that within two years, these huge craft soaring on aërocurves will lift much greater weights with the same engines. Also, their wings may be made to rival the birds in soaring on ascending air currents. Starting with gas-chambers full to give the greatest buoyancy, and with engines running at top-speed, the air-ship would be driven swiftly, to a height of two or three miles, where it could travel with chambers one third empty at a speed that would keep the ship afloat. At top-levels, it is possible for the air-ship to be driven seventy miles an hour through the thinner air. Great flights by some birds of passage are not easy to explain even by the winds. Carter, a Colorado naturalist, killed an English heron. He explained this foreign bird's presence by suggesting that it had come with a flock of travelers. Many passage-birds seem to fly very high, which would explain why they are seldom seen. Science has recently shown that mechanical flight is perfectly feasible at vast heights, where the machine, finding thirty per cent. less support, gains thirty per cent. in speed, with little more energy than at sea-level. For the same reason, birds would fly at these altitudes. G. Gätke, a German naturalist, says they fly four miles a minute two miles high over the island of Heligoland, in their spring travel from the continent to England.

THE EVOLUTION OF AIR-SHIPS

THE evolution of air-ships, now taking place, confirms the writers' statements, a year ago, in an article called "The Aërial Battleship." When Count Zeppelin began his experiments, it was thought necessary to have a house for his air-ship, and that house to float on water, to avoid jarring the craft. Three years ago the German government presented to the inventor a perfect floating house on Lake Constance, costing $150,000. The government recently returned it to the builders for $15,000 as obsolete. The Count has since announced his plans for a ship nine hundred and eighty-four feet long, with one thousand horse-power, to carry three hundred passengers against any storm. It

will not be possible to house a craft of that size.

Count Zeppelin always asserted that the larger ship was the more efficient, and in fact air-ships have been built larger and larger, as have steamships, and speed has increased in proportion to size and greater engines. Major Gross, an earlier critic of size, built his last military air-ship three hundred and seven feet long, and mounted four motors; as a consequence, it makes thirty-eight miles an hour instead of twenty-eight, which was the highest speed of his first craft. Vickers Sons and Maxim are building a dirigible of the Zeppelin type for the British government, more than five hundred feet long. Four engines are expected to drive it forty-eight miles an hour.

AIR-SHIPS AS FREIGHT CARRIERS

ACCORDING to present indications immense air-ship hulls requiring no housing will be built for increased cargo; such ships should be able to compare with ocean vessels of equal size and high speed, even in stanchness. This will bring the air-ship into the freight classification for

From a photograph

ZEPPELIN III IN THE FLOATING SHED ON LAKE CONSTANCE

The stern is shown with the stability fins which carry the vertical rudders. This shed built by Count Zeppelin was supplanted by the shed built by the German government at a cost of $150,000.

From a photograph

GROSS III, THE FASTEST AIR-SHIP SO FAR CONSTRUCTED

The ship is shown at the air-harbors in Bitterfeld, about fifty miles southwest of Berlin.

the carrying of urgent mail and certain articles of commerce. Such freight might be carried in an air-line at sixty miles an hour, and more, by a man-made cloud, which is not inconceivable when we consider that the Wetzel air-ship, now projected in Germany, is being planned to transport thirty-seven tons of passengers. Immense supplies of gas would be required; but that cost would be negligible, owing to the saving of leakage through the burning of hydrogen as fuel, which offsets the weight lost by consumption of gasolene. Such an air-ship's earning capacity might be substantially greater than that of a ship on the water. It would not require shelter, being heavy enough in a storm to lie on the ground with the inertia of a log. The inertness of an air-ship, half a mile long, is considerably greater than its bulk; this is a long misunderstood feature of the craft that has caused a vast waste of money. A mammoth air-ship can be operated by the same crew as a small one, as easily as one chauffeur handles a racing car of any size. It has been demonstrated that a large air-ship can go farther and faster than a small one, and the shorter trip would mean relatively less fuel, and smaller loss of gas.

EXPENSE OF AN ATLANTIC AIR-VOYAGE

THE expense of air-shipping steadily decreases with experience. In operating a transoceanic service, one week would undoubtedly be allotted to each of forty-eight annual voyages. The crossing would take two to three days. Engines and ships would be overhauled after each trip. Air-ships of twenty thousand cubic meters displacement would need to be refilled twice a month. A new process for producing hydrogen, makes the inflating of ships the size of the Zeppelin IV cost $526, as compared with $3091 a year ago. Gas drawn from the chambers and burned in the motors, to compensate for weight lost by the consumption of gasolene, would cost $155, leaving $198 for the gasolene consumed. Docking, overhauling, and repairing between trips would not exceed $250. An air-ship costs $144,600; it will last four years if regularly overhauled; a credit of $300 for each trip would represent material that could be taken from an obsolete ship to refurnish a new one. A captain now receives $3856 a year; two helmsmen, each $2410; and three engineers, each $1446. This personnel would need to earn $301 each trip, but by transferring the crew from incoming to outgoing ships, $200 would be a conservative estimate for wages. Roughly the expense of each trip would be about $1203. If twenty passengers were carried at $120 each, the fare on a first-class steamship, the returns would enable the air-liner to pay a handsome dividend and lay aside a fund for better wages to more expert officers. The captain must be assisted by a navigating officer, both drawing $8000 to $10,000 a year, according to the training and service demanded of them, which includes expert skill in astronomical and meteorological calculations, and wireless telegraphy.

AIR-SHIPPING INVESTMENTS

THE extent of European investment in air-ships, air-harbors, and aërological stations is not appreciated in America. A new air-harbor at Hamburg, near the mouth of the Elbe, will be finished this year at a cost of $200,000; another at Kiel will be ready in May, and others at Dessau, Lübeck, Eisenach, and Baden-Baden, on later dates. Those at Hamburg, Lübeck, and Baden-Baden belong to the Zeppelin Navigation Company; the others to other corporations. Competition has already impelled the Zeppelin Company to build larger ships, because the local traffic it had planned to enjoy, with smaller ships, and a minor outlay of money, is being sought by two or three other companies that can operate smaller ships as cheaply and as well. The German Air-navy League has asked the municipal authorities of Glatz, Austria, to lease to the Zeppelin Company grounds for an air-harbor, as a part of the plan for local traffic between the cities of Saxony, Thuringia, Silesia, and Northern Bohemia. An Austrian company is arranging to operate short lines between Vienna and neighboring resorts. The Zeppelin Company has announced that its new ships will make regular trips from Cologne to London, in eight hours, by using the prevailing winds. The quickest connection now is by express-trains and cross-channel turbine steamers, requiring thirteen hours.

The Italian government is building air-harbors at Venice and Verona; and a new dirigible for its navy will have twelve thousand cubic meters displacement, to make possible the carrying of explosives. In Germany, the non-rigid Schuckert airship of fifteen thousand cubic meters is nearly finished.

THE AIR-SHIP OF 1915

FROM the standard of present development the air-ship of 1915 may be conceived as having a hull of rigid construction, one thousand feet long and eighty feet beam, with accommodations for one hundred and twenty-five to one hundred and fifty passengers, and a crew of forty-two men. The new air-liner will resemble a submarine, or rather a flying-fish. All its parts will be compactly built into the hull. Its underbody, eight hundred feet long, twelve feet wide, and nine feet high, will extend between the elbows fore and aft where the hull begins to curve toward its pointed bow and stern. The underbody will hold seven passenger and eight operating sections, after the fashion of a compartment sleeping-car. A continuous passageway will extend from end to end. The prow glazed with artificial mica will furnish an aërial observatory. Its interior will be a series of grill galleries, connected by steps. Here will be the "bridge," the air-liner's nerve-center, with signal radiation to all parts of the ship. A narrow gallery will reach the extreme nose, where a small exploring gun, swung on a universal-joint, can be fired toward most points in space. On its several platforms will be the navigating deck, the helm, the "wireless," the chart-room, and both meteorological and astronomical "observatories." Below the "bridge" will be a hatchway to the main passage in the forward underbody of the ship, where there is a companionway which is the ship's portal. Abaft of this will be the captain's cabin. To starboard will begin the main passage and state-rooms, with all doors opening on the passage. Next to the captain's quarters, in sequence, will be officers and engineers' state-rooms; officers' ward-room and mess; the barbershop; the first motor compartment; the toilet room; passengers' state-rooms; passengers' living quarters, a central lounging, reading, and

Drawn by W. T. Benda.   Half-tone plate engraved by Robert Varley

A FORECAST OF THE AIR-SHIP OF 1915—OVERTAKING AN ATLANTIC
LINER IN THE ENGLISH CHANNEL

dining saloon, the width of the ship. The saloons, glazed with openings of artificial mica, can be transformed into open deck-space, by sliding side-ports. At the stern will be the steward's quarters, where all cooking will be by electricity. Meals will be served in each saloon, the pantry service being operated by escalator, passing through the "hold," which will be attached to the air-ship's entire underbody. Table service will be delivered through a trap in the saloon floor. Telephone and electric annunciators will connect each section with the steward's quarters. As only twenty-five passengers will be accommodated in each section, but one steward will be required there. All bed covering will be of the lightest weights, because elektron heaters carrying the hot exhaust of the motors will keep the temperature automatically even, while flying at frigid altitudes. When flying low in the tropics, the air-ship may be perfectly cooled by ventilation. Only hand-baggage will be permitted for the quick passage, other "baggage" going by steamer or express air-ship.

The sides of the "hold," or tunnel, five feet high and eight feet wide will be lined with continuous tanking, containing gasolene fuel, to be forced upward into the engine-rooms, as needed. The outside of the "hold" will serve as the air-ship's rounded keel, and will enable the craft to float on water; elastic buffers for landing will be fixed under each engine section. The eight motor compartments will each be equipped with one two hundred-horse-power motor, transmitting energy by short steel belts, in flattened tubes, to one propeller on the same side of the hull, and to auxiliary engines operating pumps that will control the gas-chambers, withdrawing expanding gas, and condensing it into the air-ship's tubular frame. They will also drive powerful fans, for ventilating the air-spaces of the hull, and the living quarters. The electric

PLAN OF THE UNDERBODY OF AN AIR-SHIP OF THE TYPE OF THE PROPOSED ZEPPELIN VI

Saloons indicated by the oblong tables alternate with the passenger sections in the centers of which are the engine-rooms.

power-plants, for lighting, cooking, and operating the escalator, will be in the engine compartments.[1]

The top of the hull, now the Zeppelin's observatory, will become a long "hurricane deck" of thin, light planking, with side-rails. Here will be kept "service" implements; two slender masts, carrying the "wireless" antennæ and the yellow "top-lights"; observatories for cloud-triangulation and taking the altitude of stars; searchlights, kite-winch and the air-ship's "boats," two small swift aëroplane "scouts,"—one fore, the other aft, with ample space for launching and alighting. The deck will be reached by small, winding openwork stairs through the hull. The hull will be divided into twenty gas-tight compartments, for sustaining the air-ship in space. Along the port and starboard sides, five sets of curved aëroplane surfaces will help to lift and support the air-ship, or steer it up and down. They will be "stepped," to avoid interference. Between them will be eight propellers, four on each side, at alternating levels along the hull.

It is believed that within five years such an air-liner will be capable of traveling seventy-five miles an hour, ordinarily, and often one hundred and twenty miles, in the upper levels. Two miles above the equator a planetary current encircles the globe at tremendous speed. The ashes of the eruption of Krakatoa were carried in this belt, around the world, in fourteen days. In ten years an air-ship driven fifty miles an hour, may perchance make that trip in eight days, flying at a speed of one hundred and twenty miles an hour or three thousand miles a day. Is it all a dream? Ten years ago a prophecy of the present achievements of German air navigators would have been received with incredulity.

[1] Since this article was prepared the writers have learned from private sources, that the airship for the British government, now being built in Paris, will be equipped with an electric lighting plant.

26.
The Sport of Flying
(1909)

THE
OUTING
MAGAZINE

MAY, 1909

THE SPORT OF FLYING

BY MAXIMILIAN FOSTER

O VER in Cairo—Cairo, Egypt; not the one in Illinois—they tell you of an American advertising agent who was taken out in the back lots of GIZEH to have a look at the sights.

"Quite a job of masonry, ain't it now?" he remarked feelingly, when they led him up to the Sphinx. "What's it for?"

The fact that no one knew rather astonished him.

"Hmph!—and from the look of it, too, seems to have been here quite a spell."

"Oh, yes." They brightened up indulgently, and to' 'm it had stood there for more than 5,000 years.

"As long as that!—and you don't know what it was used for?" cried the high priest of publicity. "Ah, say now!"

Such was the fact, however, and he turned away in disdain.

"Great Scott!" he grunted fretfully. "Five thousand years in the same place, and no one knows why! Huh! Didn't advertise, I suppose!"

In a way, this is the same sort of trouble that seems to affect the flying machine. Why? Well, because for five thousand years man has been trying to flit along the highway of the air, and now that the Wrights have managed to do it, mighty few persons besides themselves seem to be at all in possession of the facts. Particularly, how they do it, and why. More particularly, what's the use of doing it anyway, now that they've gone and done it?

"You see," said Mr. Charles R. Flint, who is the financial agent of the two Dayton sky-fliers, "the Wrights are what you might call too shy and too modest. I said so once to Wilbur, and do you know what he answered?"

Mr. Flint paused long enough to chuckle.

"Wilbur said to me, 'Mr. Flint, the best talker and the worst flier among the birds is the parrot.'"

Which is one good reason, perhaps, why the world at large knows so little about the Wright flying machine.

But in a few months now—say, a year at the outside—the new flier is to be as definitely advertised in the United States and

Europe as are the motor car and the bicycle. Of course, it will take much longer to make them familiar to everyone; yet nobody should lose sight of the fact that the Age of Flight is really here—that the man bird is fledged at last, and already on the wing. If you care to join him, too, the way is open, because the Wrights' flier is now on sale. Price, from $5,000.00 to $10,000.00, depending upon style and horse-power. Deliveries immediate.

Now get it out of your head, in the first place, that flying is an exceptionally dangerous pastime. To the contrary. And, at the same time, clear your mind of the idea that the Wright flier is not suited for ordinary man. If you will ask the Wrights themselves about the future of their invention, ten chances to one, their first effort will be to deprive you of a lot of of highfalutin notions. One of them is the general impression that they are going to put the railroad out of business. They grin when you suggest things like this—or that the ocean liner is doomed. And when you inquire whether the motor car is now on the way to the scrap heap, they try hard

to look polite and interested. The truth of the matter is, that the Wrights never miss a good chance to club an idea like this over the head, hitting it a good, solid thump before the idea has even had time enough to sit up and take notice. Why? Well, that's easy, too. Because the flying machine, as they will patiently tell you, seems to lack a probable, or even a remotely plausible chance of disturbing, in the least way, the present methods of transportation. Instead, it only adds one more factor to the facility of travel; and as for its first utility, hear what the Wrights themselves have to say:

"Sport first of all. After that, its use in exploration and in war. And after war . . . Oh, well, you can guess as well as we can."

But this idea, new as it will be to the average American, has already been grasped abroad. To-day, in France, there are already nearly a hundred persons who have ridden in the air; and the number is growing constantly. In America, however, a scant dozen would fill the list—a statement that many will accept as evi-

Aërodrome "Silver Dart," in position for the start to fly.

Photograph by J. A. D. McCurdy.

"Red Wing," ready for trial.

dence of the American's more conservative regard for his neck. But if you'll stop to think, you'll see this can't be true; for the most daring, and the fastest and best drivers of motor cars are from the United States. Necks have nothing to do with the case. It's because, over on this side of the ocean, we haven't had the chance.

IS FLYING AS DANGEROUS AS MOTORING?

Of course, there is a certain element of danger in flying, as there is in every sport. But granting that, it is still a question in the minds of those who have tried both flying and motoring, whether the aërodrome, at its average gait of thirty-eight miles an hour, is not a safer vehicle than the automobile when it goes tearing up a road at the same rate of speed. And as between riding in an aërodrome and in a Vanderbilt cup race, ask any one who has tried which he believes to be the safer. Farman, who has given up cup racing to go into aviation, smiles when you put the question, and promptly chooses the flying machine. Furthermore, I'm told you couldn't get the Wrights into a racing auto unless you dragged them into it, and then sat on them. Because, as the two respect-

fully and earnestly submit, they have an extremely anxious regard for both life and limb.

One of the usual questions put to Orville Wright, at the Fort Myer tests, was whether flying is hard to learn.

"That depends," he answered always. "Some persons learn to run a motor car without any trouble at all. It takes others longer. Some never learn."

Pinning him to the fact, I asked whether this was the case with the aërodrome.

"It seems so," he answered, after a moment's cautious reflection.

But this question, asked by so many in a spirit of idle curiosity, is of first importance to any one considering flying as a sport. If you are a motorist, the flying machine with its engine, levers, rudders and supporting surfaces, will be more or less easy to understand—much easier, in fact, than the involved mechanism of a motor car. But in running your auto, the road is in plain sight before you, its hills and vales and turnings clearly indicated and every obstruction visible before you come to it. Furthermore, you can nearly always tell at a glance where your auto is likely to skid or bore or crimp its forward wheels. In the air, however, sight will aid

Photograph by A. Radclyffe Dugmore.

Orville Wright at Fort Myer, Va.

you very little. It is all a matter of sensation—of *feel*. Still further, the road through the air is a highway among hills and hollows, a path filled with innumerable grades and pitches, cliffs, gulfs and precipices, all invisible and all in a state of chaotic, violent unrest. You must keep this in mind if you wish to fly. In motoring, you see your road; in flying, you know it only by the feel.

THE SIMPLE CONSTRUCTION OF THE FLYING MACHINE

As for the machine itself, there is very little in it that is not reduced to the utmost simplicity. In fact, one is astonished to see how really simple it is—astounded that so plain and uninvolved a mechanism should have solved a problem that has vexed the world for ages.

One looks hard to find in it the fearful and the mystifying, and one finds it isn't there. Here, if you please, are two cloth-covered surfaces, one above the other, each slightly concave, and, in dimension, six and one-half feet fore and aft and forty feet from tip to tip. Out in front—say, about where a wild goose would hold its head—there are two horizontal planes, also one above the other, and sixteen feet in width and two and one-half feet fore and aft. This is the forward rudder, which steers the machine up and down and also serves to hold it from pitching. Astern, about where the tail of the wild goose would be, are two six-foot, parallel planes set upright—this, the rudder that turns the flier from side to side, and, at the same time, which helps to keep the aërodrome on an even keel. A system of light wooden stanchions and steel piano wires truss the body together, and under all is a wooden skid—a sledge with narrow runner on which the aërodrome rests when it alights.

On the lower wing, a little to the right of midships, stands the engine, a four-cylinder, gasoline motor of the usual type. By a chain and sprocket gearing, it drives the two propellers, which revolve astern in opposite directions. Then there are the two seats set amidships on the forward edge of the lower wing; and, in front of them, the three levers that operate the aërodrome in its flight. The one on the left works the forward rudder; the two on the right, set side by side, so that they may be grasped together in one hand, serve a double purpose—to steer from side to side and to maintain equilibrium. All very simple—yes.

TO FLY YOU MUST KNOW THE CHARACTER OF THE AIR

But without a clear knowledge of the air and the air's unruly character, the Wrights had never succeeded in flying. And every man that wishes to fly must learn about it, too.

Bluntly speaking, the average person knows nothing whatever about the atmosphere. Ordinarily, he regards the air as like so much water—as a great deal lighter, of course, but not differing in other respects. If it be still air, it seems to him to be like unto a stagnant pool; if the wind blows, it takes on the semblance of a flowing river. And, in each case, he is wrong. In the first place, the air is never still. In the second place, the only condition in which water draws near to the air's wild turbulence is when the river flows like a Niagara that has burst from between its banks. Even then, the water in its unrest, would fall far short of the atmosphere's riotous inconstancy. For there are always currents of heated vapor flowing upward, and currents of colder vapor flowing downward; and through this commotion, all driven onward in the tossing of the wind, whirlwinds go corkscrewing up and down and to and fro, spinning like tops, or rolling like barrels or scaling at every angle like a boomerang. Then too, the wind, moving forward, advances in huge waves like the billows of a storm-tossed sea; only there is a difference from the troubled ocean or from the leaping, whirling maelstrom in that the air never sticks to one given line or plane of direction. If, by chance, it did, man would have learned long ago to fly. But until Langley, Chanute, Pilcher, Lilienthal and then the Wrights themselves began the study of the air, the world was as far from solving the puzzle of flight as it was in the days of Darius Green.

Now in venturing upon this turmoil, two things must be provided for—balance and support. A plane surface resting inertly on the air, maintains three points in one—

the center of gravity, the center of area and the center of pressure. But if you tilt up the front edge and move the plane forward, the center of pressure—which is also the center of support—instantly leaps away from the center of gravity and of area. At every change in the angle of the plane, the pressure center changes, too. Therefore, when it gets far enough away from the center of gravity, the plane— whether it be a card, or a square of wood, or an aëroplane—promptly upsets. So

is kept from wandering fore and aft by the forward rudder—a device, by the way, which the French have borrowed with or without credit to the Wrights—usually without, it may be said.

In operation, it works like this: Say that the center of pressure starts to slide aft, which would tend to make the machine dive headlong like a kite. To correct this, the rudder is bent to throw up the flier's nose in the air; it responds instantly, and, regaining the normal, drags back the cen-

Photograph by J. A. D. McCurdy.

Aërodrome "June Bug" ready for flight.

what the Wrights have done is to build a machine in which the pressure center—the point of lift and support—is kept constantly near the center of gravity.

It's easy enough to build a machine that will rise in the air, for every plane surface or a surface with flat curves will do that if there's enough power behind it. But once in the air, unless the travel of the pressure center is restrained, that same vital point of support will ultimately slide off toward one edge or the other, and tumble the flier to the ground. In the Wright machine, it

ter of pressure to its proper point. Much, in fact, like the bubble in a spirit level.

KEEPING THE EQUILIBRIUM

As to the balance sideways, you need only to watch a bird floating in midair to see how the Wrights maintain their equilibrium. If you watch closely, you will note when a sudden gust tips the bird off its balance, that it twists its wing tips, presenting one to the wind at a greater angle than the other. If the wind tips the

Wright machine, the operator does precisely as the bird. He warps the two main supporting surfaces—the wings—so that the side tilting downward inclines itself to the air at a greater angle than the other wing. Instantly, that side begins to rise, and when it has reached an even keel, the wings are flattened again, and the machine glides onward.

One needs to see it only once to understand. Orville Wright showed it to countless visitors at Fort Myer, and each one seemed to catch the idea. "Watch," said

shaped themselves to face the air at a greater angle; the right-hand wing ends to face it at a lesser. Also, in this movement, the rudder turned to the right.

During a flight it works this way: Say that the machine tilts over to the right. At once, and almost instinctively, the operator feels the aërodrome career, and to correct it, pulls the two levers that control the wing tips and the rear rudder. Thereupon, the right-hand wings are warped so that they present themselves to the air at a wider angle; the left-hand wings are

"June Bug" in flight.

he, grasping the two right-hand levers that stood side by side.

He pulled the levers over, and the two supporting surfaces—the upper and lower wings—warped themselves in opposite directions, at either end. The right-hand wings twisted themselves so that their rear edges were lower than the edges in front. The left-hand wings warped so that the rear edges were higher than the forward. In the general movement, the rudder turned to the left. Then he reversed the lever, and the left-hand wing ends

warped to present themselves at a lesser angle. Naturally, the wider angle of the wings on the right tend to lift that side—as they do. But, at the same time, the wider angle presents a greater drag, tending to slow down that side of the machine, while the left-hand side, opposing no drag to air, slides on at unabated speed. If not corrected, the machine would whirl around as if on a pivot—skid, in fact, just as an auto does on slippery asphalt. And that's where the tail rudder comes in. It moves to the left, and opposes a drag to the wings on that side by steering against them. Thus, the machine's head is held straight ahead, while the right-hand wings are raising the flier to a level. And once its equilibrium is adjusted, the lever is moved forward until both wings are at the same angle. Furthermore, if you care to, you may steer the machine in a circle in the same way. Throw her up at an angle, cut your rudder lever free, and then warp your wing tips. If you do it properly, she will take the turn in a much shorter circle than if you do it with the rudder alone. It requires about seven hundred feet for the Wright flier to circle. No bird of the same size could do it in less, for, like the birds, the aërodrome turns in a circle proportionate to its size.

Simple, isn't it? Virtually only two levers to handle, no brake to bother with and nothing in the line of a clutch to keep your feet as busy as your hands. And so evenly and closely adjusted is the running of the Wright aërodrome that the operator may sometimes sit back and let the machine practically guide itself. I mean that, too. The Wrights are often able to remove their hands from the levers, and glide along like the bicyclist who leans back and lets go of the handle bars. In quiet air, of course—just as the bicyclist tries his stunt only on a smooth highway.

LEARNING TO FLY

There are two ways of learning how to fly. The first—and the more cautious—is to make your first flutter in a gliding machine—*i.e.*, a machine with smaller wings and without the engine and propellers. The Wright glider also lacks the tail rudder; and, in using it, the operator lies at full length on the floor of the lower wing instead of sitting upright. In other forms of gliding machine—notably the Lillienthal—the aviator hangs suspended, a rather perilous way of doing it, however, and only necessary in the clumsy type of gliders that depend largely on acrobatics to maintain their equilibrium.

To-day, a variety of gliding machines are offered for sale. A. M. Herring, who was an associate of both Langley and Chanute, offers a light glider at $300, f. o. b. New York; and advises the beginner not to try actual power-flight until the art of gliding

has been mastered. But the Wrights have practically discarded this means of instruction. They take the beginner into the air with them, and ride him around a while. In the machine used for instruction, there are two sets of levers—one under the control of the teacher; the other in the hands of the beginner. Thus, if the neophyte makes a mistake, the trained operator is instantly able to correct it. Count de Lambert, the first of the Wright pupils, was allowed to operate the machine alone, after an experience that was not much longer than it would take to learn how to run a motor car. He says he could have done it sooner, if Wilbur Wright had been willing to let him try it. But the Wrights are not taking any risks. They wish to make the world understand that their flier is not the dangerous machine many persons think it to be.

In a gliding machine of the proper type and properly handled, you will find a wide range of sport with a minimum of danger. But don't go at it in the same haphazard way that so many persons tackle the bicycle or even the motor car. Because, if you do, you are likely to be astonished at the surprising evolution a gliding machine will perform in the hands of the untutored. Herring told me of a case in point.

"Doctor Chanute and I," said he, laughing, "built a glider which worked to perfection. After I had tried it out, Doctor Chanute's son said he'd like to try it, too. So climbing to the top of a sand dune, he lifted up the glider, waited for a gust and then started running. Instantly, the machine sprang into the air and climbed upward; and there, before we knew it— there was young Chanute away up overhead—as high as a housetop, if you please —with his legs still working furiously. It had happened so quickly, that, in his mind, he was still running."

I asked Mr. Herring what followed then.

"Oh, nothing. The machine was perfectly balanced, and when the gust died away, it settled softly and safely to the ground."

Then he sighed regretfully. "If he'd only thought to tilt the machine a little downward, he'd have made a record-breaking glide."

But there is no reason—after the art has

The Wright flier in action.

Photograph by A. Radclyffe Dugmore.

Flying when the air is still.

been explained and then shown to the beginner—why any one should not learn how to glide. The best ground to begin on is the seashore—a sweep of sand with a dune to start from. But any plain will do, providing there is a slope high enough for launching purposes. One with a drop of about one foot in six is about right. It is not too steep to run upon, and once launched, you have plenty of room to coast in.

The glider may have two hundred square feet of supporting surface—or even three hundred; for even with one of such large area, you will be astonished to find how light it becomes in a wind. Facing the breeze, you wait until a gust sweeps steadily up the slope, and then race forward directly into the wind's eye. You may run ten feet or twenty—it all depends on the power of the breeze—but presently, your feet leave the ground; you stride as if on stilts, and then you clear the sand altogether, and throw yourself into place. Shooting forward, the glider darts down the slope like a toboggan, and you are fairly launched in midair.

A glide of fifty feet is a good beginning. In time, you may learn to scoot along for a clear hundred yards. Herring claims the record with a circular flight of more than nine hundred feet, of forty-eight seconds'

duration. Theoretically, there is no reason why gliding flights may not be prolonged indefinitely—flights like those of such birds as the condor, eagle, vulture and buzzard which scale along for hours without the movement of a wing. The Wrights say it is merely a matter of practice. "Yes," they tell you, "whether it be a rising current of air or something else that sustains these birds, it is just as well able to sustain a flying machine, if man once learns the art of utilizing it."

You can readily understand this, if you've ever tried a glider. There are moments, during the toboggan-like shoot of the machine, when you actually feel it rise. It does, in fact, rise, because it has been lifted by the wind glancing off the sloping face of the hill. Beginners feel an instant inclination to hold down their machine; but a practiced operator allows it to keep on rising, and then when it has reached the highest point, tilts it forward and goes coasting downward again.

Another thing. It is not necessary, either in gliding or in power-flight, to go ticklishly high in the air. In a power machine, if you try it over a level plain, you can fly just as well ten feet off the ground, as you can a hundred feet up. In a glider, if your hill has drop enough, you can skim along a few feet over the surface, flying for great distances directly parallel to the earth. In machines like the Wrights—ones that require no movement of the operator's body to balance and to steer—it is an extremely simple matter, because the machine is guided as easily and definitely as a boat.

But if your ambition is to essay at the beginning actual power flight, the Wrights will accommodate you. At the moment, they have five fully equipped machines for sale in France; and in addition, the Lazard Weiller Company, which has bought the French rights, is making fifty more. And as soon as the United States Government tests have been completed, the Wrights will begin manufacturing at Dayton. Full instruction in the art of flying goes with each machine.

To soar in a Wright flier is an experience that seems to have no parallel. One needs only to see it floating by overhead to understand the enthusiasm of those who have ridden in it. Or in any type of flying machine that really manages to fly. The first two men I asked about it were J. A. D. McCurdy and F. W. Baldwin, of Hammondsport, N. Y., whose work in the Aëronautic Experiment Association has put them into the front rank of aviation. They hit the nail on the head, when I asked them what flying felt like.

"You have a sense of exhilaration," said Mr. McCurdy, "a feeling of freedom and delight you can get in no other way."

"Of bounding along without jar or vibration," added Mr. Baldwin.

In launching the Wright aërodrome, a pylon—or tower—and a hundred foot monorail are used. Under certain conditions of wind, however, Wilbur Wright has been able to rise directly from the ground, and, in all probability, the launching way will shortly be abandoned. But assume now, that the flier is to be launched by the present method.

Out in the open, usually on a gentle slope, stands the tower with the single rail stretching away from it. A small truck, with its two wheels set in tandem, is placed on the upper end of the track, and on this the aërodrome is straddled. Then a half ton weight is hauled by a pulley-block to the apex of the tower; and the rope that holds it is led down to the ground and run through a second pulley.

This is fastened to a wire that stretches out to the end of the monorail, where it turns on a third pulley and is brought back to the machine. Thus, when the weight is dropped, the flier is hauled forward along the rail at a speed fast enough to lift it. Once in the air, its propellers and the broad wings do the rest.

Now turn and watch them crank the engine; it will interest the auto man as much as anything else about the machine. Because the motor is cranked by turning the two propellers, and again, because it lacks a carburetter. Instead of that, the gasoline feeds into a tube set beside the cylinder heads, and is heated by the exhaust from the first and fourth cylinders, and instantly vaporized. To charge the cylinders for the first one or two explosions, a rag soaked in gasoline is held over the air intake. A quarter turn of the propellers sucks in the charge; another quarter turn gives compression, and usually, the third quarter turn gives an explosion sufficient to start the light fly-wheel revolving. Then, with the two nine-foot double-bladed screws revolving at a speed of about four hundred and fifty turns a minute, the flier is ready to start.

You take your place in the seat placed beside the engine; the operator takes the other. Straightening the levers, Wright gives a nod, and the weight falls.

SENSATION OF FLYING

All who have had the fortune to ride in the aërodrome unite in their description of that first sensation. There is no jerk in starting, though the machine leaps forward with a powerful swoop. Then comes— with some—a brief sense of nausea, a feeling as if the blurred ground were dropping away from beneath. A slight thrust of the left hand lever lifts the flier's head; the ground drops away still faster, and then, as the machine climbs into the air, one's eyes adjust themselves to the proper focus, and the surface of the earth below seems to be ripping past at railroad speed.

By this time you have forgotten the clack of the noisy motor, the flap and whirr of the propellers, the grinding of the chain and sprocket gear that drives them. All vibration has practically ceased, and you float along with a sense of springy ease and buoyancy such as you can gain from no other means of locomotion. That you are flying fast, you know only from the roar of the wind in your ears and the slight difficulty you have in filling your lungs with air—the same sensation one gets in racing against the wind in an auto. Then comes the first turn. The machine rises to it, taking its own angle sideways, just as a motor car leans on the banked curve of a racing track. You have no sense of leaning sideways, though—no feeling that you must tilt yourself as you do when the auto turns a corner; for you sit upright, the aërodrome slanting of its own volition to the necessary angle and slanting you with it. A glass of water, set on the floor of the flier, could be carried around curve after curve, and still not lose a drop.

And there is still another thing to astonish you. In the French machines, which rely largely on the shifting of the operator's weight to maintain balance, one dare not move in his seat. In the Wright aërodrome, however, you may lean forward or lean back, or from one side to the other. As a matter of fact, it is said that a two hundred-pound man might sit far out on one of the wings, and yet not capsize the machine. Because the balance of the Wright flier, as you have been told, depends not upon the agility of the operator to move from side to side, but is controlled by warping the wing ends. The French couldn't borrow that idea, because the Wrights had it patented before the Frenchmen heard about it.

If you fly diagonally into the wind, look down and note from the ground what happens. You are sliding sideways at a terrific speed. The machine does not alter its course; its head is held without change in the same direction, but still there is that startling drift. Watch a bird flying across the wind, and you will see this duplicated. Its head points in the direction it wishes to go, but in a stiff breeze, it will drift nearly as fast sideways as its speed in forging ahead. A boat without keel or centerboard, in tacking into the wind, does the same thing, but in a degree much less marked.

But when this happens, don't do what one of the Wrights' assistants did, the first time he was taken up. Happening to look down at the moment the aërodrome was slanting across the wind, he gave a wild yell, and leaped up with his arms about a stanchion. He thought the world was sliding out from under him. But he hadn't learned much about flying then, as another story about him shows.

"Say," he observed, when the first machine built was shown to him; "all you got to do is to put feathers on that to make it light enough to fly."

Once in the air, you will be astonished at the ease with which the machine is operated. No strength is required, nor any great degree of haste. When the machine begins to tip, it tips slowly enough to allow the operator time to figure out how we must correct it. A slight movement suffices, a thrust of the lever through an arc of a few inches at the most. You know by experience what little effort is required to steer a bicycle—or, carrying it further, how a motor car responds to the slightest turn of the steering wheel. In the aërodrome, just as light a touch —if not a lighter one —is all that is required, a touch about as light as that which swerves a bicycle from one side of the road to the other. There is no strain against your hand; the machine answers instantly.

Once you are in flight, the senses of

Photo. by Dugmore.
Going it easy.

Aërodrome "White Wing," a highly successful type.

feeling becomes developed to an unusual degree. You feel at once the least deviation from an even keel, the fore and aft pitching, the tilting to one side or another. Furthermore, when the machine butts into an aircliff you know it, as you know when it drops off into one of those gulfs lying between rising hills of the atmosphere. In running into a massed up bank of air, your flier slows down; when you strike a sharp declivity, 'it leaps ahead like a toboggan on a heavy pitch. Then you feel the flier lift as it meets an upward shoot, each one of these sensations as clearly defined as if you really *saw* the road on which you travel. Not that the machine bounds and bumps and staggers when it reaches these thank-you-marms of the air, because every movement of the aërodrome is springy and modulated—as buoyant as if the flier were a bird indeed.

And as to the safety of it all, reflect on what the Wrights have said and proved in their operation of the aërodrome. The accident at Fort Myer has nothing to do with the case. A defect in construction, combined with the fact that it happened while the machine had no chance to alight in the open, caused the tragedy—one that

is not likely to occur again to the Wrights. Assume now that the engine does stop. The uninformed believe that in such a case the machine will tip over and hurl itself to the ground. To the contrary. A short time ago, while Wilbur Wright was flying at Le Mans with Capt. de Girardville, the propeller chain broke—an accident somewhat like the one at Fort Myer. Shutting off his engine, Wright merely headed for the ground, and came drifting downward as lightly as a bird. A few days before this, he had given another demonstration. Stopping his motor at a much greater height, he began describing spirals in mid-air, alighting at the end so gently that the machine scarcely disturbed the dust.

In landing under ordinary conditions, it is almost impossible to tell when you first touch the ground. When it strikes, the flier may slide along on its runners fifty or a hundred feet, but unless you have thrown it down at too abrupt an angle, there is an entire absence of jar. Sometimes, you are not even aware the machine has landed until it comes to a halt. But go try it yourself; it is well worth the while.

And take this from those that know. Flying is the coming sport.

27.
Western Men
Who Would Fly
(1910)

Western Men Who Would Fly

By Pitt P. Hand

THE great outdoors of the country is destined to be the source of the most widespread experimentation in air-travel as well as the favorite exhibition ground of the successful aviator.

Western America to-day, without having as yet• produced a single air-ship of world-famous success, probably could enroll a greater percentage of air-travel experimenters than the eastern or southern states or the nations of Europe.

The advanced stage of the new passion in the public mind is shown by the recent offer of a prize of one hundred dollars to the schoolboy or girl who constructs the best model of a flying-machine by the Pacific Aero Club of San Francisco. This offer already has inspired hundreds of schoolboys who are past masters in the art of kite-flying to spend their hours seeking to conjure up a box-kite that will prove the ideal type of a heavier-than-air sky-car. This 'movement to encourage even the schoolboys to delve into air-ship invention has received the general approval of educators, and flying is now a part of the Western curriculum.

At a recent competition in composition in the Fremont Grammar School of San Francisco, the two medal winners, Frank Dowsett and Irwin Meyers, each fourteen years old, took "Aviation" as the subject of their successful essays and betrayed a thorough study and remarkable understanding of the air-travel problem.

Long before Bleriot sprang to world-fame by his epoch-making feat of flying over the English channel, two young Westerners were constructing a machine which, it is now discovered, is almost a prototype of the French wizard's monoplane. These two inventors are John W. Hudson and Clifton O'Brien, of San Francisco, who now have a perfected monoplane with which they confidently expect to surpass the feats of Bleriot. Their machine, differs from Bleriot's chiefly in that it is equipped with a revolving engine. The engine has seven cylinders and its revolutions acts as a gyroscope, doing away with the necessity of a flywheel and acting as a balance.

When the great international aerial tourney riveted the attention of an astonished world upon Bethany Field, at Rheims, France, last August, and in one week brought aviation from the status of a hazy dream to that of a splendid living reality in the public mind—it gave a tremendous impetus to experimentation already under way throughout the West. The great Los Angeles meet was a still greater stimulus to Western inventiveness.

Pioneer Biplane Inventor

San Francisco has a pioneer air-ship inventor in the person of Sylvester M. Williams, a retired photographer sixty years old, residing at 816 Oak street. Mr. Williams is one of the earliest, if not the very first, of all experimenters in the field of heavier-than-air flying-machines or aeroplanes, lifted without the sustaining force of any gas bags. He has worked upon the problem since boyhood, and during forty years of active experimentation has made and discarded more than twenty distinctive ships and models. Now he has perfected a biplane, for which, after many tests, he makes claims that are sensational. The Williams machine as now perfected, is declared to be an actual commercial utility. The inventor declares that in it he will be able to fly from San Francisco to New York, to pass safely through any kind of weather, any storm or atmospheric condition, and to carry fifteen passengers or their equivalent in weight.

"The Wright brothers, Curtiss, Latham, Farman, Bleriot and the rest are to-day just where I was years and years ago," declares Mr. Williams. "I determined to refrain from producing publicly any aeroplane that was a plaything or dangerous and not perfect for safe public travel and commercial use. Now I am ready and have a biplane-aeroplane that will mark the longest forward stride yet made in aerial navigation, and will prove a world-wide sensation."

Mr. Williams has won honor in other fields of invention. He is the inventor of a flashlight photographing device, which was awarded first prize in competition with improved methods at the exposition in Chicago. Also he is the inventor of the retouching method and the enameling process now in general use in photography everywhere. These inventions have yielded him a comfortable fortune.

PACIFIC AERO CLUB'S MACHINES

If one-half of the air-craft now in course of construction are successful in mastering the law of gravitation, the West will be able to send a formidable and novel fleet of flying devices and a horde of sky-pilots to the next aerial tourney to compete with the wizards of the East and of Europe The Pacific Aero Club, a new organization embracing devotees only of San Francisco and environs, already enrolls over fifty heavier-than-air machines.

One San Francisco lad, Cleve T. Shaffer, of the Potrero district, has perfected a soaring machine that he is now manufacturing for the market. He has the first air-ship factory in the West and is advertising for business. The Shaffer glider is marketed as a pleasure device. The pastime of scudding over fields at lightning speed is recommended as entirely safe and most exhilarating. Shaffer is twenty years old.

While building his gliders for the trade Shaffer, in a shop established in the rear of his home at 302 Holyoke street, is fitting an enlarged glider with a power motor which he declares will make of it a biplane-aeroplane superior to those of the Wrights, Bleriot, Curtiss, Latham, Paulhan, and the other aviators already famous.

Shaffer is secretary of the Pacific Aero Club, the lively little organization of air-travel zealots which has sprung from the widespread interest in the new field of experimentation in San Francisco. The story of Shaffer's efforts to solve the aviation problem is inspiring. Though a mere boy, he is a "pioneer" in aerial experimentation. Without funds and without any suggestion, support or encouragement from older persons, Shaffer as a boy of fifteen years, at a time when aviation was a subject engaging the attention of only a handful of men in the entire world, began persistent and systematic experiments. The lad became the laughingstock of his home district in the Potrero hills. He was looked upon as a freak, a child with something wrong in his make-up—because of his unquenchable mania for air-travel experiments.

FLIES LITTLE SISTER

Now he is considered a prodigy, and is honored with the secretary-ship of the organization of all the most successful local experimenters. Vindication has come to Shaffer fully, for the contagion of the "air-ship idea" has spread to such an extent that his next-door neighbor, Alfred Biniartz, who for years was constant in his ridicule of the boy, has contracted the passion, constructed a model, and to-day is a confirmed aerial experimenter.

Shaffer began as a little boy by building box-kites, which embody the primal principle of all aeroplanes, biplanes and monoplanes. He built and flew box-kites of varied sizes and patterns by the score, studying their antics in the strong winds that sweep from the ocean at all times of the year. In conjunction with his kite tests he made a study from life of the sea-gulls—the most perfect and graceful soaring birds known. From observations of the graceful gulls, he fashioned wings and planes upon his best box-kites and watched their

The biplane glider built by Alfred Biniartz of San Francisco

the field at top speed with the towline. As the machine dived downward into the air the boy pulled harder and ran faster and faster. It dipped and plunged, but in the face of the stiff sea-breeze, with its little human freight, it mounted upward, steady and true, and finally soared.

It was Shaffer's greatest kite. Here he had embodied all the merits, all the tried princi-ples, all the origi-nal ideas develop-ed in the making and flying of a hundred kites dur-ing two years of unflagging toil. The boy sailed his

effect upon the flights. It was original experimentation with Shaffer, for in those days there existed no publications upon aero-nautics, and he had no advantage of precept or advice from the ex-perience of others.

The neighborhood was startled one day by Shaffer lugging from his shed to the hilltop the most gigantic and grotesque box-kite they had ever seen. It was a framework of bamboo, strongly wired, with stout cloth of window-shades forming the covering of the planes and wings. With Shaffer trudged his little sister — the children silently and determinedly clamber-ing to the top of the loftiest hill which was surrounded by grassy fields. Little Miss Shaffer mounted the lower bars of the frame after it had been perched at the edge of a sharp declivity, and the lad stood at the bottom holding a stout rope attached to the front of the kite-aeroplane.

With all in readiness for this crucial experiment, Shaffer gave the rope a tre-mendous jerk, launching the machine off the precipice, and then started running across

Prof. Jos. Hidalgo, of the University of California, and Herman Bulask, student and mechanic, discussing plans for their projected aeroplane

little sister between sixty and seventy-five feet in the air—raising and lowering her at will. She was unterrified, and so was he.

Then the neighborhood awoke to Shaffer. The scoffers became interested supporters who proffered aid. The men who had laughed at him now praised and encour-aged him. After this the flying of men and boys on Shaffer's kite became a common sight in the Potrero. With a team of two or three fleet runners carrying the tow-rope against a strong wind, Shaffer went up to dizzy heights. Shaffer, meanwhile, with meager resources and primitive methods, has proceeded with the perfection of his biplane glider, until now he is able to step off the crest of the hill and soar and pirouette over the fields in marvelous fashion without any motive power whatever. Adventurous persons who have watched his flights have given him orders for similar machines which he is now constructing. Meanwhile, he is attaching to his latest and largest glider a small engine whose propulsion will take the place of the tow-rope and give him a full-fledged aeroplane. For his flights with power Shaffer is constructing a seventy-five-foot tower, to the top of which he will hoist his machine for the starts.

Youngest of Aviators

Youngest of all the San Francisco aviators who have attained some degree of success is Clyde Payne, Jr., fifteen years old, and a student in the Lowell High School. Young Payne has constructed a biplane without power attachment after the pattern of the Wright brothers' machine, performing all of the work himself in a barn back of the family residence at 1350 Jones street. The beardless aviator claims an improvement on the Wright invention, however, in the form of a balancing device designed automatically to maintain the equilibrium. The machine constructed has two canvas planes twenty feet long and three and one-half feet wide, one four feet above the other, and with power is estimated to have a lifting-power of four hundred and twenty pounds.

The lad has soared successfully in the sand-dunes beyond Golden Gate Park, and is ambitiously planning a larger machine to be driven by a powerful gasoline engine. He declares that in this he will fly over downtown San Francisco.

College Men at Work

Another young Californian whose ideas have followed closely those of the Wright brothers, although reaching his conclusions by independent and original work, is Herman Bulask, a student of the University of California at Berkeley, who is also a practical mechanic and machinist. His aeroplane will resemble the Wrights', with the same motive power, but is operated upon entirely different principles which the inventor confidently believes are superior.

Bulask has experimented in aeronautics continuously for more than three years past, and is now constructing an aeroplane which combines all the best points proved by tests with many models and experimental craft. He has had as an enthusiastic and valuable associate in his work one of the University professors, Joseph Hidalgo, instructor of languages, who now shares his confidence that they have solved aerial navigation; at least, as regards the heavier-than-air machines.

The University inventor declares that aeroplane travel is neither difficult nor dangerous, as all flights may be made along a slight elevation from earth. He expects to see his ship attain tremendous speed, however, and to fly the five hundred miles from San Francisco to Los Angeles, surmounting the high Tehachapi mountains, within the next few months.

These inventors have gone into the study of aeronautics deeply and exhaustively, and their calculations are based upon scientific principles and tests.

Few accidents, none of consequence, have marked the extended experiments in this section of aerial travel. Joseph Bettancourt, John Driver and Bertram Aber, of San Leandro met with several minor accidents in flights with a novel type of glider, but undaunted, they are now preparing to attempt a flight from the top of the hills above Lake Chabot across San Leandro to the bay at an elevation of eight hundred feet, which is the loftiest ascent attempted in machines without power in San Francisco.

Back to First Principles

Perhaps the most interesting and radical departure of all the novel contributions by Californians to the world of aeronautics—certainly the one that has attracted the most widespread attention and comment from the scientists actively engaged in the great problem of overcoming the law of gravitation—is the product of Charlemagne Sirch, a civil and electrical engineer of Los Angeles, who has perfected and marketed a number of mechanical inventions of note during the past five years.

Sirch, resolutely disregarding the dictum of most scientists, goes back to first principles and adapts methods which were used at the very beginning of any travel by human beings above the surface of the earth. The first device that ever carried men upward from the earth was a crude sack of ordinary sheeting filled with heated air and smoke from a bonfire by the two brothers Montgolfier, at Annonay, France, in 1782. One of these brothers, while the two were seated at a café table after a repast, carelessly threw a lighted match into his empty coffee-cup, then cast a partly-crumpled tissue-paper napkin on top of it. By mere chance the napkin had been formed into a bag, and the hot air rising from the smouldering match gathered within and raised up out of the cup the first known balloon. The brothers were impressed, pondered, and then began experimenting.

J. C. Irvine, President of the Pacific Aero Club

Leonard H. Lane, Mechanical Engineer, West Berkeley

From this small incident grew the common hot-air balloon with which adventurers have been making ascents and parachute drops all over the globe for over a century.

The two discoverers became zealous and daring aeronauts. In the greatest balloon of their career they ascended several thousand feet in the air and carried with them on a platform a cook stove weighing nearly one thousand pounds, from which the hot air was conveyed upward into the big cloth bag by means of a long stovepipe.

Awe-struck multitudes witnessed the frequent ascensions of the Montgolfier brothers throughout Europe, and they were hailed as the conquerors of the air. In their ascents they used damp straw as the lightest fuel available, carrying it in sheaths attached to ropes which trailed downward from them for hundreds of feet. When their fuel supply was exhausted and the air cooled they settled slowly to earth.

Modern practice never has improved upon the original hot-air balloon. Rather have subsequent changes in minor detail been steps backward instead of forward in the utilization of this method of air-travel. There has been no attempt at long-sustained flight by heated air. Later flights were made without carrying fuel or heating apparatus; instead, the latter-day aeronauts have lashed their bags to earth, filled them to the limit of their capacity with heated air by means of petroleum fires emptying out of earthen caves, then have shot swiftly to enormous heights and immediately dropped to earth in parachutes.

Then to clinch the abandonment of hot-air bags as a part of modern aeronautics has come the generally-accepted verdict of aeronauts and scientists that this means of sustaining power has reached its utmost development and that it is worthless in the utility of the problem.

To Harness Hot Air

Now comes inventor Sirch with a return to this primal principle. Sirch proposes to harness the lifting-power of torrid pure air, and to keep his air heated while in flight, but to improve upon the cook stove and wet straw as a method. This has proved a rather startling announcement, and has attracted wide attention in the scientific world, being coupled with sane, mathematical and plausible plans. Indeed, many leaders in aerial experimentation, upon thorough examination of Sirch's remarkable plans, have declared that it is entirely possible that he has found the key to a most important method of aviation. The calculations of Sirch, upon which he already has perfected American and foreign patents, are declared to be as simple and absolute as mathematics regarding the lifting-power of heated air and other fundamental principles. Heated pure air has considerably greater lifting-power than hydrogen-gas, at the same time being non-expensive and non-injurious to its containing-bag.

The details of this air-craft, which the inventor has christened "The Sirch Transport," are no less surprising and interesting than its radical basic principle.

Sirch has evolved, to contain the heated atmosphere, a rigid bag in the form of a projectile, through the center of which runs the major shaft of the metal frame. The covering itself is an invention, being of canvas subjected to a patented treatment of gelatine and asbestos, which renders it impervious to fire or water. The bag, which is divided into eight chambers, is held rigid by stout ribs extending out from the central shaft that traverses it from end to end. At each end of the steel shaft is a revolving gasoline engine coupled to the propeller-blades. Both engine and propellers whirl with the shaft as their axis.

Thus the horizontal main shaft, rigid as an arrow, is driven through the air by the two engines upon its ends, being sustained meanwhile, by the bag of heated air which surrounds it. This gives it the compact, direct, rigid traveling force of a projectile.

The method of maintaining the necessary high temperature of the air while in flight aloft is in consonance with the other unique features of the machine. This is done by utilization of the exhaust from the gasoline engines which whirl the propellers, and is declared to be the most simple and certain part of the device, if it is somewhat unique. The constant explosions of the gasoline drive the propellers as in the automobile, but the heat properties in the automobile and in gasoline engines generally, escape and are utterly wasted in the hot blasts from the exhaust pipe. In Sirch's "transport," the exhaust pipe from each engine is diverted to travel by means of circular coils of pipe similar to the ordinary radiator, through the chambers of the bag, thus keeping the air therein constantly at high temperature.

EXPECTS TO COMPETE WITH RAILROADS

The carriage and pilot-house of the "transport" hang close beneath the bag, held rigid by steel braces leading from the main shaft. A long hanging platform or deck provides access during flight to the engines and propellers at either end. It carries also a small and simple device for a supplementary supply of hot air, which is conveyed directly into the chambers from apertures beneath. The bag need not be air-tight, as the hot air rises—and explosions, such as wrecked Zeppelin are impossible.

As an aid to flight, but of minor importance, are attached two long planes or wings,

which are "reefable" and may be extended or drawn in at will to take advantage of favoring winds or air-currents.

Sirch flatly declares that in his lifetime his "transports" will become competitors of the transcontinental railroads in the carrying of both freight and passengers. He has constructed several small types, each of which he declares have proved true to the uttermost every essential principle of his machine. He has now commenced to build a large example of his ship which he says will carry twenty passengers from Los Angeles to San Francisco, with fuel, provisions and comforts for the trip. Sirch is president and general manager of the Sirch electrical and testing laboratories, a manufacturing corporation with a large plant at the corner of Sixth and Hope streets, Los Angeles.

DIRIGIBLES IN DISFAVOR

The Pacific Aero Club, the organization of San Francisco aviators, is in its infancy. It has a membership of about one hundred only, but every man enrolled is a consecrated devotee of the new passion for travel in the air.

Almost to a man, the Aero Club members are toilers in the field of heavier-than-air machines. In fact, the balloonist is looked upon as a "back number"—as one misguided—wasting time with a disproved, discarded, impracticable and academic form of air-travel. The balloon is a known quantity—the aeroplane is a fascinating uncertainty—the balloon is an economic failure for air-travel—the aeroplane is a partial success.

The aeroplane aviators point out, first of all, that the balloon is so expensive as to preclude practical commercial utility or such general use as to be of value. The cost of hydrogen-gas and of the silk containing-bags is very great, the work of proper inflation considerable, and the deterioration ruinous. A silken balloon is made worthless by fifty successive inflations with hydrogen-gas. Control is made exceedingly difficult and the length of flights are definitely limited by expansion, contraction and escape of gas under varying atmospheric conditions.

The Aero Club members therefore have relegated ballooning to the realm of futility, and are devoting all of their energies toward perfecting flying-machines which will raise and carry weight without the assistance of any bags of gas whatever. They are interested only in straight "heavier-than-air" flying-machines.

Not ten per cent of California air-ship experimenters, however, are members of the Pacific Aero Club. Its membership comprises only the most confirmed and devoted "cranks" on the alluring new field of endeavor. Recently, the Aero Club gave an "Air-ship Show" at the Dreamland Rink, San Francisco, which was the first exhibition of its kind given on the Pacific Coast. Twenty-five machines and models were shown, and students and inventors delivered lectures upon various phases of aeronautics.

Charlemagne Sirch, Electrical Engineer, Los Angeles

Sylvester L. Williams, a pioneer California aviator

The types were amazing in their variety, and ranged all the way from an ordinary wind-wagon, or sailing-vessel on wheels, to helicoplanes and aerocycloids of the most fantastic patterns. No imagination could conceive the strange devices produced by these wits of the air-ship world.

The "air-ship passion" has hit at random, and struck men and women of all age, occupation and circumstance in life, as an examination of the Aero Club membership list discloses. The members include capitalists, professional men, mechanics, scholars and dilettantes.

FANTASTIC AEROCYCLOID

The president of the Aero Club, J. C. Irvine, is a manufacturer of dies, stamps and medals. He has invented a most fantastic machine, a sort of air-velocipede, which he has named an "aerocycloid," and in which he proposes to pedal straight up to the skies. Accompanying this article is a photograph of President Irvine's "aerocycloid." It is an arrangement of fans which revolve between a double-wheel, propelled by a chain attached to pedal and sprockets located at the seat of the manipulator below.

One may ride into the air on Irvine's machine by foot-power just the same as we now ride horizontally along the ground upon a bicycle. The inventor has proved the lifting-power of his aerocycloid, and he is now developing the idea by attaching planes that will enable him to soar upon the wind. He may travel in any direction merely by going to a height where he finds the proper air-current, then drifting along by aeroplanes on the breast of favorable billows. The leg-power of the pedals will be supplemented by a small motor and folding wings will be attached to assist the planes in breaking too-rapid descent.

Irvine named his machine an "aerocycloid," because of its strong resemblance to a bicycle.

There are two wheels mounted at the top of a light bamboo frame, on which rests the engine and the seat of the driver. These wheels revolve upon a fixed shaft, and at points of the periphery of the wheels equidistant from each other, are huge round planes, fixed on revolving shafts. The power is conducted from the pedals and engine below to the big wheels by bands extending around the periphery of the large wheels. On one of these is a big sprocket from which bands run to smaller sprockets on the planes. When the big wheels are turning the sprockets conduct power to the planes, and these turn also, making half a revolution on their own axes each time the big wheels make a complete revolution. This brings the planes at different passages through the air, going down or coming up, at correct angles for lifting.

In the position shown in the picture the propelling-planes are exerting their whole force in lifting. When the proper height is attained, the sprocket-wheels are rotated to give the propeller-blades proper angles creating downward and backward air-currents, and the machine travels forward. By reversing the position, the machine will travel backward, accomplishing satisfactorily something which no other machine has thus far attempted.

The aerocycloid is built upon the gyroscope principle and the weight of the machine is below the center of lift. Thus, if it should lose the line of incidence—for instance, if it should become overbalanced by a sudden gust of wind, the rapid rotation of the propeller-blade would right the whole contrivance immediately. It has no rudder, but direction is easily changed by retarding the action of one or more propellers, very much as direction is changed by a side-wheel steamer, through stopping the starboard or port wheel.

The inventor claims for the aerocycloid many advantages over the common type of aeroplane. In the first place it has a much more rigid construction—it is not so great in length, thus requiring less space for housing, for alighting or rising. Again, it has a straight upward lift, thus enabling it to arise even in a crowded street, and descend in the same place, whereas an aeroplane must have plenty of "sea-room" to perform both actions, and the least interference with its delicate planes means a broken machine. Third, it will stand still in the air, hover or dash, all of which are great conveniences in reconnoitering, and for active warfare, as well as for pleasure.

The picture of the aerocycloid shown herewith is that of a model fitted with a three-horsepower engine. With this Mr. Irvine succeeded in lifting one hundred and five pounds, or thirty-five pounds per horsepower, which is more than any flying-machine of any type has thus far been recorded as doing.

The vice-president of the Aero Club is Charles C. Bradley, an official of the Crocker National Bank, where the headquarters of the organization are maintained and weekly meetings held. Bradley is the inventor of a biplane. Joseph Master is treasurer of the club.

The Aero Club proposes to hold regular exhibitions at frequent intervals to interest the public in aeronautics and give inventors full opportunity to display their ideas. Also the organization will establish a fund from which financial aid may be given to worthy inventors in their work of experimentation. A proving ground, with proper elevated

mounds and storage sheds for flying-machines, will be established and maintained.

Two college instructors, Professor Bruno Heyman, teacher of mechanics in the Lick School, and Professor Joseph Hidalgo, teacher of romance languages in the University of California, are among the active members of the club. Prof. Hidalgo's monoplane model has attracted much attention for its perfection of detail. Joseph Rosenthal, a well-known capitalist, is one of the most active members in promoting aerial experimentation.

Other members of the Aero Club who are active participants in the sport, and who have supplied themselves with models of machines from which they are building actual flying-machines are A. C. Pillsbury, J. Z. Posadas, Jr., C. C. Bradley, Captain P. A. Van Tassell, George Stanley, A. C. Watkins, Claude De Haven, Leo Kowalkowski. There are innumerable others who have been engaged in designing machines which are as yet merely on paper, but which will take form as soon as the designs are completed.

DENTIST BUILDS HELICOPLANE

It has remained for a dentist, Dr. A. J. Hiniker, to take the lead in the club in the range of the more complex machines. Dr. Hiniker has invented and built a "helicoplane" which was exhibited at a recent air-ship show, and attracted wide attention, because it is absolutely unique and the only machine of its kind ever evolved. The "helicoplane" is a combination of the two principles embodied in the heliocopter and the aeroplane. It is now being fitted with specially-designed engines and, while its possibilities are conjectural, all the experienced aviators declare it certain that it will ascend and also navigate, only its speed and flexibility being in doubt.

The helicoplane is unique, for while the heliocopter and the aeroplane have been familiarly known for sometime, the possibility of uniting the two in one machine and thus getting the best action from each seems to have occurred to Dr. Hiniker first.

The aeroplane construction is a simple enlargement of the box-kite principle. It consists of planes which are presented to the air surface at different angles, according as the driver would rise, soar, fly or descend. The machine is dragged through the air by a propeller in front and takes the name of monoplane, biplane, triplane, and so on, from the number of planes. The Wright machine is a biplane-aeroplane, having two planes one above the other, between which the driver sits. The Bleriot machine, the one to first cross the English channel, has only one plane and is therefore a monoplane. Triplanes are not popular and none of them have achieved any distinction in the realms of the air.

A heliocopter is an altogether different thing. An aeroplane lifts by being forced against the wind, exactly in the same manner as a kite lifts when it is pulled against the wind. A heliocopter rises by the fast revolution of a series of vertical propellers.

When you were a child you often amused yourself by twisting a piece of spirally-cut cardboard about one end of a lead pencil, rapidly revolving the pencil thus equipped by dragging it through the hands, each moving in an opposite direction, quickly releasing the thing and watching it soar upward as it continued to turn from the momentum imparted. When you did that you were experimenting with the principle which governs the present-day heliocopter, probably the most scientific of the flying-machines of the present.

The uniting of these two principles is what Dr. Hiniker has attempted, and those scientists who have examined the machine, both with and without club membership, are unanimous in their praise of it and their belief in its possibilities.

Having the resistance of the aeroplane in its lift and the direct assistance of the heliocopter principle in combination, it is believed it will be more steady and more sure in the air than any other form of flying-machine that has, as yet, occurred to the mind of man.

A Giant Heliocopter

The heliocopter, or top-principle lifter, has a number of devotees among the California inventors. In fact, the costliest of all the machines constructed in California have been built upon this principle.

Peter and W. P. English, father and son, have constructed in guarded secrecy at Sather station, Fruitvale, near Oakland, a heliocopter so mammoth and elaborate that they have already expended upon it nearly $10,000. This token of confidence in success of the idea follows one year of experiments which have amply proved

the lifting-power of the apparatus. The Englishes, who are practical machinists, have incorporated a million-dollar company to handle their heliocopter.

The English has at its top two gigantic adjustable-disk propellers, lying horizontally at each end of an upper truss, each of which by forced spinning is capable of lifting nearly one thousand pounds. The propellers are twenty feet in diameter and are driven by a seventy-five horsepower, eight cylinder, water-cooling gasoline engine. Two curved planes with eight hundred square feet of supporting surface for soaring extend over the top of the machine. This auxiliary aeroplane canopy being of finest prepared silk. The framework, which is of nickel tubing and brass, provides an operating platform at the bottom, which bears seventy-five per cent of the weight and gives equilibrium. As the total weight of the machine is six hundred and fifty pounds, the great and powerful propellers are figured to provide such a tremendous surplus lifting-power, that the completed heliocopter will easily carry four or five persons.

The idea of the machine is to make a straight ascent by the horizontal whirling of the propeller-wheels, then travel at will both by soaring on gravity and by propulsion. Upon reaching the height desired, the propellers can be deflected by levers on the operating platform to vertical positions and utilized for driving the ship horizontally through the air while it rides on the sustaining power of the planes. Before commencing the construction of the large machine, the lifting-power of the arrangement was thoroughly tested by means of small models. The men have been at work on their large machine for six months past and expect to make a public flight over San Francisco bay before the close of the year. The English machine is kept under close watch in a large, specially-constructed shop at Fruitvale. Few persons have been permitted to inspect it and no photographs or drawings of the detail of its construction have been permitted.

Ascends on Compressed Air

Another most interesting air-ship of the heliocopter type under construction on an elaborate scale in San Francisco is that of Leonard H. Lane, of 1158 Francisco street, West Berkeley. Lane, who is a mechanical engineer, has spent several years in study and experiment, from which he has evolved what he terms an "automatous heliocoptic aeroplane" that is remarkable in its detail. His machine, which will cost slightly in excess of $5,000 for construction, is more than half completed, and it also is being handled by a stock company controlled by the inventor.

This inventor kept his secret ambition to solve air-travel so well that the first information his wife had of the reason for his prolonged absences from home and considerable expenditures was when he came sailing down from the skies into the front yard one evening. Now his wife has developed into his most enthusiastic and intelligent helper in perfecting the great machine with which they both count on winning fame and fortune.

Lane's "automatous heliocoptic aeroplane" possesses several distinctive and entirely original features not included in any other California air-ship. Firstly, its propelling power is the expansion of compressed air, and this fundamental departure Lane has guarded zealously as to its detail. Secondly, the aeroplane feature is composed of automatically-opening and closing shutters or valves of aluminum. Thirdly, its lifting propellers all revolve around one central shaft, making the equilibrium as absolute and certain as that of a spinning-top.

The aeroplane portion of Lane's machine which covers the top like an enormous umbrella, is twenty feet wide by thirty feet long. In traveling this will present its broad side forward. The entire plane is composed of a series of thin sheets or plates of aluminum, similar to the scales of a fish. When the machine, in response to the whirling horizontal propellers, shoots upward, these

plates hang downward, permitting the air to pass through without hindrance to the rise. When the desired height is attained horizontal progress may be begun either by tilting the machine slightly downward and soaring or by the use of a secondary propeller at the front of the ship. The sideward motion automatically closes the valve-like flaps, and when descent is begun they are slammed shut by the air-current, and form a perfect parachute for safe and slow descent. Supplementary to the main aeroplane are two side gliders or wings, which aid in sustaining the ship in flight or descent. For steering there is a two-way tail or rudder.

It is in his motive power of compressed air that Lane has his most radical departure and claims his greatest exclusive merit. Lane, in simple, proposes to create a gale beneath the sustaining surfaces of his ship, devoting a portion of this energy to driving his lifting propellers. The mechanism of the ship looks like two gigantic bicycles, laid sidewise, one on the top of the other. There is concentration of power for lifting by double whirling circles about the central shaft. The propeller-disks whirl about their own axes, and the wheels themselves revolve on their carriages around the big central shaft. The two sets of wheels go in opposite directions, compelling an even balance. The motors which generate the compressed-air power are placed with the operator's seat in the hanging carriage below. The machine complete weighs four hundred pounds.

"My system simply is to create the 'turn of the wind'—the thing sought and necessary for all aviation by artificial means," says Lane. "I can create by expansion of

Aerocycloid, the fantastic air-craft built by President Irvine of the Pacific Aero Club

compressed air a gale of from fifty to two hundred miles per hour, and in my machine I simply throw this tremendous power beneath a circular kite. I have proved its ample lifting-power. My four-hundred-pound machine will have a lifting-power of two thousand five hundred pounds."

Lane made five flights by means of compressed air last September and created a sensation with a cheap and primitive device designed simply to demonstrate the practicability of his theory. With a crude machine operated by hand and foot-power, surmounted by a small balloon and meager spread of wings, he rose from an open field in West Berkeley to a height of seventy-five feet and floated about over the tops of the trees and houses to the amazement of the townspeople. He remained aloft for seven minutes on one occasion, pumping desperately with hands and feet to continue the explosive expansion of air beneath the wings. Finally, exhausted by his terrible exertions at the pump-handles, he descended slowly, the wind by a peculiar chance wafting him and his strange device down to his own dooryard, where his astounded wife greeted him as he floated through the treetops and for the first time learned of his long-cherished ambition. On this and successive flights, Lane lifted a total of one hundred and sixty-two pounds dead weight with the compressed-air power.

WHIRLING DISK-LIFTERS

A third heliocopter of ambitious design and expensive construction, founded upon the same principle of lifting-power as that of the English and Lane machines, but different in other essential details, is that of Charles Stanley, an aviator whose enthusiasm and confidence is undaunted by the loss of a completed air-ship by fire on the day before he was to make his initial flight. The Stanley ship is in the last stages of equipment at No. 68 Fifteenth street, Oakland, and the inventor announces that he will surely circumnavigate the San Francisco bay and peninsula before next New Year's Day.

The two horizontal-lifting disks of the Stanley machine are fifteen feet in diameter. At either end of the ship are supplementary propellers eight feet in diameter; one pushing and the other pulling the craft horizontally through the air. Large monoplanes extend the full length of the ship at each side, which are to be utilized for soaring when the vertical lifters have raised the machine to sufficient height, and also to break the fall of the vessel in event of mishap to the engine. A fifty-horsepower gasoline engine furnishes the power.

Stanley also has devised a dirigible balloon which embodies the unique principle of reverse heliocopters that will pull the balloon down to the ground at any time without the necessity of releasing any hydrogen-gas from the envelope. This balloon, like the enormous Zeppelin craft, has a rigid envelope, the gas-bag being encased in conical aluminum shields which prevent sagging and flattening from air resistance and permit of high speed. There are propellers at each end, and Stanley claims he will attain far greater speed in this dirigible than that attained by Count Zeppelin.

WEST OFFERS ADVANTAGES

The splendid hills and vast open spaces of out-door California are an alluring invitation to soaring, and the result has been a vast amount of effort in the branch of aviation devoted to scudding and gliding on the winds without power. Many machines of various types, ranging all the way from mere shoulder-wings to broad, tent-like planes, have been constructed and tried with differing degrees of success.

28.
The Prince
of the Power
of the Air
(1908)

MR. STEDMAN'S FORECAST OF AN "AËRONON OF THE TWENTIETH CENTURY"
(REPRINTED FROM HIS ARTICLE "AËRIAL NAVIGATION,"
IN THIS MAGAZINE FOR FEBRUARY, 1879)

THE PRINCE OF THE POWER
OF THE AIR

AËRIAL NAVIGATION A MENACE TO
BRITISH SUPREMACY

BY EDMUND CLARENCE STEDMAN

Mr. Stedman was engaged upon this article at the time of his death on the morning of January 18, 1908, and the first paragraph was his last written words. As the reader will perceive, the subject is one in which Mr. Stedman for many years had taken more than merely speculative interest. The article is printed from a full but obviously not a final draft, with slight transpositions and omissions,— among the latter chiefly an incomplete résumé of what has been accomplished or undertaken in aëronautics by various governments.— The Editor.

THIRTY years ago, having business with the most restless and formidable of American financiers,—one successful in getting hold of railways and telegraph on his own terms, and applying something like genius to their development,—I asked him why, with his engineering bent and imagination, in view of what seemed to me fairly close at hand, he was not moved to devote a befitting sum—say five per centum of the year's profits—to experiment in construction of a flying-machine or, rather, of a dirigible aërostat. He replied very mildly, in his best vein of cynical humor, that life was short, and he would leave that field, and the means of exploiting it, to his heirs; for himself, he preferred the modest competence obtainable from roads for which he had an exclusive right of way to gains wrested from the atmosphere—a region where there was no monopoly of road-beds, and where the world at large could cross and even use his track. Possibly he had some premonition that he was to die comparatively young. For all then said of him, I admired his intellect and liked his courteous ways; and, taking one thing with another, I trust he may have gone to some clime whose habitants are equipped with plumes which render artificial means of flight superfluous.

In the autumn of 1878 I wrote an extended paper entitled, "Aërial Navigation (a priori)," which was published by "Scribner's Monthly," now THE CENTURY MAGAZINE, in February, 1879. Its acceptance, bearing in mind the state of opinion on this topic twenty-eight years ago, showed both open-mindedness and courage, and a willingness to follow Dr. Hale's motto, "Look forward and not back."

The paper opened with a confession that its writer rode a hobby, and a hobby early bestraddled; for it was as a youngster on a vacation, before the Civil War, fishing at Greenwood Lake and watching the perch move below, up and down, back and forth, in the shallows, that I conceived the idea that the fish model should be the first to insure measurable success —however advantageously progressive ingenuity might imitate the bird and arrive at the idea, in time, of a flying-machine heavier than the air. Of course I knew little of the mechanics of resistance,— who did?—but my instinct was that the fish, totally immersed in its fluid element, was a palpable prototype of an "aërobat." This word I coined as a companion to "aërostat"—the word still properly used for a gas-bag that is not propulsive and dirigible at command. "Aëronon" is an equally good word, and "aëroplane" exactly expresses the new machine on the kite principle. At this time I went so far as to make some rude and crude diagrams, merely to show the application of certain principles; so I may confess myself sorry that they were reproduced then, for the paper already is yellow with age. Two other pictures were added, giving my notions of what might be expected at the end of twenty-one years, and possibly to lend a little more picturesqueness to my exposition.

First, I proceeded to show the utter failure of the slightest advance, over a hundred years earlier than my paper, upon [the Americans] Rittenhouse and Hopkins's use of hydrogen for ascension of a gas-balloon in 1783. Among the causes of the failure, I cited: (a) the impotence of an aërostat that is forced to

lose ballast to compensate for the loss of gas; (b) the globular shape of the balloon, with its car hung far below, as if a fish shaped like an inflated bladder had tiny fins suspended by a ligament; (c) misconceptions caused by the use of the word air-ship—an aërial machine being in one element only, and not in an elastic and an unelastic element; (d) the futile attempts to capture and include the secret of flight, the study of the bird having had then only one outcome, namely, that its hollow bones furnished the natural combination of lightness and strength; (e) there had been no deliberate and scientific attempt by skilled engineers, and with co-adequate means, to navigate the air—all experiments having been relegated to the ignorant enthusiast, the crack-brained theorist, the would-be inventor, who, each in turn, spent only a few hundred or a few thousand dollars on his respective failure, where the aid of capitalists and governments was required. In contrast with the $5000, the most which any of these novices had expended, I referred to the readiness with which capital had placed $500,000 at the disposal of Captain Ericsson to build a steamer to test his caloric engine for marine propulsion. This showed that capital is provided when conditions are understood or even imagined.

Offsetting this failure, the fact remained that there was nothing in nature against the solution of the problem, which was wholly a mechanical one.

I condense briefly the long series of statements of what seemed to me then essential to reach an outcome:

(1) Forget the shape and uses of the old balloon: what was wanted was an air-traveler, governable at will. Forego attempts to construct a flight-machine until the principle of the fish model is thoroughly developed and utilized. The first confidence of the people at large must thus be gained. The submarine torpedo-boat was cited.

(2) An aërobat must resemble its model in being so delicately upheld that the slightest motive power would elevate or depress it. Further on, I termed this condition "buoyant equipoise," and predicted the use no less of the vertical screw above or below for this purpose, than of the propeller in front or rear for

horizontal traveling; the aërobat to be so weighted as to float naturally a short distance above the earth; and to be dependent upon its motor for change of elevation.

(3) Every particle of advance toward unity of design was a gain. The machine must contain its power and freight within itself, at least as near as possible; must be an integral structure, not a motive appendage dragging an aërostat high above it with an adverse leverage proportioned to its flexibility.

(4) As to form, attention was invited to the shape of the elliptic fishes—to the fact that a pickerel will change its locality so swiftly that the eye cannot follow the movement; that the trout and salmon dart up the swiftest rapids; that the porpoise plays round the fastest steamer. Consideration, also, was given to the law that, although the air packs in front of a projectile like snow before an engine, and the resistance increases as the square of the velocity, yet the law is modified by the shape of the moving body; and that doubtless the side of the body, even not less than its head, shares in this modification.

(5) Motive power, and its application by means of the screw, was considered, and how the benefit for the invention would be determined exactly by the advance in producing engines that would utilize greater proportion of the energy produced, and give vastly greater horse-power for each unit of weight.

(6) Coming to structure, it was held that the aërobat must be solidly framed and protected, not flexible; must be greatly longer than its beam, and divided into upper and lower chambers, if possible; must have a rigid framework, and in the end be made so large as to permit a metallic covering. Here aluminum was dwelt upon, the lightest of plentiful metals; the scale of reduction noticed in its cost; and the prediction made that it would soon be so cheaply produced as to be available. Some years afterward, attention was called to its greatly reduced price, in a letter to the "New York Tribune," supplementary to an article by Professor Newberry in the same newspaper. But at a long period later, Clarence King gave the writer his opinion that steel, on account of its greater ductility, would furnish the greater strength for the same weight, and that the structure, if large, must be bulwarked at the front.

(7) Finally, questions of money, safety, steering, and the field of motion were discussed; as to dimensions and outlay, it was claimed that these must be on a grandiose scale, proportionate to the greatness of the enterprise, before practicable results could be reached; that any smaller demonstration would be merely a working model, which might warrant the application of the services of the best engineers to produce an adequate one.

One point also remains to be made. Two cuts in the article illustrated air-travelers of the near future, one of which, after the earlier stages of navigation, would be considered a clumsy affair, a kind of "Dutch bottom." The other was far more elongated, and a kind of "aëronon of the twentieth century." (See cut page 18.) Finally, it was shown that the gradual lines of advance should be through increase of lifting and propelling mechanical power, which should finally be so great as to meet the views of those claiming that atmospheric navigation can be effected only by a machine far heavier than the air.

About the time when that article was in hand, I had very fresh in mind the old Commodore's monition, "Sonny, don't prophesy unless you know!"—a monition strengthened by the fact that, within a few weeks after he himself said that he never bought more than he could pay for, his brokers temporarily suspended payment until he could raise money on the lender's terms to receive his own purchases. But I did not consider my forecast a prophecy,—that is, I did not look upon it as containing much left to the fates or chance,—it seemed to me but the reading and interpreting of a text already inscribed on the wall; not the promise of things hoped for, but the evidence of things not yet seen by the average eye. And I repeat that time has warranted the confidence of conviction upon which I acted.

For the problem was even then solved in so far as that portion of it was concerned which was only the precedent to the other, and which is the only one in open practice at this writing. I made no claim to the invention of anything: so far as this was concerned, my work was *a priori,* abstract and not concrete. Anthony Pollok of Washington, a trained engineer no less than a great and successful patent lawyer, the hero of the Goodyear litigation, and later the very protagonist of the Bell telephone war and victory, believed in my general theory, but held that even a model would not secure a patent for that which was in the air and, willy-nilly, "dedicated to the public" by its feeble experimenters. What can be patented are the special devices for applied results. Not the man who sees or expounds, but the man who does the thing, is the only legitimate patentee of modern inventions—or, more likely, the capitalist to whom he assigns them.

I will not deny that in day-dreams I often fancied myself doing the thing; but my own theory was against any partial experiments. Sometimes, with something of the childish pride which always accompanies our sleep dreams of levitation, I used to lie with shut eyes imagining the glory of appearing over New York, soaring above the course of Broadway, circling about the then "tall Tower" or Trinity spire, as a beginning of a straight course for Washington and a landing demonstration to Congress on Capitol Hill. Nothing at that day—not even news from Mars—could have been more amazing to the public. The man who should have done it would have made his name as unforgettable as Christopher Columbus. Yet now the evolution has come on so gradually, from the day of De Rosier in France and Rittenhouse and Hopkins in America to the beginning and latest of flights of Santos-Dumont and Count Zeppelin, that nothing short of an unexpected battle in the air would astonish us, in the proper sense of the word. Have we not had the search-light, the sky-scraper, wireless telegraphy, the automobile, all within this period? The truth is, the public imagination is so trained upon invention and discovery that everything is possible to it. The error now is in favor of encouragement to inventors—just as in the literary realm there is too facile a process for making and selling worthless books, as a result of the copyright law and the transformation of our forests into printing paper.

In the summing up of the article, the writer "let himself go"—if he did not rise "upon the wings of prophecy"—in contemplating what doubtless would be the effect of man's final conquest of the air, the only region as yet unadded to his domain. Presuming that if all things seen be regarded as a fanciful day-dream, I implied that the race had first to attain majority to be intrusted with the consequent illimitable freedom. Earlier, the gift would be fatal. I now feel like adding this: During my own life, no epoch-making invention has ever come until it was needed. Until the means of traffic and travel on the sure and firm-set earth had been thoroughly exploited, and it was time for flight, invention and capital never seriously essayed the problem, which is to be, after all, a greater advance for the twentieth century than the railroad and telegraphy for its predecessor. Moreover, until those former processes had steadily increased the economy of energy, and the advance toward perfection of mechanical motors, serious effort was impossible. As to the effects of aërial navigation, I said that the first and obvious one would be to make Decatur, Illinois, a seaport. I might as well have said Denver or San Moritz, the new ocean being everywhere and every spot on earth, from the Victoria Embankment to either pole, a "port of entry." Fourier's idea of the slower growth of overgrown cities would follow, and the multiplication of smaller land-locked centers of habitation, culture, and trade. I showed that Fourier's mistake was in urging us to effect, by a forcing artificial process, what only time and evolution could bring about—the desired distribution of population throughout the land. I showed that the change must be gradual; the art of aërial navigation long in perfecting; our primitive vessels and motors as rude as was Stevenson's locomotive; freight would long move, if not always, by water and rail; mails and express packages, and passengers would be the first transmitted; and a picture was drawn of the swift dropping of the great newspapers into towns and villages everywhere. Space was devoted to the thrills of wonder and ecstasy pertaining to the luxury of flight, which would render all former travel tame by comparison. And, those twenty-eight years ago, the article enlarged on the check upon the arrogance of monopolies,—the great transportation companies,—whose license and immunity and freedom were dwelt upon, including their evil control of law-making and practice. Aërial companies of course will be chartered, but who could impede the right of way upon these higher than the high seas? The quick adjustment of science to the new opportunities was predicted; meteorology, discovery, astronomy from the clear upper air, geology—in every direction knowledge would be amazingly increased.

Eventually new mechanical and manufacturing industries would arise, marked by grace, lightness, and strength. A new profession of aëromanship would exercise the labor of a countless army of trained officers and airmen; a new poetry and romance would have birth. Landscapes painted between earth and skies would take on a new universe of drawing, color, light, and shade. The ends of the earth would be visited by all. Sportsmen would have the world for a sporting-ground; the yachts of the air would be christened with beautiful names—Iris, Aurora, Hebe, Ganymede, Hermes, Ariel, and others not derived from the pure springs of Aryan beauty.

Above all, and influencing all, a new departure must at once be made in political science and international comity. Boulevards would be virtually abolished; laws and customs must soon more closely assimilate; free trade must be imperative and universal; the Congress of nations no longer would concern itself with academic questions. War perforce would come to an end, after perhaps a few destructive experiments; there would be no "ghastly dew" from "the nations' airy navies." Death-dealing aërial vessels and squadrons would be maintained solely for police surveillance over barbarous tribes and nations. The dawn of a Saturnian age at least would be at hand. I closed with an appeal for the liberal expenditure of a single government, or even of one of the moneyed corporations or some multimillionaire, of that former time, toward a solution of the problem. With or without their efforts, I said the result was even at our door.

The appearance of this article brought the writer into business. The general reader found it interesting. Fellow-wri-

ters thought it an ingenious flight of fancy, the verisimilitude of realism and romance, akin to Locke's "Moon Hoax," Poe's adventure of "Hans Pfaall," "MS. Found in a Bottle," "The Gold-Bug," "M. Valdemar," "Arthur Gordon Pym." A fellow-member of the Century Club—Newton, an accomplished engineer—said that between ourselves I "meant it as a fake," and looked upon me incredulously when I assured him that I was in dead earnest. All this I expected, but I had not foreseen the instant attention the article gained from people in Europe and the States, who, it appeared, were concerned about the prophecy. I soon learned of the existence of foreign aërial societies from their official committees. From that time, for several years aspiring and impoverished inventors sent me diagrams, theories, even models. I have a great box full of such matters accumulated in those years. Despite newspaper scoffing, and the banter of minor engineers, and the raillery of my really learned friend Newton, who soon after died, I was surprised and gratified to find that various distinguished professional experts expressed great interest in my views, and, allowing for such defects as would be expected in a long article not based upon a full study of a subject, in the main coincided with them, so far as the coming solution of the matter was concerned. Notably so, Mr. Chanute, that able, open-minded, and distinguished civil engineer, official, and inventor, who has been the most able and hopeful thinker on the subject from that time to the present day. The talks with him and the views he gave me from his full knowledge made me quite content to have ventured with that paper at that time. At the date of my paper, I think he was the chief engineer of the Erie Railway, and soon afterward made his earlier experiments to test the relative resistance of the atmosphere to differently shaped railway cars, moving at different velocities. He never lost sight of the subject either by word or act, keeping step with every advance both in dirigible aërostats and in gliders heavier than the air. Toward the latter he directed in the end his chief interest, and he has always claimed that only two questions are left—those of stability and power. He has been the friend and confidential ally of the Wright brothers, and his paper on their motor-flyer, forming the opening chapter of our Aëro Club's volume, informed the experimenters of Herring's automatic gliding-machine, run by a light yet strong gasolene motor. He himself also constructed a multiple-winged machine, which was "demonstrated" near Chicago in 1896.

In addition to the general and quasi-imaginative forecast of what would be the results of aërial navigation, I ventured, from the progress of what in 1878 had already to be observed, to make certain chronological expectations; to wit, that by the end of the nineteenth century, dirigible air-travelers, substantially on the fish model, would be making at least twenty miles an hour in perfect calm, and that from this they would soon advance to three times that potential. All would depend upon the inventions and improvement of motors; upon the shape, and structure of the machines; and upon the engines and steering-apparatus, and so on.

As a matter of fact, within five years (in 1884) a dirigible flight of a spindle-shaped machine, at the rate of fifteen miles an hour, was executed by La France; but the structure, and its motor and steering-apparatus, were too primitive to justify any confidence in its practical utilization. The weight of this motive power was near 170 pounds to the horse-power. Little advance was made for years, but in 1890 Maxim demonstrated that a heavy aëroplane could be made at least to rise from the ground, and since then we have had the daring and brilliant experiments of Langley, Lebaudy, Lilienthal, Herring, Chanute, and others, culminating, up to date, in the motor-flyer of the Wright brothers and the tetrahedral designs of Professor A. G. Bell. Unquestionably Santos-Dumont gave the greatest new stimulus to the campaign, and fired the public imagination by both practical and dramatic success with the aërostatic air-ships, which his fortune enabled and his ambition nerved him to build and navigate successively, and also by his prize-winning dirigible flights in full view of the French capital, continued for years; and soon ambitious demonstrators, and governments were imitating and striving to excel him. Motors weighing only one pound to the horse-power have been produced. Structure has been refined and strengthened. The vertical screw has been taken in hand. Not only private capital, but that of governments, is devoted to the competition. In France, speeds of over twenty miles an hour in a calm were attained in the first lustrum of this century. Germany, instantly alert as a military nation, has reached the greatest success thus far with Count Zeppelin's air-ship, its buttressed frame, its large proportions, its actual calm-speed of thirty-eight miles an hour, its double motors. Previously *La Patrie* had gone from Paris to Verdun, a distance of 187 miles, in six hours, forty-five minutes, but making 23 miles an hour when not helped by the wind. The most successful machines have demonstrated my early protest against car-leverage by placing the car and motor close to the end of the aërostat, and Zeppelin's magic attachment almost reaches my ideal of an integral moving body. The account of all this, regularly taken by me from the press for a quarter-century, is well condensed and illustrated in Mr. Augustus Post's first handbook of the Aëro Club of America, with plenteous other matter. This book,[1] the club, the experiments of its enthusiastic members, show how thoroughly the demonstration that the problem of aërial navigation is solved has entered into the mind, and has promoted the contests of sport and venturous amateurs, as of governments and savants. At this moment the highest mechanical genius of the world is applied to the perfection of motors and dirigible aërostatic ships, and to the solution of the problems of power and stability for aëroplanes and tetrahedral kites. Of all the dirigible fish patterns, those by the Germans are the most successful, and certainly most conform to my requirements of unity, rigidity, and front strengthened like the head of a fish; they are also the largest, profiting by the fact that, as Mr. Carl Dienstbach states it, "By the law of air accumulation in front of a moving body, the resistance becomes proportionately less for one big body than for many small ones," together equaling

[1] This volume was compiled by the Committee of Publication of the Club: Mr. W. J. Hammer, Mr. Israel Ludlow, and Mr. Augustus Post, Secretary of the Club.

it in cross-section. This has virtually justified my argument for liberal outlay and magnitude of dimensions. Finally, at the present writing, England has waked up to the necessity of grappling the problem as a war measure, and her engineers are at work. Then our Government, viewing with sympathy the efforts for ultimate achievement and management of the aëroplane flyers and gliders, sees that the dirigible is already accomplished, and needs only a little further application to military needs, and has gone to work itself, with all the advances of other governments to start with. I conclude that the era of life and government as effected by man's conquest of the air is upon us; that certain radical results are to follow, as surely as the simple invention of the elevator has quadrupled the residence capacity of any given area of city, and the toy-bicycle, first, and the automobile later, have revolutionized road-building—to take only two of the modern inventions of general utilization; and that the aërial age is yet in its infancy.

But at this moment I am not half so much intent upon rehearsing my "told you so" as about completing the train of results which would follow upon even initiatory navigation of the air. For, in fact, I made the strangest possible omission—an omission that to me would be incredible, if I did not plead the absolute incredulity at that time prevailing as to the solution of the problem at all—a problem then classed with the squaring of the circle. It is true, I reflect with complacency, that I did devote picturesquely eloquent passages to what would follow man's conquest of the air, and I did say, as all have found obvious, that it would make war a hideous impracticability. But of late—that is, since the appearance of Captain Mahan's masterwork, in 1893, on the "Influence of Sea Power in History"—I have wondered how it was that, going at such length into the corollaries of the German nature, I could have failed to think of the one result—of that glaring concrete type which most impresses the unreflecting average class,—most instantaneous in existence, and most dramatic and startlingly recognizable and to be reckoned with.

When four grand armies of Germany, France, Great Britain, and the United States find themselves in possession of aërostats manageable for flight and military use, the very first question in world-politics to be asked is, How will this affect the foreign policy and international status of Great Britain, now for two centuries demonstrably the Princess of the Power of the Sea, and by the same token unassailable whether in her insular stronghold, or upon the waves which Britannia has ruled? The question is not, What of her colonies, where her scepter guides the sun around the globe, but, What of the nucleus of Great Britain? What of the tight little island, mother and defender of them all? Is there to be,—can there be?—a Prince of the Power of the Air? For if there is, then the distinction, the unique advantage of the British empire vanishes, and Great Britain must take her place on a level with all the other sovereign great powers. This may not, will not, imperil her safety; but it must reduce her pride, her vaunted superiority, and her prerogatives, to the common international denominator. Either this must eventuate or the assent of historians and history to her insularity and her sea-domain as the basis of her greatness has been purely chimerical—an illusion upon which her supremacy has been as well assured as if it were fact.

It is no illusion. Her sea-power, supplemented by her statesmanship and valor, has forwarded her growth and sustained her greatness. It must cease to do so from the decade in which the atmosphere enveloping the globe becomes man's greater ocean. So far as war is concerned—as the deterring factor, the "Last Chantey" of the waves as dominating alike London's "gossiping Mall and Square" and "The naked shingles of the world" will be sung, and a new song may be sounded in the empyrean, the way of a ship in the sea—of an eagle in the air.

"The sea is a wide common, over which a man may pass in all directions." Thus writes Mahan, and he adds that there are certain trade-routes "which controlling reasons" have led men "to choose . . . rather than others." But, after all, the surface of the sea, with its trade-routes, bears to the upper ocean the fancied relation of flatland to actual space. The atmosphere has no continental borders, no island coasts. The sea is "cabin'd, cribb'd, confin'd," not "broad and general as the casing air." Yes, supremacy in peace and war has indeed depended upon sea power, and "man's commerce on secure ports where his ships could lie in safety"; and such ports set close together against all waves and against all winds have made Britain what she is. So from the date when Anglo-Saxon and Norman blended on English soil, two concepts have possessed the national mind. First, a perfectly clear understanding of the source and muniment of the national greatness, and, second, that apprehension, often dormant in tranquil periods, but alert at the least suggestion of trouble with the first-class neighboring power. Every true son of Britain feels that the vital spot of the empire, the source of energy, is the tight little island: threaten it, and a tremor runs throughout the colonial system; pierce it, and, for the moment at least, paralysis must ensue.

For this reason solely, our transatlantic kinsmen,—from whom we derive, however mixed the increased immigration, our own equipoise,—as heroic a people as any men on earth, and the most steadfast when once in fight and the battle goes wrong, are periodically falling, without apparent sense of the grotesque, into funks which the less brave and competent seldom display. Their hysteria is that of a people long immune, whose insularity is wealth and comfort. To those who have nothing to lose, but everything to gain,—the gipsies and the free-lances among countries, the proletarians of the world, however ignoble in war,—the Britisher's spasms of alarm afford diversion. Nothing has added more to the gaiety of nations than English governmental opposition, and the reasons given for it, to the tunnel—thrice cabled to halt—between the coast at Cap Blanc-Nez, in France, and that below Shakspere's Cliff "near Dover." More reasonable, of course, has been the national attitude toward a succession of suspects and rivals. First, within memory of those now living, it was France, the hereditary foe; then, for half a century, Russia—the one power that would seem Great Britain's natural ally in mutual exploitation of Asia upon latitudinal lines; and now Germany, whom, it must be confessed there is manifest reason for dreading not only as a trade-rival,

but for her masterful determination to figure in all respects as what an English school-boy would call "one of her own size."

Concerning Germany, and all uninsular compeers, she has had much reason, hitherto, for complacent reliance upon the principle laid down by Mahan: "If a nation be so situated that it is neither forced to defend itself on land, nor to seek extension of its territory by way of the land, it has, by the very unity of its aims directed upon the sea, an advantage as compared with a people one of whose boundaries is continental. This has been a great advantage to England over both France and Holland as a sea-power."

But when he says, elsewhere, "if she maintain her navy in full strength, the future will doubtless repeat the lesson of the past," the world, once awakened to what aërial war-power means, will enter a demurrer. Is, then, the lesson of the past, which depends upon the unique insularity, so surely to be repeated? There are portents to the contrary: the shadow cast by Zeppelin's air-ships—even by the heavier-than-air scouts appearing across the horizon; *La Patrie* dropping out of a clear sky into an astonished village in Ireland; and the promise of aërial creations which shall flock at the mariner's hallo, and skim and hover like ospreys on the track of the seafaring fleet.

And what of England, the country which of all has most to lose and least to gain? How is she contemplating the era when all nations equal her in possession of the atmospheric ocean, the higher seas? When the aërial fleets of the world can pass as readily as her own not into, but over, the Cinque Ports; over St. Paul's, and Lombard Street, and Buckingham Palace; over Windsor, over Manchester, and Birmingham, and Sheffield; over the length of the fairest, strongest, securest, most historic, and richest of argosied realms, from Land's End to John o' Groat's,—from her new naval base at Rosyth to the borders of the Mersey?

Major F. S. Baden-Powell, late of the Scotch Guards, summed up the whole matter, last year, with so quiet a significance that one would think there could be no other subject so occupying the mind of his countrymen. "If in the future all nations adopt air-ships for war, much of our insularity will be gone, and we must make due preparation."

But in the event of England's loss of insularity, what preparation, or equality of aërial equipment, can restore to her a specific supremacy like that,—with all it includes,—which is possessed by her, so long as sea-power is the sovereign power, and "Britannia rules the waves"?

Recalling the past, it is atypical, to say the least, that all England is not at this moment evincing for once a just apprehension; not of defeat in war or even of violence at alien hands, but of the falling-in of that concession of specific immunity which has been a sound warrant for the "gude conceit of hersel" so little relished by the envious. A like apathy, however, prevails in other countries most concerned, in some of which the people at large express a full realization of what is soon to affect modes of life and international liberties and restrictions. The sub-jugation of the atmosphere has not come impressively like the steamboat of Fulton, or the "What hath God wrought" over Morse's wire, but has crept slowly from the diversion stage to the utilization of advanced engineering and equipment.

Who can doubt that the actual condition is understood in the chancelries of Europe—it must be that cabinets and rulers have an inkling of it, that British statesmen know what it means, else why are they watching so intently the efforts made by one another? England, as usual, is letting others pull the chestnuts out of the fire, ready to profit in imitation of what others may produce; although, even she, at last, has tested, rather unsuccessfully, a dirigible air-ship of her own.

And yet, if the statesmen of the great powers really appreciate what is coming, why do they insist so on the increase of their navies?

DR. BELL'S COMMENT ON THE FOREGOING ARTICLE

THE letter which follows, written in response to a request from the Editor of THE CENTURY that Dr. Bell would read the proofs of this article, is here printed with his consent:

Many thanks for the privilege of reading Mr. Stedman's article, which I return. I see nothing to correct in it.

While of course the bird is Nature's model for the flying-machine heavier than air, Mr. Stedman is undoubtedly right in looking upon the fish as the true model for the dirigible balloon. It is certainly noteworthy that the dirigible war-balloon of to-day already approximates the fish-like form predicted by him.

He is also right I think in supposing that of all the nations of the world the interests of Great Britain will be most vitally affected by progress in aëronautics. For it is obvious that sea-power will become of secondary importance when air-power has been fully developed through the use of dirigible balloons and flying-machines in war. The nation that secures control of the air will ultimately rule the world.

Yours sincerely,

Alexander Graham Bell.

WASHINGTON, D. C., March 16, 1908.

29.
A Week of Flying
(1909)

L. A. Shafer

THE GRAND WEEK OF FLYING

By MAXIMILIAN FOSTER

Author of "Corrie Who?" etc.

A T Rheims, for the week, they offered history of both kinds, so that one took his choice. There was the old, established brand, the mediæval—a little of the Vandals and the Huns, something of the Roman, and a good deal of the poor epileptic peasant girl, Joan, and her contemptible king. One saw her statue in the square before the cathedral; and, appropriately enough, Joan had her back to the plains of Bétheny. For out there was history of the other sort, the type that marks progress, a new era in the world. It was a wide swing through the arc of events—on one side the Dark Ages, superstition, and the smoke of poor Joan's funeral pyre; on the other, Science and the breaking of new roads, the opened highway of the air.

Close upon half a million persons walked

within a stone's throw of the spot where the peasant girl had handed a doll his kingdom—and how many remembered?—or cared? New kings obstructed the view—Wright, Latham, Blériot, Curtiss, and their kind. One forgot the monstrous egoists who gave the world history of the other sort—war, famine, and plague—and turned one's back on Rheims. Out beyond lay Bétheny, where they made history of a better brand.

There were three roads to the big plain out beyond the town. You walked, motored, or bought a ticket at the *Gare des Voyageurs* and then fought your way aboard one of the queer little French railway cars, whose outlines suggest the road coaches from which they sprang. *Fought* is the exact word, too; for though Rheims had expected a crowd and prepared for it, the inpouring host was far beyond its most hopeful anticipations.

Countless thousands walked, peasants from the nearby communes, and the small bourgeoisie of the town, all cheering and chaffing together. They chaffed when your motor pulled up to save you from killing them—cheered when you shot on again. They cheered the trains that dragged along the high embankment—they were positively entranced if a train got stalled with the traffic. A crippled motor drew the crowd's fire, and, at sight of it, they revamped the familiar catch-call of "Get a horse!" into a newer phrase: "*V'la, m'sieur! Il faut q' vous achetez un aeroplane!*"—Monsieur should buy himself a flying machine. They were a jolly mob, those tens of thousands.

Those with a franc, three francs, or ten or twenty francs to spare, placed themselves within the enclosure; yet as joyous as they—and perhaps much more comfortable—were the thousands camped outside, crowding with their *panniers* and campstools and baby carriages and what not to every coign of vantage: the roadside along the fence, the fields, the little wooded knolls—everywhere, in fact, so that the course of ten kilometres was banked around from start to finish as if by a flowering hedge.

One draws deep on his reserves of the superlatives in dealing with Bétheny, and then, at the best, falls short. Here was the field, for example, a course that reached beyond the view, fading at a distance into the soft, hazy smoke of those August days. One came out from between the grandstands and marveled at the sweep of undulating golden plain, a vast terrane bare of hedges, fences, walls—

clear of all obstruction, save here and there a chance array of haycocks that were more than once dispersed by the fans of those monstrous birds passing overhead. Beyond, on its heights, lay Rheims, an impressionistic background seen through the haze in all the marvelous color tones that come on August days in France—purple, violet, blue—hues the palette might never hold, such was their depth and softness, their wonderful brilliance and variation. The square gray towers of holy Notre Dame rose high above all else; and, of a quiet nightfall, one could hear the bell's chiming stroke through the rattle of speeding motors, the hum of the crowd, and all the stir and life on Bétheny plain. The old and the new, indeed!

But the crowd gave heed to one thing only. A murmur rose, spread, and then burst into a roar of swelling applause. Over at the left, a level spread of turf reached northward beside the highway of Neuchâtel; and there, in the elbow of the roadside trees, things had already begun to happen. The sharp rattle of an unmuffled motor clacked on the air like musketry; the clamor grew, and one surged with the crowd toward the boundary of the course. Against the stiff, metallic foliage of the roadside trees, a great snowy fabric raised itself, sped forward along the gentle slope at railway speed, and then took the air with a grace and ease that left one gaping in admiration. That hoarse murmur of the crowd keened to a higher octave, and then died swiftly. One shouts little when he marvels. Here came the first of the machines, and the throng held its breath.

It was Latham, as it chanced, the young Frenchman, hardly more than a boy, who drove the Antoinette monoplane. Here he came now, his fifty horse power motor tuned up to the limit, and aimed for the starting line between the grandstand and the judges' box, 350 yards away.

In the face of sights like this, one naturally gropes for a telling simile. Here, one said at the first breath, is a bird, a mammoth thing of snowy plumage, supreme in the air to which it was born. But no bird ever buzzed and hummed on its flight like this: so there came swiftly another image. Here was a monstrous mosquito hawk, the devil's darning needle that goes boring up and down the summer air, its wings whistling as it darts and twists and turns. There you had a likeness—But the huge fabric of metal, cloth, and wood, droning by at the speed of a railway train, moved, after all, with a poise and majesty that eventually thrust out of mind all efforts to compare it to any known thing.

For this was a creature by itself; and as the vast engine winged onward through the quiet air, the talk of its busy motor dying in the distance and its wings outstretched like the pinions of a floating gull, one gasped as at the supernatural, at some uncanny and unbelievable thing of dreams.

Now, down toward the fringe of trees, a second motor raised its staccato, barking clamor. Then another joined. One reached far out across the palings, and gaped anew. There, in the dishlike flatness of the hollow, a half dozen spreading shapes blanked out with their array of gleaming, snowy white the background's heavy foliage. There were some with a ship's spread of cloth; others that were smaller, more birdlike in type. Three were in place now, their motors humming in a steady drone.

Here it came, another monoplane. "BLÉRIOT!" roared the crowd, as the machine resolved itself out of the parked white shapes below. For him and his flyer one found a likeness early. You, too, perhaps, on a listless Carolina day have seen the buzzard essay his rise from the ground. He spreads himself, his wings held wide, and, with dangling legs, strides on until he gains speed enough to lift himself. So it is with the Blériot type of 'plane. Of course, the wings don't flap; their main supporting surfaces are rigidly fixed; but, all the same, in the suspended *chassis* one gets a near image of the legs and dangling claws of our old friend of plantation fields and sky.

Yet here, too, comparison failed, once the machine inclined itself from the earth and scaled away upon its course. Rocking slightly from the last kick of its wheels against the uneven ground, it bored higher in the air; and then, as its driver got the feel of the breasting wind and set his gear to meet it, the 'plane swung to a level and held it steady as a church. So it drove to the southward, the exhaust of its motor crackling in the summer quiet; and, careening to the turn beyond, dipped over the rise and was gone.

One type passed and another came. Latham had gone and then Blériot; and as the crowd hummed its approbation, another of those immense, appareled birds kicked itself from the earth and soared across our ken. It was a Wright biplane now, an entry of the Société Ariel; and from the big 25 painted on its tail, one knew Lefébvre was at the levers. One watched in interest, for here was a new figure in the sky, a youthful exponent who, in a phrase, had learned his flying in a correspondence school. Laugh, if you please, but nevertheless this is the truth of it. Lefébvre, they told one, wrote for a machine, got it, and in something under a week had grasped the art of aerial navigation.

At Bétheny, he cut capers in the sky that always amazed, and, if the truth be told, sometimes terrified. Others got into the air, steadied themselves, and then wore away with a majestic dignity of power and pace. They were akin to the great soaring birds— the eagle, condor, osprey, and their like. Here, as one soon enough perceived, was the sparrow. But, sure of himself and always clever, Lefébvre cut upward till he got his height, and then, with his planes slanted steeply on the curve, he wheeled to the course, and, with a springy, bounding flight altogether unlike the level swimming of the bigger, heavier entries, darted off upon his journey.

In fact, each type of flyer, and perhaps even each separate flyer of all the entries in the field, had a distinctive style of its own. With little practise, one got to know each of them at a distance. One saw the great Antoinette engine poking its nose through the blue, and there was no mistaking its poise and certitude, however great the distance. Nor could one err in picking Blériot, tilting at a dizzy pace over the dips and hollows of the plain. Curtiss one knew from afar by the speed and the light springiness of his biplane, its headvanes, stretched out in advance, cutting the air like the forebody of a wild fowl homing to its nightly rest. His was a sprightly engine of flight; it had an abrupt and startling quickness all its own, so that one never quite overcame the habit of gasping when the intrepid driver cut corners at every pylon. And if, by chance, there were one of the big Voisin biplanes touring on the line of view, the onlooker, at the contrast, gave even a deeper gasp. For these French biplanes, big and clumsy beyond all others, went trundling by with the stability and power of a Dreadnought.

Flight after flight was essayed, and in turn succeeded—not a mere hop, skip, and jump off the earth and back again, but the steady touring of a ten kilometre course, six and a quarter miles of it, and all with the regularity and speed of a railway engine. Nor was it a mere spurt out and back again. Farman, at 4.20 P. M. on Friday, crossed the starting line in the *Grand Prix de la Champagne;* and for hour after hour swung round the ten kilometre course until one grew almost weary following him. Mile by mile he rolled up the distance, until, after 3 hours, 4 minutes, and 56 2-5 seconds of unbroken flight, he came to earth again with a record of 180 kilometres. In that time, his height from the earth ranged between ten and forty feet; and the ease with which he took his levels and kept to them was a convincing evidence that the aeroplane has reached a high stage of control and tractability.

Yet Farman's record is confusing. As a sustained effort in mechanical flight it is admirable, well worthy of achievement; but any of the other machines on the course—bar one or two exceptions—could have made it, too, had they been provided with tanks of a greater capacity. And that they were not doesn't mean that they were unable to bear the weight. On the contrary. In the Wright service machine, for example, there is a surplus capacity of more than three hundred pounds above the weight of the pilot that drives it. Reduce that into additional gasoline, and the gasoline into miles, and you find a radius of action that compares favorably with that of a motor car. For flight to-day, be it understood, depends in its *extent* upon little more than the supply of fuel.

There were eight events on the Bétheny program—seven for aeroplanes and one for dirigible balloons. Among them, they covered the four requirements of speed, endurance, carrying capacity, and height; and in each event a world's record was established. Not that these records count for much, however, for there is hardly one of them that will endure, once a single machine is created out of the manifold lessons of the meeting. But as an index to the world of the advance in aviation, they are momentarily invaluable.

One finds it difficult to reduce to generalities the results of the week at Bétheny. A favorite phrase was that Rheims had beheld a new age born, that the world had been witness to the dawn of a new and vital era. Yet that will hardly pass muster when one recalls the fact that the two Wrights had won their mastery of the air four or five years ago. It hits closer to the mark to say that at Bétheny a new age kicked off its swaddling clothes—or that it deplumed itself of its pin feathers.

But one vast and comprehensible fact stuck firmly in the heads of those that viewed the spectacle. In effect, it was that a great and extraordinary, almost incredible progress had been achieved during the past year both in the art and the mechanics of this conquest of the skies. So great, indeed, is the advance that mechanical flight is not only firmly established as a reality, but has touched close to the point of real commercial utility.

A year ago, the world watched the Wrights in flight with extremely divided opinions. In one camp and another, it was a much argued question, now that the secret had been grasped, whether mechanical flight could be applied in any practical way to the uses of the times. To make flying a commercial possibility, the Wrights, it was said, would have to devise a means of automatic balance. So, for a year, the matter rested. Automatic balance—that was the cry!

But at Bétheny no machine was yet equipped with it. Queerly enough, one hardly looked for it, nor could one suppose that such equipment would add greatly to the stability of at least one or two of the machines. Of course, the skill of the individual operator had much to do with this; yet, on the other hand, no machine can attain flight in the hands of the most practised pilot unless it has been designed on stable lines. In this, to the eye of the uninitiated, the Wright 'planes seemed to be deficient. They flew, of course, with power and with certainty, yet with a jerky, bounding motion altogether unlike the steady, even progress of the Antoinette monoplane.

To explain this without technical detail, it may be said that the Wright machine, like a short and stubby boat, rose and fell upon the waves of air; the Antoinette, longer, heavier, and more powerful, cleft a passage through them. To say now which is the better would be unsafe; for time alone can prove that. But in comparing the two from the standpoint of the spectator on the ground, it *is* safe to assume that the Antoinette type embodied more popular requirements than any other form of machine.

It remains to be said, however, that the present Wright machine responds more instantly to control, and offers, at the same time, a greater efficiency per horse power than any other type. And consider this, as well: Of the thirty-one other entries on the Bétheny course, there was not a single machine that in some essential detail did not violate the Wrights' basic patent, as it stands in the United States. Whether or not the courts will sustain them remains to be seen; but whatever the case, the details embodied in the original Wright machine are indispensable features of all mechanical flight. The astonishing part of it, however, was not so much that these ideas had been borrowed, as the way in which they had been developed within a single year.

The Antoinette monoplane which, though first only in the contest for altitude, won foremost popular honors, was a big flying engine —sizable in length, however, rather than in breadth and depth; and of the most graceful proportions. The two supporting surfaces, clothed in snowy white, were inclined at the identical angle at which the wings of a soaring hawk are set, so that, viewed head on from a mile or two away, one had to look twice to make sure this was not some stray barnyard marauder out upon a killing. In the underbody, too, there was the sharp, clean run of breastlines and waist noticeable in hawks and falcons, a trim, incurving front comparable also to the bow of a racing launch. Clear abaft to the waist it was sheathed with cedar plankings; from there on, the fishlike shape was carried out in canvas.

In the other French machines, notably among the biplanes, there was wanting, somehow, an air of reality. Those immense, double-decked fabrics could not fulfill one's cherished visions of the manbird. Even the Blériot machine, in its close likeness to the birds, fell short of one's ideal—what though one confesses this to be only the poetical side of the matter. For in this type of flyer there was an abrupt and fussy nervousness—more or less akin to a teal duck's darting flight— that got on one's nerves while watching it. So it was with the Curtiss and Wright biplanes. They seemed too abrupt in their movements; as if too much were depending on the pilot's skill and faculties—too little on the poise and confidence of the machine itself.

But the Antoinette, in Latham's hands, fulfilled all one's wish. It was real, vital. One who has watched some bird of prey idling through a placid sky can form for himself an image of this power-driven flyer, of its shapeliness, its poise and repose and ever confident sureness.

On Sunday, the final day at Bétheny, one had a finishing evidence of its abilities. Toward nightfall, the wind dropped to a whisper, and over the shoulder of distant Rheims arose the harvest moon, gray and round. To the north lay the Neuchâtel highway, banked deeply with its hedge of watching thousands; on the south, a deeper, blacker hedge could be seen—the other thousands that lined the upper course and stretched far into the distance along the barrier fence. Absorbed, the crowds watched where over the fields a quartet of scaling aeroplanes wheeled and flitted to and fro like sails on a running sea.

Then, out of the skyline's dusty haze, Latham came into view, head on and snoring up toward the turn at a speed of forty-five miles an hour, or thereabouts. Delagrange, in a smaller Blériot monoplane, held the course ahead, but on a level fifty feet below; and as the two made a race of it along the left-hand board of the course, the crowd hung breathless on this contest in the skies.

The Blériot monoplane hustled, its engines tuned to the limit; and, with its curved surfaces drawing like the head-sails of a clipper, careened to the turn and came bundling down the stretch. One saw the smaller engine held a reserve of speed in plenty behind its wings; yet the Antoinette, touring steadily onward, overhauled the chase as if the bird below were squatting on its roost. A roar went up from the crowd. One saw Latham peep downward over the gunwale; his machine forged ahead, and then, in a tremendous burst of speed, the two drove by the tribunes with the Antoinette straight over Delagrange's head, and pulling to the lead with every turn of its propellers.

Another roar leaped to the throats of the volatile French assembly. In the open stand where lunching and watching went on together, high France and his wife went delirious with joy. They climbed to their chairs and wildly waved their napkins. They beat riotous tattoos with knife and fork on chinaware. They took bottles of Madame and Monsieur of Rheims—huge quart fellows, empty or full, it made no matter which—and with them drummed resounding bass *obligatos* on table and floor and railings.

But of a sudden the noise cut short. "Oh!" said the crowd, in the same note as when a train leaps the rails, or some one falls off a roof, or a ship sinks out from under. "Oh!" it said.

Latham, driving by overhead, swerved suddenly. In the poise of a stooping hawk, the Antoinette dropped its head and shot earthward at a steep incline. One guessed instantly in the breathless moment the cause, for the barking rattle of the exhaust had stopped. A minute particle of dust had gagged the carburetor and cut off the supply of fuel; the engine failed, and, waiting for the tragedy, the whole course stood breathless.

It seemed inevitable. The eye leaped instinctively to Delagrange below; the swerve, however, had carried Latham to the left, and the lower 'plane went on, scuttling out of peril, all unaware, so it seemed, of its narrow squeak. But the tragedy still impended. The Antoinette was high enough, if it struck earth headlong, to be wrecked into scrap; yet not high enough, one thought, for room to scale to an even keel, and so to take its landing gently. But the driver had his wits about him; his machine was geared to answer to a touch. . . . By chance, have you ever seen a falcon sweep from overhead, and then, close to the grass, spread itself and skim upward at an easy slant? In plain view of the watching grandstands, Latham's hand reached out and gave two quick jerks to the controlling wheel at his side, a movement about equal to the twist one needs to guide a motor car around a rather narrow turn. Like a thing alive, the dropping 'plane responded. Its engines, cranked by the still revolving blades, caught their breath anew, and, dangling its wheels just over the top of the outfield stubble, the Antoinette swooped upward on the air again and bore away to its landing over beside the highway trees.

By this time, it seemed that the world had seen and felt enough in the eight days at Bétheny to content it for a while. Yet for the last moment—the final hour of the show—there was reserved a spectacle that outdid all the rest in emotion, sensation, thrill.

Night came on quickly now. Twilight spread, and in the haze the round harvest moon loomed red and large. Overhead, a big Voisin biplane trundled by, Paulhan at the wheel, going with a steadiness that drew the usual murmur of applause. Wheeling inside the right-hand pylon, he cut a long, upward curve across the field, his headgear pointed high on the stiff climb before him. Then, as he wore away, Latham came after, and, in his train, Farman, Rougier, and Bunau-Varilla. In wide circles, each one had his try at scaling into the heights above; and the crowd, sensing the emotion of the sights to come, paused in its rush for the exits, and stood gazing, spellbound, upward toward the quiet sky.

Farman passed, still climbing, the broad planes of his machine quivering like the sky-cloths of a full-rigged ship. His form, crouched over the lever, had reduced itself to pigmy size, yet still his flyer's headgear pointed up toward even greater heights. There was a heavy sureness in it all—a magnitude and solidity that in a way robbed one of a feeling that this was flight. It was amazing, of course,—yet it produced the kind of stupor one would have felt to see a ship's tophamper free itself and go off on a voyage through the clouds.

But the immense and startling apparition passed, and there came that other flyer—Latham again, drifting on soundless pinions high above the upturned faces of the throng, so high and free that a low and prolonged whisper of admiration spread, then burst suddenly in another rousing cheer. For here was flight—real flight—the manbird fulfilling to the last degree the popular, enthusiastic dream of what flight should be. Five hundred feet above—at that time the greatest measured height reached in an aeroplane—the broad and shapely fabric swam through the skies, floating in its thin medium with all the grace and power and volition of any of Nature's creatures of the air. Outlined for an instant against the moon's yellow round, it made a picture such as one may safely say the world had never seen before; and, gently turning on its course, silently bore away into the rising loom of darkness that had spread across the plain.

So ended Bétheny, the curtain falling on that last, completing tableau of the conquest of the air. It was the dramatic climax to a week of emotions such as no other spectacle might provide. Of its fruits, one might speculate endlessly. They seem to be illimitable. Aviation, for one thing, acquired an impetus that will go far toward settling mechanical flight on its proper base, both as a sport and as a commercial utility. France, it was evident, has entered the field with its characteristic spirit and enterprise, with all its energies directed toward investigation and improvement, so that it is safe to say now that another year will see the aeroplane firmly established in every field to which it is adapted. Though America and the two Wrights made flying possible, France is now far in the lead. Over there, they have grasped the possibilities; they have made a wide leap in the single year in which mechanical flight has been before the public view; and as an aid to scientific effort—certainly as a vast and astounding spectacle—it would be difficult, indeed, to match the week at Rheims.

30.
The Business Side
of Aviation
(1911)

The Business Side of Aviation
The Money in Flights and Machines

It seems at first glance somewhat premature to rank the new art of flying among the accepted and recognized branches of industry; but on close examination of the actual state of aviation affairs at present there is found ample reason for doing so.

In the past three years an astonishingly large field of commercial and business activity has been built up, that has to do solely with aeronautics.

There are few who have stopped to realize the suggestive fact that more than half a million men are now actively engaged in some industrial enterprise that has to do with navigation of the air.

To fully appreciate the significance of the commercial side of aviation, a knowledge, or at least an acquaintance, must be had with demands on a flying machine, its uses and the commodities whose manufacture, sale or exchange constitute "the trade."

Aeroplanes at present are used in three distinct ways--for sport or convenience, in war or postal service, and as a means of profit in exhibitions, etc.

The use of the aeroplane by sportsmen and its use by individuals or corporations as a convenience, is the field best developed at present, and for which the greatest future is predicted.

The use of aeroplanes in war seems already definitely assured.

Exhibition flying, however, is likely, and in fact has begun to decline, although races if sufficiently exciting are likely to persist.

A great impetus to the use of aeroplanes by sportsmen is bound to come soon, with the further perfecting of the hydro-aeroplane.

The Trade

The market for aeroplanes is of considerable magnitude, as indicated by the volume of sales made by the various companies. M. Bieriot has sold several hundred aeroplanes since the spring of 1909, when he first began manufacturing them on a large scale. He has almost been outdone by the Voisins and Henri Farman, while the enterprise of Esnault-Pelterie, Sommer, Breguet, Nieuport, and a score of other constructors in France brings the total of actual sales to a surprisingly large figure.

A single-seater Bieriot monoplane costs 24,000 francs, and a two-seater, 28,000 francs. This is also the price of Voisin biplanes. A Breguet biplane costs about $6,000 and an Antoinette monoplane is even more expensive.

In general, the range of prices in France is from 15,000 to 30,000 francs.

In England the cost of "all-British" machines like the Valkyrie and Howard Wright runs from $1,500 upward, the price of English made machines being much lower than for those of foreign make.

In the United States there are not over a dozen large and established manufacturing firms, with the Wright, Curtiss and Burgess companies as recognized leaders. The Burgess Co. has sold more than thirty machines, the Wright Co. two or three times as many, and the Curtiss firm also a consider-able number. The average price of American machines is $5,000, although the Burgess Co. charges $7,500 for a biplane of the Wright type equipped with a Gnome motor. The sales here are at present much less than abroad.

It may be conservatively estimated that the sales of aeroplanes to date, both here and abroad, amounts to about 1,500. Placing the average price paid for these machines at $5,000, it becomes evident that the volume of business is represented by an outlay of well over $7,000,000.

In England, for example, the import trade from January to August, 1911, is represented by $177,000, and the export trade by $70,000, thus giving an insight into the magnitude of the trade between England and foreign countries. The exports of France and the imports of America are greater, all statistics proving that France leads the world in the aeroplane industry.

The Bieriot factory employs about 600 men, and is replete with the most up-to-date facilities. The Wright Company has an equally efficient plant of modern buildings, shops and assembly rooms. In fact the growth of most aeroplane factories has been phenomenal, and yet the real lasting market for the aeroplane has been but slightly reached.

Greater even than the trade in aeroplaning, as a unit, has been the activity in the supply and demand for aeroplane accessories from motors and propellers to the minutest parts of metal or wood.

There are fifty or more established firms in this country alone, doing a large business in parts of aeroplanes, like ribs, struts, joints, etc. As in France, propellers are being designed and manufactured by more than ten firms devoted to this alone.

In France the Chauviere Company is a large corporation employing many hundred men, with extensive shops, and turning out countless propellers for all types of aircraft.

Many of these separately manufactured parts never get to be used in a full fledged aeroplane, but serve merely for purposes of experiment.

The motor trade is also large, especially in France. The Gnome company pays dividends that few "industrials" ever reach, and its business grows apace. Many American motors are showing excellent qualities and are much preferred here to the higher priced foreign motors.

Aeorplane supply houses abroad have ceased to be a novelty and are rapidly becoming a necessity. Even special clothing for aviators is now being made, leather being a favorite material. Numerous kinds of map cases, portable buffets, helmets, searchlights, and horns are offered specially for aeroplaning.

There is also much done in France in the manufacture of instruments for aeronautical work, speedometers, recording barographs, altiscopes, sketching cases and specially mounted compasses.

Coincident with the large trade in aeroplane supplies and in aeorplanes themselves, there has arisen a large number of firms in France, acting as aeroplane brokes, receiving orders and transmitting them to the manufacturers. Dealers in second-hand machines and supplies are also springing up, but their field is still very limited--a second-hand aeroplane is a dangerous investment at best.

Lagagneux, the all-around French aviator, who has made records with both
monoplanes and biplanes.

Claude Grahame-White, England's leading aviator. He has won many
cash prizes.

Weyman, the American, who won
the Gordon Bennett Cup race
this year in England.

Louis Breguet, first to carry live
load equaling weight of
machine.

Even the profession of the law is called into the aeroplane field to a great extent the number of flourishing patent attorneys giving an indication of the amazing number of patents applied for.

The model aeroplane also plays its part in the industry and many model manufacturers sell several hundred of these toys at prices ranging from $1.50 to $20. Gliders, motorless aeroplanes, are also manufactured and sold, especially in England, where "gliding" is becoming a hobby.

The number of corporations applying for certificates in various States, although only a few survive, gives a further indication of how active the field of aviation is becoming from the business side.

The Art

It is not only in the trade and manufacturing of aeroplanes that a large volume of business is found. Activity of another kind, but of equally great importance exists in the cultivation and practice of the art of flying.

A large number of men are employed by private individuals to fly their machines for them, and many manufacturers have a regular staff of expert birdmen to test, exhibit and instruct others on their machines.

Few persons appreciate the actual cost of flying and what it means to keep as delicate a machine as an aeroplane in perfect order. Atwood in his great St. Louis-New York trip, is said to have made over $6,000 in prize money. It is understood on good authority that this failed by a large margin to pay his expenses.

To keep an aeroplane in perfect trim two or three trained mechanics are required. The wages of these men are $30 to $35 a week each, and often more.

A Burgess-Wright aeroplane of the kind used by Atwood requires four gallons of gasoline an hour in flight, the gasoline costing about 20 cents a gallon. Oil, motor accessories, spare spark plugs, etc., also cost a considerable amount. The aeroplane, itself, practically used up in this grueling campaign, cost $5,000.

In addition Atwood has large expenses for rents of fields and hangars, as well as damages to property, and in his own traveling expenses, his manager's salary, etc., are found other sources of expenditure. The grand total amounts to well over $8,000--a rather expensive way to travel.

At the recent aviation meets many of the contestants suffered heavy financial losses. In most cases, however, the losses fall on the manufacturer who supplies the machine and who employs an expert to handle it.

The earnings of some of the aviators at the recent Boston meet are: Ovington, $11,782; Milling, $6,200; Sopwith, $6,022; Grahame-White, $5,224, etc., down to Ely, at $150; and others with no winnings at all.

At Nassau, Sopwith won $4,850, while Atwood and Lieut. Arnold won only a few hundred dollars.

There are other sources of revenue, however, in the actual flying of aeroplanes.

Passenger carrying at $25 to $50 a head is becoming customary in this country. In England and France, regulation booking offices have been opened where reservation can be made. The price is from $10 upward.

Manufacturers and aviators also make a considerable charge for instruction of pupils. In France, $150 is the usual price for a full course. If breakages are to be included, the Voisin Company charges $500.

At many aerodromes in England, where their location seems to be definite, hangars and the privileges of the field may be rented at $500 a year. The rent of the hangars in France is about the same.

The business of aviation is thus growing apace and the possibilities that are offered in the flying field for the development of industrial enterprises can probably be as little conceived of at present, as could the future of railroading one hundred years ago.

Glenn H. Curtiss, winner of the Scientific American trophy, first to rise from water in a biplane.

Louis Blériot, France's premier monoplane inventor, first to cross the English Channel, July 25th, 1909.

Wilbur Wright, the elder of the two brothers who built the first practical aeroplane.

Morane, the former Blériot pilot, who has invented an exceedingly fast and efficient monoplane.

31.
A Chamber of Horrors
(1911)

A Chamber of Horrors
Wild Designs in Flying Machines
By Marius C. Krarup

Every one of the aviation machines shown in the accompanying illustrations is dear to its maker or designer and to his friends. Every one of them has something in its construction which is promising, sensible or brilliant to men whose ability in the ordinary walks of life has been sufficient to enable them to save or borrow the money wherewith to substantiate their faith in aviation. All but one are proudly photographed ready to fly at the word "go." Yet only the one not so pictured ever made a start. The others probably still cherish the convictions which created them by means of occult or theoretical qualities, the nature of which the uninitiated beholder may only surmise. Here is a problem for the psychologist to solve. Mechanics alone scarcely furnish the key to its correct solution. The shrewd observation that it is better to get into the "game of aviation" wrong than not to get into it at all in its beginning may have shaped many of the hasty creations which abound in the shops of amateur aviators the world over. They are evidence of a widespread desire to become identified at almost any cost with a movement clearly destined to be more conspicuously picturesque in its unfolding than any other which civilization has ever wit-nessed, and prodigiously fruitful in physical, scientific and financial adventure. These odd structures are claims staked off on the hills of golden promise, and the cheerful prospectors confidently expect to "grow up with the country," and to reap the rewards which come to all sturdy pioneers. A single unproportioned thought, "given his act" contrary to the advice of Polonius and embodied in steel, wood and fabric, is boldly offered as the entry fee, and lo! the world generously accepts it. For it is not after all proof of courage and energy, those primary traits of character which are as much needed for progress as mere insight, which grows with what it feeds upon and may be acquired. These men shall have free passes to glory and advancement, provided they stand by their claims, work them and guide their next steps a little more closely to the sum total of dry facts and experiences from which real flying aeroplanes have been evolved.

The unproportioned thoughts manifested in the various machines are not without interest. The edgewise tumble has haunted the maker of No. 1. Of this he is sure: So long as the motor and propeller are kept working, these drums will uphold whatever they are capable of upholding, whether the wind tosses them to one side or the other. Pivoted as they are to the elegant trussed frame, they afford means for sustentation, for steering and for fore-and-aft balancing, all combined in a single mechanical conception. If the propellers cease propelling, simply tilt both drums forward for a gradual descent. Should the impact with the earth be a little hard, the structure offers the same advantage which has served Latham so well in his Antoinette flier; namely, that there is much material to be broken before the shock reaches the aviator's

Fig. 1.—This designer was haunted by the fear of edgewise tumbling. He did
not know that drums are inefficient lifting surfaces.

person. It seems almost a pity that the laws of the atmosphere will not
permit drums to act as efficient aeroplane lifters.

The machine shown in Fig. 2 is the contribution of the Marquis
d'Equeuvillay. It may be imagined that the scion of a noble house has
started his train of thought with a profound respect for the magic strength
of a bicycle wheel. By developing its great principle of centripetal
stresses it should be possible to produce a very light framework rich in
capacity for areas, strong and yet deformable at its ovalized periphery,
and, Eureka! with motor and aviator centrally located and applying the
vital forces of propulsion and control from the rigid hub, the very
deformation of the rim and planes might be utilized for steering and
balancing. Note also the forethought evinced in shaping the upper
planes with a self-righting curvature.

If two planes are better than one, then three planes are better than two.
This is the simple and powerful idea embodied in the apparatus pictured
in Fig.3, and which is known as the Bousson-Bourgnis. It is common
to many triplanes. In addition, an abundance of rudders, generous in
size, and a certain flabby flexibility in all the areas, testify to an active,
energetic misunder-standing of nearly all the leading principles in
successful aviation. The head-on resistance is enormous. What might
perhaps have been gained by using perfectly elastic materials shaped and
proportioned so as to return an equivalent in work for the power
expended in bending the planes back, is squandered through the
acceptance intead of unresponsive materials, endowed with an inert flexibility rather than resiliency, the bending of which, under the influence of

Fig. 2.—A marquis's idea of applying the principle of centripetal stresses.
Too much head resistance here.

air resistance, means mainly the generation of heat from molecular friction and the consequent wasting of the power employed for overcoming the air resistance.

Stoeckel's monoplane (Fig. 6 in this series) was expected to work a revolution in aeroplane dynamics, for it is equipped with a motor of only twelve horsepower driving two propellers of very modest diameters located far below the level of the planes and the bulk of the air resistance. Under these circumstances the machine should immediately tip over backward the moment the wheels leave the ground, but the designer has

Fig. 3.—If two planes are better than one, three must be better than two, argued this designer, taking no account of the head resistance.

Fig. 4.—Here the eye rests in peace, for compared with standard designs
the variations are more conspicuous than radical.

placed an inverted canoe, also useful as a sunshade, lengthwise over the central portion of his machine, and in this device he must have anticipated special virtues, not only the feeble merits of an undersized parachute, but something extraordinary in the way of balancing effect, since it is otherwise an axiom among aeroplane builders that the power and the air resistance must be kept pretty well in line. As a wind wagon skipping nimbly over the aviation field the compact Stoecker, with its short wheelbase, should have real merit, however, not to be despised for meets, particularly if the inverted canoe, as the illustration suggests, may be tipped and utilized to preserve the balance.

The largest aeroplane in the world is shown in Fig. 5. It was constructed at Dunstall, near Wolverhampton, by Lieut. Seddon of the British navy. It is equipped with two 80 horsepower engines and its planes measure an area of 1,000 square feet. The boldness of the figures and of the mechanical execu-tion, with the great hoops and sweeping curves suggesting the expert in Spencerian handwriting, almost disarms criticism, numbing it with the query: Can this be possible? Can this be what we are striving for and what we are coming to? In that case, would it not be better to leave aviation alone until a more advanced mastery of materials shall have made it possible to accomplish it by simpler designs? The large hoops, crossed with others like them and tied at the crossings, give great freedom in producing any desired relation between the planes. By mere changes in the angles and the points of contact of the hoops, practically the same framework may be utilized for a number of ex-perimental variations, and perhaps it may be assumed that the designer has been actuated by this consideration, knowing that the tandem arrangement of planes has been found unfavorable to equilibrium, but knowing also that no large aeroplane construction can be expected until this difficulty shall have been experimentally overcome. But the design looks more theoretical than inspired.

The engineer responsible for the example in Fig. 7 has also tackled elongated construction, being plainly actuated by hopes of escaping from the problem of lateral equilibrium. As for the necessary sustentation, fancy this scow being sucked forward through the atmosphere at great speed by the innocent little propeller, and the friendly mind will readily perceive how the bow will throw powerful air waves upward against the flying-fox membrane extending from the gunwale, fairly lifting the structure; and, moreover, the hollow of the scow will create a vacuum-- the vacuum being a highly favored phenomenon among independent

Fig. 5. – Here is a huge machine which seems to have been designed by one who admired the sweeping curves of copybook penmanship.

aeroplane designers, nearly always produced without special expenditure of power--to fill which a mighty upward pressure from the atmosphere underneath will automatically assert itself. The hand wheel in front of the operator seems to connect with a simple rudder at the top for side steering, and the perfect lateral balance produced by the narrow con-formation and the low center of gravity (really permissible with this shape) should render all other and auxiliary steering means superfluous. For up-and-down steering perhaps the aviator slides his own weight forward and back-ward.

The seven machines mentioned and illustrated in the foregoing might have been proposed and built whether Lilienthal, Maxim, Langley, the Wrights and Bleriot had ever gathered data for aviation or not. But on the Diapason mono-plane (Fig. 4) the eye may rest in peace. As com-pared with standard design, its variations are more conspicuous than radical. The tail and side-steering apparatus have been cut in twain and moved to the two sides; the *ailerons* have been moved rearward. The arrangement makes room for a large propeller, and, while the equil-ibrium seems more sensitive, the means for maintaining it and for steering may at the same time have been improved. The machine is said to have flown with some success, and it would be rash to assert its superiority or inferiority in comparison with other models depending on control by rudder actionIt accentuates this feature, making even stronger demands upon the aviator's agility than the standard type.

Recent Aeroplane Accidents

During the past month there have been many accidents. In several of these the aeroplane has caught fire in the air, and the aviator has been burned to death or killed by the fall. One such accident occurred in France on September 2nd, another in Spain two days later, and the third, in which two men were killed, happened in Germany on the 7th ult.

Fig. 6. — A monoplane that was expected to "revolutionize" aerodynamics and didn't.

Maron, the French pilot of the Savary biplane, was the first victim of this type of accident. He experienced a bad fall on the 2nd ult. His machine caught fire, and when it struck the ground, he was incinerated under the debris. Lieut. de Grailly, of the French army, also fell and was burned to death on the 2nd inst., owing, it is claimed, to the breaking of a wing of his R.E.P. monoplane. Capt. Camine, with the same make of machine, was killed by the fall due to the same cause. On September 5th, M. Leforestier, a French aviator, fell to his death at Huelva, Spain. His machine, which was of his own construction, is said to have caught fire in the air.

Two other men who were victims of this kind of accident were Lieut. Newmann, a German military aviator, and M. Leconte, his passenger. While making a cross-country flight on September 7th the machine caught fire when at a height of sixty feet, and fell to the ground, instantly killing both aviators. The same day, Paul Senge, another German aviator, fell and fractured his skull at the town of Karlsrube.

Two days later Herr Eyring was killed near Stuttgart. On September 29th, Capt. Englehardt, Germany's premier military pilot and the first man whom the Wrights taught to fly in that country, was killed by a fall, while his passenger, Herr Sedlmayer, had his skull fractured and received other serious injuries.

In England, Lieut. Cammell, a seasoned Bleriot pilot, on the 18th ult., fell to his death while making his first flight in a Valkyrie (English)

Fig. 7.—Fancy this scow being sucked forward through the atmosphere at great speed by the innocent little propeller!

monoplane. He had been aloft 10 minutes and was making his second wide circuit, when the monoplane turned over and dropped 90 feet to the ground. Capt. J.J. Frisbie, Louis Rosenbaum and Cromwell Dixon were killed in America when flying at State fairs. The last-named aviator, a youth of but 19, fell 80 feet into a stone quarry at Spokane, Wash., on October 2nd, owing to his turning too sharply to avoid hitting some telegraph wires, and sliding down on end as a consequence. A few days before, at Helena, Mont., Dixon had flown over the Rocky Mountains to Blossburg, a small town 18 miles away, and back again. Blossburg lies in a deep pocket in the mountains, from which wild ducks and geese escape with difficulty after battling with the air currents sometimes for hours. It took Dixon twice as long--22 minutes--to attain the necessary altitude of 7,000 feet at Blossburg as it did at Helena. The trip out and back across the 6,200-foot Mullins Pass was made in 15 and 17 minutes respectively. Dixon was given a $10,000 purse made up by several men who witnessed his flight. He delivered a letter from Governor Norris. This is the second time a Curtiss biplane has crossed the Rockies. Ely was the first to accomplish this feat at Butte, Mont., last spring.

On September 25th, at the Nassau Boulevard meet, Dr. Clark, a trick bicyclist, had a fatal fall in a Queen monoplane. He was unable to accustom himself to moving the warping control lever outward instead of inward when turning. A sharp turn to the right, caused by improper warping, resulted in the instant development of gyroscopic force by the revolving motor sufficient to make the machine dive vertically to the ground.

32.
Airships

⊛⊛⊛

Two American
Conquerors of the Air
(1908)

AIR-SHIPS

BY DAY ALLEN WILLEY

use the word "air-ship" for the various de-
s of mechanism by which a man can move
ugh the air; but strange as it may seem, the
1 cannot be found in the dictionaries, so
ntly has it been coined. And in any case it
word that seems misleading; for the name
p" is associated with something that has sails.
air-ship, as we know it, is usually a bag con-
ing gas or hot air, which is driven in various
ctions by an engine and steered like a boat,
a rudder. It is useless without its gas-bag,
cannot be kept in the air merely by its ma-
ery. Really the aëroplane can more correctly
alled an air-ship, because it has wings or sails
nst which the air-currents press and thus aid,
only in holding it above the ground, but in
ng it motion.

we call the aëroplane an air-ship, it is not a
idea by any means; for as far back as 1879
arly thirty years ago—Victor Tatin, a
1ch scientist, made one which went through
air at the speed of twenty-five feet a second,
ver a quarter of a mile a minute. As those
e the times when the modern gas-engine, such
ve use in the automobile and "power-boat,"
unknown, compressed air was the motive
e. It passed from an air-chamber into two
ellers which forced the aëroplane through

the atmosphere as a boat goes through the water.
This air-ship, which made its successful flight at
Meudon, near Paris, had two "wings" of light silk
stretched on wooden frames which kept them
distended. These wings or sails could be turned
in different directions like the sails of a yacht,
only, instead of being arranged up and down or
in a vertical direction, they were nearly horizontal.

It is worth while to describe Tatin's air-ship
because nearly all which have since been tried
have been modeled with sails or wings. Of
course, each type is different from its fellows, but
usually in the number and shape of the sails. No
man has invented a type which is without them,
but the inventor has wrought such wonders with
the engine that a motor has recently been built
in Europe which actually has a power equal to
the strength of a hundred horses. The ordinary
steam-engine of this force would weigh so much
that it could not be used for even the automobile,
saying nothing of air navigation; but this European model is so very compact and light that two
men can easily carry it on their shoulders. This
is because it requires no heavy cylinders or boiler,
which would be needed if it was operated by
steam. No, its energy all comes from the explosion of gas. It has little tanks or cylinders into

each of which a tiny spray of gasolene or some other inflammable oil is thrown, mixed with air. This vapor is fired by sparks from an electric battery. As it explodes it generates a gas so powerful that a little of it has as much strength as a much larger volume of steam—a strength that sends the motor-car whizzing along the highway at the speed of an express-train, and the power-boat rushing through the water at the rate of twenty to thirty miles an hour.

Yes, the vapor engine, or whatever you choose to call it, has done more to make the real air-ship a practical device than anything else; but until recently, only the craft which had the gas-bag was capable of going into the air and making a journey of more than a few miles, in spite of the hundreds of kinds of wings and engines that have been fashioned. A few of those who would navigate the air as the sailor navigates the sea, have tried both the wings and the gas-bag. Santos Dumont, the young, Brazilian who has made himself famous by what is termed the "dirigible balloon," has experimented. with the "flying-machine" or aëroplane as well, but the greatest distance he has ever gone is only a few feet com-

wings so that they could fly like a bird. ing to this out-of-the-way corner of North C lina to keep the rest of the world from kno of their experiments, they made several gli machines, as they called them—boxes of canvas held in shape by wooden sticks. T were open at the sides and not unlike the kites which are so much in use nowadays. tening a box upon his shoulders one of brothers would make a running start on the of a sand-hill and leap from the top with wind facing him. This plan was so succe that one of the Wrights made a flight of t hundred feet before he again touched the gro The trials, however, led them to give up the of flying like a bird without some other f than air-pressure, so they designed several engines for their aëroplanes, and with the ai one of these they traveled a distance of ov mile without touching the earth, and "flew high as sixty feet above it.

The Wrights have designed types of aëropl for use in France as well as the United St. The American design was accepted by the U States Government for military purposes aft

BALDWIN'S DIRIGIBLE (OR "STEERABLE") AIR-SHIP.

pared with his balloon flights. One of the first, if not the first, successful aëroplane to be built in the United States was that with which the Wrights "flew" about a mile above the bleak sand beach of Cape Hatteras, North Carolina. The two brothers, who lived in the city of Dayton, Ohio, became convinced that they could construct

had made an aërial voyage lasting over an h and at an elevation at times of 250 feet above earth. In September, 1908, Orville Wright formed this successful feat with Lieutenant Fr P. Lahm, the aërial expert, as a passenger. aëroplane, which is the most practical de which has yet been built in America, is forty

STEERING AN AIR-SHIP UPWARD BY SHIFTING THE MAN'S WEIGHT ALONG THE CAR FRAME.

length. Its weight without passengers is 850 nds, including a gasolene motor having the ver of forty horses, which has driven it ough the air at the rate of thirty-nine miles an r—the speed of a fast railway train.

Besides the box-kite there is the old-fashioned ign still used by the boys fond of kite-flying. s is the kind where two sticks are fastened the form of a letter X and a crosspiece at-

will easily lift a man into the air, so much strength has it. Taking Professor Bell's idea, the late Professor Langley, of the Smithsonian Institution at Washington, designed a flying-machine with three or four wings made up of kite-cells of the tetrahedral form. This made a flight over the Potomac River but fell into the water and was ruined. In France a score of other inventors have tried to excel the achievement of Santos Du-

TWO AIR-SHIPS STARTING FOR A RACE.

ied, the upper opening of the X being smaller n the lower. That great scientific kite-maker, fessor Alexander Bell, as described in ST. HOLAS for October, 1907, has changed this n into what he calls the tetrahedral kite, which

mont, but, as we have already stated, no machine has yet been tried which would remain in the air more than a short time, and the distance covered has been a mere trifle compared with the voyages of the dirigible balloons.

A simple explanation of "dirigible" is contained in the word "steerable." The dirigible balloon, which is what most people mean when they say air-ship, is simply a balloon which can be directed—its movements guided and controlled so that it travels in the direction desired by the aëronaut or navigator. It is just as much of a balloon as those which rose above the earth in the days when the great bags were driven here and there before the air-currents, and a man who

call the stern. The great French bag called *Patrie* was of this pattern, as it was believed th the smaller bags aided to steady the larger o when in motion, and permitted the steersman guide it more accurately with the rudder.

Below the gas-bag, however, are many diff ent contrivances. Of course there is the engi possibly two or three, if the air-craft is ve large. The basket in which aëronauts of form days usually ascended is replaced by a car whi

THE TRIAL ASCENT OF THE AIR-SHIP *DIRIGIBLE II* IN ENGLAND.

chanced to be in the "basket" or perhaps hanging on the trapeze-bar had no control over them except to open the gas-valve and lower himself by allowing the contents of the bag to escape. The shape of the bag, however, has been greatly altered. It is usually in the form of a huge cylinder, narrowing gradually to a blunt point at each end, the greatest thickness of the cylinder being over the machinery. The reason why the bag of the modern balloon is shaped like a cigar or banana is because it offers less resistance to the air when moving in a horizontal direction. Sometimes three or four smaller bags are attached to the rear end or what the seaman would

may be partly inclosed in glass as a protecti from the weather. A narrow platform extendi beneath the center of the bag allows the navi tor to reach his engine and his ballast-bags ha ing in rows in the rigging, and from this platfo he may move the huge rudder by means of ropes or wires which extend from it to the pl form.

Running this sort of an air-ship is very mu like running an automobile, except that the na gator must keep his craft far enough aloft well as headed in the right direction; but moving enough weight beneath the back part the bag he can throw the front end at an upwa ne and thus ascend as he goes forward. If vants to descend he can reverse the position ne weight or release some of the gas by open- the valve in the bag. Should he wish to nd vertically, he can do like the old-time aëro-

Lake Constance, Switzerland, was about 420 feet long and was driven by two engines having the combined power of no less than 170 horses, while the great bag contained when filled 375,000 cubic feet of gas. This air-ship in its trials rose to a height of over 1000 feet above Lake Constance, carrying, not only the machinery, but twelve passengers, and while in the air moved forward at a rate of over thirty miles an hour, the navigator turning it in circles and guiding it as easily as the motorist guides his touring-car on the ground. While this craft met with an accident and was destroyed, another of the same model has since been completed that excelled its performances.

Several of the European countries have designed dirigible balloons to be used for military purposes. The one designed in England is called *Nulli Secundus*, and after being completed made a trip from Farnsborough, where it was constructed, to the city of London, circling around several towers in the city

COUNT ZEPPELIN'S EARLIER AIR-SHIP, MORE THAN 400 FEET LONG.
Photographed in flight by E. Frankl, Berlin.

t—throw over the sand-bags. The engine nds on the size of the balloon, which is usu- large enough to hold it in the air with the engers, even should it break down or stop n some other cause. It may be of five or ten more horse-power, but it is always sufficiently erful to whirl the big wooden, canvas, or ninium blades of the propeller which, fas- d underneath the rear of the bag, does the e duty in the air that the screw of the ocean r does far beneath the surface of the sea. h its assistance the air-ship may travel at a of twenty miles an hour or more, even inst the wind.

e most successful dirigible balloon was proba- the *Zeppelin*, so called from its inventor. It by far the greatest air-ship, if it may be ned such, yet constructed, while it had a rd for attaining the greatest speed and lift- the heaviest load yet borne aloft. Count Zep- n is a German officer who has spent several rs in studying the problem of air navigation. air-ship, which was built on the shore of

and finally returning to its starting point. *La Patrie,* the French air-craft, also made several journeys of the same length guided without difficulty, but, unfortunately, broke from its fastenings and was carried out to sea some time ago. The United States has several types of war balloons and has recently asked inventors to plan air-ships which can be used for military purposes. American genius, however, has been successful in building models which are as practical as any of the European types. One of the first to be completed was the design of Dr. William A. Baldwin, which was exhibited at the Oregon Exposition in 1905. With it Roy Knabenshue described circles in the air, moved over the city of Portland, and returned to the place where the air-ship had risen from the exposition grounds. Since then Mr. Knabenshue and other navigators have guided their crafts through the air, some of them manœuvering over the city of New York itself.

The latest design of Dr. Baldwin's air-ship has been accepted by the United States Government for military service.

TWO AMERICAN CONQUERORS OF THE AI

BY C. H. CLAUDY

WITH PHOTOGRAPHS OF THE WRIGHT AËROPLANE IN MOTION

ALMOST every boy knows the names of the Americans Wilbur and Orville Wright, and their aëroplane which has astonished the whole world.

It consists of two surfaces of cloth, stretched on wooden frames and held apart by struts, a horizontal rudder in front, a vertical one behind, and an engine driving two propellers; there is

hand planes will move as one, and so that the left-hand ones will move as one. When right-hand ends are bent or warped *toward* earth, the left-hand ends of the planes are or warped *away* from the earth. Both end both planes, of course, warp in either directio will, but the ends warp always together. B

ORVILLE WRIGHT.

From photographs by Hollinger.

WILBUR WRIGHT.

nothing particularly startling about this. The meat of the invention lies in the shape of the surfaces and the fact that this shape can be altered in the air.

Both ends of both planes, that is, the frames on which the cloth is stretched, are movable, not upon hinges but by bending the frames themselves, that is, bending under pressure, just as a rattan cane bends. A simple system of chains and wires and a lever controls this bending or "warping" of the planes, so that the two right-

second lever, the rear or vertical rudder-pla are turned very much as a rudder is turned in water. Still a third lever operates the front horizontal rudder-planes, which steer the air-s toward or away from the ground.

It has been known for years and years, e before Lilienthal gave his life to prove it, tha certain surface of a certain form would supp a man's weight in the air if it is kept going slower than at a certain speed. To keep up speed, a motor and propellers are used instead

THE WRIGHT AËROPLANE IN FULL FLIGHT AT FORT MYER.

THE WRIGHT AËROPLANE APPROACHING.

the flapping stroke of the bird. But the balancing! There was the difficulty of the whole matter! Lilienthal and Pilcher, his pupil, balanced themselves by throwing their weight from side to side as they hung to their "gliding machines." Once they were not quick enough, and their lives paid the penalty. Something else than an athletic shifting of weight was necessary.

That something else the Wright brothers found. When they are in the air and a gust or a puff of wind, or a shifting of their own position, or any other cause makes the machine tip, a lever is moved, and two planes warp down a little on the end that is canting toward the earth. At the same instant the two opposite ends warp up. The ends which warp down immediately offer more resistance to the air through which they are moving; the ends which move up offer less. The result is that the machine ceases its tipping and rights itself. Before it tips the other way the lever is moved so that the air-ship again moves forward on an even keel. In going around a corner, the trouble with aëroplanes has hitherto been a "skidding" through the air, a sliding away from the true course, somewhat on the same principle that a boat will not sail well across the wind without a center-board. Now, when the Wright machine is to go around a corner, simultaneously with the shifting of the rear rudder the planes are warped to such an extent that the whole machine cants over and goes around the corner leaning against the wind, just as a bicycler takes a curve leaning against the centrifugal force.

There does not appear, as yet, any limit to the things which these two unassuming American gentlemen can do with their machines. They seem to go at almost any speed they please, stay up about as long as the fuel for their motor holds out, and perform any sort of evolution. Only one serious accident has marred their success,

and that was owing to a weakness of the structure, not of the machine's principle.

The world needs flying-machines for many purposes—and one of them may well be to make war so terrible that no nation will ever fight.

It is a matter of pride to all who know them, know of them, have seen them fly, or heard their conquests, here and abroad, that the best and, indeed, the only really successful conquerors of the air, thus far, is the invention of two American men who are now themselves the foremost flyers of the whole world.

CONDUCTOR: "UJIJI JUNCTION! CHANGE CARS! STEP LIVELY, PLEASE!"

WHEN ANIMALS FOR THE CIRCUS COME FROM AFRICA BY AIR-SHIP.

33.
The Aerial Battleship
(1909)

WAR IN THE AIR

FROM A DRAWING BY G. A. COFFIN

McCLURE'S MAGAZINE

AUGUST, 1909

THE AËRIAL BATTLESHIP

BY

CARL DIENSTBACH AND T. R. MacMECHEN

ILLUSTRATED WITH DRAWINGS BY G. A. COFFIN
AND WITH PHOTOGRAPHS

"Heard the heavens fill with shouting, and there rain'd a ghastly dew
From the nations' airy navies grappling in the central blue."

IN the fall of 1908 the third airship built by Count Ferdinand von Zeppelin was bought by the German government, officially commissioned as a warship, and given a military crew. On May 29, 30, and 31 his fifth and last ship, the Zeppelin II., made, without landing, a flight of thirty-six hours, covering 850 miles. This flight would have carried it from German soil to London, Paris, Vienna, or Stockholm, and back again. In secret trials by the German government during March, a rapid-firing gun, capable of throwing nearly sixty 1.9-inch shells a minute, was fired with entire success from the deck of the Zeppelin I. This means the end of armies within the next ten years. The situation, about which there is now the densest popular ignorance, should be understood.

A savage very naturally would consider a ship of iron a physical impossibility. He is accustomed only to rafts. Our present civilization is in exactly the same position with regard to the navigation of the air; it is accustomed only to balloons. A Zeppelin airship is not a balloon, but a true ship—exactly corresponding to an iron ocean ship. It has a strong, rigid hull; it is sustained by displacing more than its own weight in the fluid that supports it; it will sink only if it leaks badly. Neither the airship nor the iron ocean ship is in the slightest danger of sinking except by grounding or collision.

It is perfectly natural that the public should be ignorant concerning the new airship. The two chief principles upon which its success is founded have both been announced in the last six years. Up to 1903 it was impossible to drive dirigible balloons by motors at any considerable speed. Every increase of power simply caused the elongated structures to plunge up and down, and throw their broadsides forward. Colonel Charles Renard of the French army then announced his discovery of the stabilizing planes — big fins, placed on the stern of the ship, like the feathers on an arrow. With these an airship can be driven straight ahead at any speed that can be applied to it.

A Huge Power-Driven Arrow

Count Zeppelin had completed his first rigid airship — a structure 384 feet long — in 1900. It was a crude thing, directed up and down by shifting weights, and capable of only a low speed. He immediately adopted the Renard planes, after they became public property in 1903; but he had built three of his ships before he discovered, in the summer of 1907, the secret of steering them up and down. This problem was solved by placing two sets of large air-planes on each side of the ship, one forward and the other aft. Since that time he has possessed, in the Zeppelin I. and Zeppelin II., two huge power-driven arrows, 446 feet long; capable of being driven at a speed of

FRANCE'S LARGEST AIRSHIP, "LA RÉPUBLIQUE," 200 FEET LONG

ments of France, England, and the United States. The last are simply motor balloons; the first is as true a ship as any on the ocean. It is protected by a cover of tough rubber-cloth, stretched over aluminum rings and ribs, each strong enough to support a man's weight; and the whole is greatly strengthened by the upward pressure of the hydrogen in its inside balloons. It is fully as strong for its purposes as an iron steamship. The airship is never strained by rolling or pitching, like the steamer, because the air acts upon it as a current and not as waves — exactly as the water acts upon a submarine; and it consequently flies on a perfectly level keel, even in a gale. It is supported by from sixteen to twenty absolutely

thirty-five miles an hour through the air; and handled as quickly and easily not merely as an ocean-going ship, but as an automobile. Nothing could be more wonderful than the control of these great craft. Turning figures of eight is a common trick; perpendicular dives have been taken at a speed that caused every spectator to believe that the ship, by some accident, was falling to immediate destruction; and irregular movements are performed that make the ship appear to observers to be "dancing and juggling in the air."

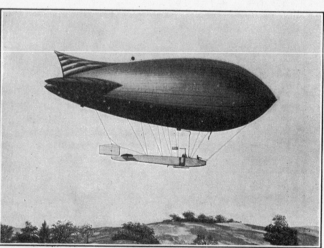

THE LAST ENGLISH DIRIGIBLE, "THE BABY," 100 FEET LONG

A True Ship — Strong and Stable

A distinction must be made at the outset between the Zeppelin airships and the dirigible balloons adopted by the govern-

THE LAST ZEPPELIN, 446 FEET LONG

THE ZEPPELIN AIRSHIP

THE GREAT PLANES AT THE STERN, AND THE VERTICAL STEERING APPARATUS AT THE SIDES, WHICH
ARE THE INVENTIONS THAT MADE LARGE AIRSHIPS POSSIBLE,
ARE SEEN CLEARLY IN THE PICTURE

separate compartments (that is, from sixteen to twenty drum-shaped balloons), whereas a ship has but five or six compartments, which are often found to be open in case of accident.

The strength and stability of these new ships are not a matter of theory or belief; they are already demonstrated facts. The Zeppelin I., under her military crew, made nineteen ascensions between March 9th and April 6th, in the mountainous country about Lake Constance, which is 1,300 feet above sea-level. Three of these were made in snow-storms; one of them, lasting seven and a half hours, in a blizzard. In another trial, the ship flew for hours, landed, and anchored safely, in a tremendous forty-mile gale. The Zeppelin II. on May 31 crushed her whole bow in while landing, spent a full day, in a heavy wind, floating on her collision bulkheads, was temporarily repaired, and then flew with her own motors fifty miles to her home port in perfect safety. No ocean steamship could have done more than this after an equally serious accident. All this time these huge craft—the size of Atlantic liners—have been landing on the ground, without special wharves. A captain attempting the similar feat of landing a great steamship upon a shore without wharves would be considered insane.

Chief Advantages, Speed and Economy

The fact is that a new instrument for the general service of civilization has arrived. Its uses, as distinct from those of ships upon water, can be clearly and definitely seen. Water being eight hundred times heavier than air, airships will never compete with steamships as freight-carriers. For exactly the same reason, they will develop double or triple the speed of the ship in the water; they will do this driven by engines of less than two per cent of the power of the steamer; and their lighter material will allow them to be built at within fifteen per cent of the cost and time that are required for the building of a first-class ocean steamer of the same length. The Zeppelin II.— 446 feet long and the largest airship in existence — cost less than $250,000, has a speed of thirty-five miles an hour, and is driven by two separate engines of 200 combined horse-power, less than that of two racing automobiles.

The engines of these ships can handle them perfectly in a gale of wind, and there is virtually no danger that both of them will break down at once — a fact that cannot be disputed since the recent trip of gasoline-motor automobiles about the earth. The present ships, and still more those that are about to be made, will be perfectly able to weather the elements continuously, like any other ship. The present shelter-houses will be given up, and they will land and be moored, when not in use, to aërial wharves sufficiently high so that by slightly tilting the sterns of the ships in the air they will be kept from thrashing against the ground. Moored in this way, they will ride out the heaviest storms with perfect safety. In short, although but five of them have now been built, they have already demonstrated their efficiency.

Germany Creates the First Aërial Gunboat

From the beginning, it has been perfectly evident that the first important use of these

which cover a space some fifty feet square. The level car of the airship proved an excellent gun-platform in the trials, and the rigid structure, twenty tons in weight, was not affected by any recoil which guns of this character give.

From the popular standpoint it seems a highly dangerous thing to fire such weapons as these in the vicinity of so great a body of hydrogen as is contained in these ships. The

THE AIRSHIP STATION AT THE GERMAN FORTRESS OF METZ; BUILT TO HOLD TWO ZEPPELINS

craft would be as warships, and the chief discussion of them in Europe, where alone the development has been followed intelligently, has concerned their employment for this purpose. The French, not having a rigid type from which guns can be fired advantageously, have proposed the dropping of explosives from their cars. But the German military experts, immediately after taking over the Zeppelin I., conceived the idea of using rapid-fire guns, and asked their gun-makers to prepare special airship artillery. The Krupps produced their gun this spring. It is a light, high-powered weapon, said to weigh about one hundred and sixty pounds — this light weight being made possible by special recoil mechanism. It fires a 1.9-inch shell, and can throw nearly sixty a minute to a distance of several miles from the elevated position of the airship. These shells are similar to those of the well-known mountain batteries, transported by pack-animals, which were used in the Russo-Japanese War. They are very efficient missiles, bursting into a shower of small, sharp fragments,

same popular belief existed for years concerning the explosive gasoline motor; yet this has been used exclusively for ten years to propel dirigible balloons, and, except for two accidents at the very beginning of the experiment, with entire success.

In the Zeppelin ship the motor is as perfectly separated from the hydrogen as the engine-room of a steamer from inflammable materials in her hold. To make assurance a certainty, so far as regards firearms, it would only be necessary to use the new Maxim silencer upon their muzzles. Tests have shown that these eliminate the flash of guns so completely that no flame can be seen, even when they are fired on the darkest night. Whether this device has been used by the Germans is not known. Their gun tests, like most of their recent developments of the airship, have been made in great secrecy — although descriptions and charts of the shooting of the airship guns have been issued in a publication circulated for the information of only their own army and navy.

THE ALUMINUM HULL OF THE LAST ZEPPELIN

THE SEVENTEEN COMPARTMENTS BETWEEN THE RINGS ARE FILLED WITH DRUM-SHAPED BALLOONS.
A THICK COVER OF RUBBER-CLOTH FORMS ITS SHEATH

A Battleship a Mile High Moving Sixty Miles an Hour

A new machine of war has arrived. It will be a ship as large and eventually much larger than present ocean battleships. It will fight from the height of a mile above the earth, and will manoeuver, during battle, at a rate of sixty or sixty-five miles an hour. The winds at this elevation average over twenty-four miles an hour, and on brisk days often reach thirty. The aërial battleships will move to windward, and sweep down these winds when passing over the enemy. In this way they can direct an absolutely certain fire upon the earth, while they are themselves practically out of danger.

The general discussion of ex-perts for a number of years has established a so-called "zone of safety," in which the last German airship, the Zeppelin II., has been built to travel in time of action. This is about 1,650 yards (nearly a mile) above the surface of the earth. The reason for adopting this level was that here the airship is out of range of the military rifle, which constitutes its chief danger. Punctures of its sustaining balloons by small bullets would not cause it to sink immediately, but would create small leaks, which would eventually bring it to earth. Large bodies of troops or large numbers of machine-guns concentrating on so great an object when it was within range would almost certainly send a percentage of bullets to the mark. The airship must, therefore, be

THE EARTH AS A TARGET

VIEW FROM A BALLOON ABOVE HOFHEIM, GERMANY, SHOWING THE SHARP-NESS WITH WHICH THE EARTH IS SEEN. ROADS ARE PARTICULARLY CLEAR, WHICH MAKES MOVING TROOPS AN EXCELLENT MARK

raised out of rifle range. This accomplished, artillery fire is left as its only possible danger.

Present artillery was, of course, not made to fire into the sky. The highest point for which modern field guns can be aimed is less than 1,200 yards. Their muzzles can be trained only seven degrees sidewise, because of the wheels on either side of them. The longest time a Zeppelin airship 500 feet long would take to pass, at battle speed, the arc thus covered, would be twenty seconds.

Wing-Shooting With Artillery

To avoid these difficulties, European gun-makers have been working on special artillery for shooting at airships. The most successful type has been produced by the Krupps. This is planned so that it can fire seventy-five degrees into the air. The rear of the gun-carriage is fastened on a pivot, and the wheels — as can be seen in the illustration on page 351 — are turned outward when the gun is ready for action, so that the gun may be trained sidewise by revolving the whole structure on the pivot at the rear of the carriage. The best experts believe that this gun will be impractical. It offers an awkward device for training the gun sidewise — especially on ground that is at all uneven; and it is believed that the first discharge of the gun, pointing upward, will either sink the wheels in the earth, or even break them. Fortress guns could be planned to reach airships more effectively, but this is of no great consequence, for the airships would not go near them. Heavy guns in the field could shoot high enough, but are too cumbersome to train on a moving object.

Moreover, discussion has developed the fact that with the best of mechanism it would be practically impossible to hit these airships at any range that they would approach in battle. Offhand this seems a ridiculous statement to make concerning a mark 500 feet long and 50 wide. But it is far from ridiculous when the distance, speed, and erratic movement of this mark are considered. The first shot by artillery is never expected to hit an object on the ground, even at known ranges. A gun is finally trained upon its target by marking the fall of trial shots upon the earth. But in firing at airships or balloons this is, of course, impossible. Captive balloons were used continually for scouting within the range of the enemy's guns in both the Boer and the Russo-Japanese War, and were infrequently hit. And careful experiments by European military officers show that, under the best conditions, with guns all prepared, it requires from five to

AN AIRSHIP ANCHORED ON AN AËRIAL WHARF

ELEVATORS AND GANGWAYS CARRY PASSENGERS TO THE SHIP; A GAS MAIN INFLATES ITS CHAMBERS; A HEAVY GUIDE-ROPE HOLDS THE STERN FROM SWINGING

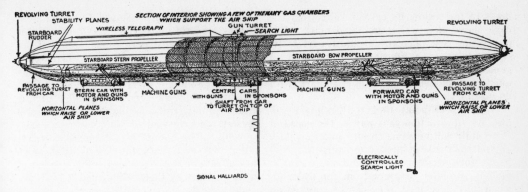

The figure is labeled with the following annotations:

REVOLVING TURRET
STABILITY PLANES
STARBOARD RUDDER
WIRELESS TELEGRAPH
SECTION OF INTERIOR SHOWING A FEW OF THE MANY GAS CHAMBERS WHICH SUPPORT THE AIR SHIP
GUN TURRET
SEARCH LIGHT
REVOLVING TURRET
STARBOARD STERN PROPELLER
STARBOARD BOW PROPELLER
PASSAGE TO REVOLVING TURRET FROM CAR
STERN CAR WITH MOTOR AND GUNS IN SPONSONS
MACHINE GUNS
CENTRE CARS WITH GUNS IN SPONSONS
SHAFT FROM CAR TO TURRET ON TOP OF AIR SHIP
MACHINE GUNS
FORWARD CAR WITH MOTOR AND GUNS IN SPONSONS
PASSAGE TO REVOLVING TURRET FROM CAR
HORIZONTAL PLANES WHICH RAISE OR LOWER AIR SHIP
HORIZONTAL PLANES WHICH RAISE OR LOWER AIR SHIP
SIGNAL HALLIARDS
ELECTRICALLY CONTROLLED SEARCH LIGHT

THE AËRIAL BATTLESHIP

twenty minutes for artillery to hit low-hanging balloons at battle ranges.

It is evident from this what success any conceivable artillery would have in snapshooting at an object an unknown height in the air, which remains in the gun's zone of fire twenty seconds at the longest, and which can assume a flight almost as eccentric as a bat's. To hit this airship at all when it is moving at full battle ranges, the artillerist must aim, not directly at it: he must "hold ahead," exactly as a gunner shoots flying ducks, otherwise the airship would be away from the place aimed at before the shell arrived there. He must not only "hold ahead," but must hold over the mark, because his gun, unlike the duck-shooter's, is discharged at an object out of point-blank range. All this with the target at an unknown and constantly changing distance.

War Becomes Wholesale Murder

On the other hand, nothing alive on the ground can escape the fire of an airship. It will be armed with rapid-fire guns, carrying shells, but its chief reliance in fighting infantry or cavalry will be upon the machine rifle. With this weapon it can turn a stream of four hundred bullets a minute on any troops within two miles, exactly as a man turns the stream of a garden hose against a tree. Its gunners can see any object on the ground with a perfect clearness, impossible of realization by any one who has not flown in a balloon. They can thus mark the striking of bullets perfectly. And the range of their guns is nearly doubled on account of their position. The fire of an airship will annihilate infantry and cavalry beneath it, as surely as the hand of God. It will not be directed long at any coherent body which could be called troops. Human nature forbids the possibility of men remaining to be shot down like rats in a pit.

Some idea of the wholesale murder of troops

possible with machine rifles can be had from the battle of Omdurman in Upper Egypt on September 2, 1898, when the English killed over 11,000 and wounded 16,000 of the Mahdi's troops, most of them in the course of three short charges. G. W. Steevens, the English war correspondent, describes the scene in his "With Kitchener to Khartum" as follows:

"The line of flags swung forward, and a mass of white flying linen swung forward with it too. They came very fast, and they came very straight; and then presently they came no farther. With a crash the bullets leaped out of the British rifles. Shrapnel whistled and Maxims growled savagely. From all the line came perpetual fire, fire, fire, and shrieked forth in great gusts of destruction. And the enemy? No white troops would have faced that torrent of death for five minutes, but the Baggara and the blacks came on. The torrent swept into them and hurled them down in whole companies. You saw a rigid line gather itself up and rush on evenly; then before a shrapnel shell or a Maxim the line suddenly quivered and stopped. The line was yet unbroken, but it was quite still. But other lines gathered up again, again, and yet again; they went down, and yet others rushed on. It was not a battle, but an execution."

The End of Infantry and Cavalry

In destroying troops on the ground the airship will take no serious risk. Its position makes it practically omniscient, so far as the movements of its enemy on the ground are concerned. Only prepared artillery can possibly hit it; therefore it will attack only when artillery is not ready. It will work to windward at a low level; then rise into the high winds of the "zone of safety," and swoop over unprotected bodies of infantry and cavalry with the speed of an express train. Or at night it will swing searchlights (steadied by wind-vanes and electrically focussed) hundreds of feet below its car, and fire from the dark above on a well-illuminated mark. Manoeuvering will play the greatest part in its development as a fighting machine, and in general its tactics will be that of jiu-jitsu—a quick and sudden blow at a vital part, with no possibility of return.

It is at this point that the aëroplane will play its vitally important part. The speed of these craft will be some twenty miles an hour greater than that of the larger ships; they will be, by their small size and rapid and eccentric motion, absolutely immune from gun fire, and, when fully developed, they can be counted on to carry at least two men and a machine rifle. Scouting aëroplanes will get in touch with the enemy while the airship is hidden below the windward horizon. Wireless equipment, for a short distance, can be carried by aëroplanes, and the airships, similarly equipped, will be exactly informed of all openings for attack, before the enemy has an inkling of their whereabouts.

Summarized, the result of the introduction of the airship into warfare will be this: If cavalry or infantry are moved over a country patrolled by airships, they will be annihilated. If they are held under the direct protection of artillery, they will be starved by the destruction of their supplies. And even when troops are protected by the best of artillery, the airship can annihilate them by its quick dashes, with practically no danger to itself. All this means simply the abolition of infantry and cavalry, and the end of land war as we now know it. The change will take time, necessarily, but even with the few German ships now afloat, we are much nearer this revolution in human history than is imagined.

The Fighting Power of Zeppelins I. and II.

The Zeppelin I., which was taken over by the German government as a military airship last year, is 446 feet long and 38 feet wide. As originally built, she had so slight a margin of lifting power that it was necessary to lengthen her by slicing her in two and inserting a compartment. This process made it possible to use the craft, but even now her relative thinness gives her a very small surplus of lifting power. Yet, handicapped as she is, this experimental ship would be able to take a crew

THE RADIUS OF THE ZEPPELIN II.

THE DISTANCE MADE ON HER TRIP OF MAY 30 AND 31 WOULD TAKE HER FROM
COLOGNE OVER LONDON NEARLY TO LIVERPOOL, BEYOND PARIS, OR OVER A
LARGE PART OF THE NORTH SEA, AND BACK AGAIN. FROM KÖNIGSBERG SHE
COULD COVER MOST OF SWEDEN, THE BALTIC SEA, AND COULD ALMOST
REACH ST. PETERSBURG, AND RETURN. FROM FRIEDRICHSHAFEN
SHE COULD GO TO VIENNA OR ROME AND BACK

of nine men over a radius of three hundred miles and back, that is, one hundred miles beyond Paris from the German frontier, flying all the time in the safety zone, nearly a mile above the earth, and still carrying two machine rifles and enough ammunition to shoot both of them continuously for three quarters of an hour. No body of troops could sustain their fire for fifteen minutes.

The Zeppelin II., also 446 feet long, has a total lifting capacity one fourth greater than that of the Zeppelin I., because her beam is 44 feet instead of 38. With the same crew and radius of action, she could carry at least four times the ammunition, and with this she could fire four machine rifles continuously for an hour and a half. In practice airships will make the first half or even more of their cruises in low altitudes, so these two ships could in reality carry more than double the weight here allowed to them. Skill in taking advantage of wind-currents — which will constitute one of the chief features in the science of aërial navigation — will also greatly increase their radius of action beyond three hundred miles and back.

But these two ships are of consequence only as indicating what the war airship will be in the immediate future. They were built — to save expenditure of money — at very near the lowest point at which the buoyancy of the rigid airship is sufficient to support the necessary frame and motor power. The tendency, both in ocean- and airships, is to build as large structures as possible. This is due to the mathematical fact, familiar to all ship-builders, that the lifting power of ships increases according to the cube of their dimensions, while the resistance on their surfaces increases only as the square of their dimensions, and the weight demanded by their structure remains always at about the same proportion to the lifting power. Consequently, as the craft grows, there is a constantly increasing margin of lifting power for cargo. Just beyond the 450 feet length in the Zeppelin airship this carrying power grows by leaps and bounds.

The German Warship Now Building

Count Zeppelin announced some time ago that he could easily build an airship with a displacement of 30,000 cubic meters — just twice that of the Zeppelin II., and two and a half times that of the Zeppelin I. It has also been announced that the ships now building at Germany's aërial shipyards in Friedrichshafen are considerably larger than those now afloat. And it is more than probable that the new craft will approach a 30,000 meter displacement. An airship of that size would be only 510 feet long — that is, but fifteen per cent longer than the two craft now afloat.

Now, an aërial ship 510 feet long and 51 feet wide could carry a dozen men a mile high in the air over a radius of five hundred miles and back; that is, it could reach every principal capital of Europe from the borders of German territory and return. It could, in addition, devote at least five tons of cargo weight to arms and ammunition. This could include ten machine rifles, each equipped with ammunition enough for a full hour's work, and two machine guns of the type built for the Zeppelin I., with two hundred shells for each weapon. Two and a half tons of dynamite torpedoes could be substituted for half of the machine guns and their ammunition, if it were desired to attack fortifications or cities. Forty craft of this kind could be built and armed at the cost of one Dreadnought battleship. And such a fleet, without opposition from other airships, could conquer Western Europe. The moment it is launched, the standing armies of Europe become an anachronism.

THE KRUPP FIELD GUN FOR SHOOTING AIRSHIPS

A Prophecy About the Navy

Something over a year ago Major Baden-Powell of the British Government Balloon Corps commented on the fourth airship, built by Count Zeppelin, as follows:

"A dozen Dreadnoughts [battleships] would be absolutely helpless if charged with the task of preventing a squadron of air cruisers from gliding above them and reaching the British coast. These air cruisers will probably soon be able to mount machine guns of lighter construction; thus they will be able to attack without having to carry missiles which are too heavy for their [present] carrying power."

This prophecy exactly states the position which the airship has attained to-day in relation to the battleship — so far, at least, as Europe is concerned. That narrow territory, where the danger of war is always greatest, is well within the radius of the German military airships. And these ships, with their higher speed and perfect knowledge of their enemies' movements, will never take any unnecessary risk, however slight, of being struck by the shells from the guns of a warship. Why should they do so in the waters about Europe? The free highway of the air lies unobstructed before them; and once arrived in a country, from their position above the land they can conquer and hold any population that is not itself protected by airships.

Navies are thus relegated at once to a new and inferior position. They will defend shipping seaports, and undoubtedly — until aërial navigation is greatly advanced — will serve as a base for the operations of airships. In the meanwhile it is not impossible that occasions may arise — especially in case of an attack by European nations upon nations of other continents — of a trial of strength between battleships and airships. Airships of the size that will be achieved in the next few years would have every advantage in such a duel.

Destroying Ships With Aërial Torpedoes

The weapons of a ship of this kind against battleships would be large aërial torpedoes, filled with high explosives. It has been popularly assumed that missiles of this kind would be simply dropped from the airship. This would be ridiculous. No possible aim can be secured by dropping any object down through a mile or more of air, filled with conflicting cross-currents. The aërial torpedo will be fired from a long, light tube, by compressed air or some similar means, with sufficient force to give it some initial speed, and a rotation which will keep it from turning over. It will consist of 150 or 200 pounds of a high explosive, like maximite, which cannot be set off by concussion, but will be exploded by a fuse which concussion will ignite; and will carry a steel cap at its end. The initial velocity, and the force of gravity acquired in the fall of a mile through the air, will give this a great speed by the time it reaches the deck of a ship. It will pass through the upper decks to the armored deck below, where the slowly burning fuse will at last explode it, and its force, directed against the sharp-pointed steel cap, will drive this through the armored deck and tear away the inside of the ship. There is no reason why this weapon should not become as dangerous as the submarine torpedo, whose explosion against the side of a warship is conceded to mean its destruction or disablement.

It is true that the battleship on sea, like the fort on land, would be the most dangerous enemy of the airship. Each can be fitted with specially constructed high-powered airship guns, which could be held always in readiness. In discharging its torpedoes, too, the airship would be compelled to run directly over the battleship. But, making every allowance for this, it is almost certain that half a dozen airships — costing less than a quarter of one Dreadnought — could destroy any battleship now afloat, or likely to be devised. With the best artillery it would be impossible to shoot them all down; while, on their part, they could make all kinds of sudden and unexpected onslaughts — at night, in foggy weather, or even on days with low-lying clouds. It has already been demonstrated that an airship can be steered electrically by a man swung in a car a hundred feet below it. By this means the airship can remain absolutely hidden in the cloud, while its navigator in the car directs its movements.

Airships a Quarter of a Mile Long?

The moment civilized nations begin to construct aërial fleets, a race in building larger structures will begin, which will make the present rivalry in increasing the size of battleships appear trifling. The airship need attain no extreme size to fight against enemies on the ground; the contest is too unequal. On the other hand, the value of the airship for fighting other ships in the air will depend directly upon its lifting power. Air battles will be won by the ships whose fire hits the others first. So the struggle between nations will be to construct ships capable of carrying the most powerful artillery possible, and, at the same time, capable of the excessive speed needed for the manoeuvering qualities which, scarcely second to gunnery, will decide these fights. For both these purposes, size and carrying power are imperative. Many of the most competent students believe that a quarter of a mile is a conservative estimate of the size that these ships will attain in a few years. And, theoretically, there is every reason to expect this.

The battleship made for fighting in the air must be built along certain definite lines. First of all, it must be able to fire its heaviest guns in every possible direction. The only positions where guns can be placed to do this are in the extremities of the stern and bow. Fortunately, this is the strongest portion of the ship, all its lateral ribs coming to a point here. These ribs will be fastened upon a strong ring, and beyond that a light spherical turret will be built, capable of holding one or more guns, with men to operate them. These guns will be directed up and down through vertical slits, and the structure of the turret will be turned to secure a side-wise aim.

In addition to these turrets, there will undoubtedly be guns on top of the vertical passageway up through the body of the ship, by which, in the Zeppelin II., the navigators now mount to the top of the hull for the purpose of taking observations. The great proportion of the machine rifles will be located in the cars beneath the hull, from which they can be fired at objects beneath and at one side.

The equipment of the ship of the early future will be devoted primarily to aërial warfare. For, if the air forces of the enemy are conquered, its land will be taken as a matter of course. The equipment for air fighting will be primarily the long-distance guns to be used for fighting other airships. But it will also include special guns — probably machine rifles — for fighting off attacks from aëroplanes. The place of the aëroplane will be very similar to that of the torpedo-boat in present naval warfare. Possessing high speed, and being almost impossible to hit at a distance, they will dart in, endeavoring to set fire to and utterly destroy the great airship by one quick blow — possibly by firing shots that will ignite the hydrogen in their balloons. The airship fleet must watch for their attack continually, and must be protected by its own aëroplanes, and at night by brilliant and far-reaching searchlights.

A Ship as Long as the "Mauretania"

It would not be necessary to build airships of enormous size to secure fighting ships of great fighting power. A ship the length of the steamer Mauretania — that is, 790 feet long — can quite certainly be expected within the next few years. Such an airship would have a total displacement or lifting power of

125 tons. She could cruise to any part of Europe from Germany, and return, without landing, at the rate of thirty-five miles an hour; and remain three quarters of the time in the battle position of 1,650 yards. Properly husbanding her fuel, she could remain in the air for more than a week, probably two, without securing more supplies. She could also devote at least twenty tons to arms and ammunition.

This ship would have a secondary battery of ten machine guns, with an average supply of two hours' ammunition for each gun. This would protect her amply, for any rushes made by aëroplanes would occupy but a few minutes at most. Going at least a mile a minute, they would not be in range more than two or three minutes, and the expenditure of machine rifle ammunition would be very small in that time. The secondary battery, then, would take half of the twenty tons' weight. The rest could be allowed for the heavy, rapid-fire guns whose fire would be directed against the enemy's airships and their ammunition.

A New Basis of National Strength

Aërial navies will be an accomplished fact at an early date, not only because they are highly efficient, but because they are cheap. The present cost of Germany's army is over $200,-000,000 a year. It has 600,000 men in active service, and 1,200,000 reserves. A fleet of 500 airships could be maintained for $15,000,000 a year, and 100 new ships added annually for $25,000,000. The incentive to replace large bodies of troops by the new instrument of war will be extremely powerful on the ground of mere economy, in the present period of enormous war taxes, which affects not only Europe, but now the United States as well; for our army and navy are now costing us considerably more than $200,000,000 a year.

Considered in a larger way, the aërial warship is simply an advance in the development of war that started with the modern battleship. Up to the present time war has been a conflict of armed populations. It is now to be a duel between fighting-machines, operated by trained experts. The number of individuals involved in war was greatly reduced by the ocean battleship; it becomes an almost negligible fraction of the populations with the still more concentrated and terrible fighting-engine that has now appeared. This means the end of the military world as we have known it. National power is no longer to be founded on the mass of fighting males. It becomes a great struggle of intellect, dependent directly on national progress in the mechanical arts and national wealth. The effect of the change on barbaric and semi-barbaric populations is too obvious to need comment. Russia and Asia are put in a new position, and the threat of the Yellow Peril is postponed for years, if not forever.

The alignment for the new warfare has already begun along the French and German frontier. The Zeppelin I. has been stationed at the military fortress of Metz; the Zeppelin II. has been assigned to the fortress of Cologne; and it is announced that the next warship to be turned out at the Zeppelin plant will have its home port at Mainz. Just over the French border-line are the two French military balloons — La République at the fortress of Verdun, 26½ miles away from the Zeppelin I. at Metz; and the Ville de Paris at Toul.

Germany's $1,500,000 Airship Plant

Germany has now nearly completed a $1,500,000 airship plant at Friedrichshafen and Manzell, two adjoining towns on Lake Constance. These plants are virtually the property of the German people. Count Zeppelin, who founded them, expended all his available funds upon the first and second of his five ships. His third was built with the proceeds of a specially authorized national lottery. For the construction of this third ship the German government built him a floating plant in Lake Constance, costing $125,000; and a year ago it paid him $300,000 when it took over the Zeppelin I. To complete his plant, the German people — in a great burst of popular enthusiasm — contributed $1,500,000 last fall. Following this, a company was formed which practically holds the plant as the property of the nation. It now contains four docks, where airships can be assembled, and two more will soon be built. In time of war these docks could turn out from fifty to sixty ships a year; the material of these craft is very light and easily handled, and its parts — motors, cloth, and aluminum frame — could be turned out at various private plants all over the country. The number of ships produced would depend only on the capacity of the docks to assemble them.

It was announced a year ago that this plant would have turned out eight ships by this winter — including the Zeppelin II., which was launched last spring. By a year from now we may expect to see at least ten, and very likely twenty, more. The next ships built will be used in commercial ventures, for taking passengers from one part of Germany to another. But these, like all the new Zeppelin ships, can be converted into fighting-craft without appreciable delay. The movement is at bottom a military one; and the Aërial Navy League of Germany — numbering thousands of members

— will be the chief source of patrons, which will guarantee the success of the new commercial passenger lines. The German government will also subsidize these lines.

In France, the popular interest in preparation for aërial warfare is not less than in Germany. The Aërial League, a great national body like Germany's, is working on a great propaganda for educating the French people as to the necessity of rapid development of the art for use in war. And the French government has subsidized a line of four airships, which will begin, within a year, to make regular trips between Paris and Nancy, near the German frontier — a distance of about one hundred miles. But in her present equipment for war France lags far behind her old enemy. The government has but three dirigible balloons now; and they are not only but a fraction of the size of the rigid Zeppelins, but Germany possesses half a dozen ships of the non-rigid type which are as large as those of France.

But the greatest apprehension naturally exists in England, a nation whose strength has been developed for centuries behind the physical barriers of the sea. With the opening of the highway of the air for warships, her position, and the position of the great kingdom she has built across the earth by the power of her navy, is suddenly changed. The development of aërial navigation finds her pitifully unprepared. Her experience with dirigibles has amounted to nothing, as is shown, beyond the power of words, by a comparison of her latest experiment, the small and awkward balloon, nicknamed by her army "The Baby," with the great, sharp, businesslike hull of a Zeppelin.

For the United States the development may be considered, on the whole, most favorable. The size of our standing army has been a fraction of that of European powers. By an instrument which does away with armies, and substitutes as a basis for military strength mechanical skill and national wealth, we cannot but be greatly benefited. It is doubtful whether any European army will attempt warfare upon our soil, if it is properly defended by warships in the air.

That the new machine of war will cause great changes in the history of nations cannot be doubted — if aërial warfare is permitted to exist. But will it be permitted? War a mile above the earth, between corps of artillery firing into huge bodies of inflammable gas, where the defeated plunge down to the ground a mass of charred pulp, will become a thing too spectacularly horrible for conception. Will civilization permit it to exist? Or does this new machine mean the end of war?

34.
Experiences in the Sky
(1908)

THE CENTURY MAGAZINE

EXPERIENCES IN THE SKY

BY HENRY B. HERSEY

Inspector, United States Weather Bureau

THE skilful aëronaut who describes his remarkable experiences in the following pages has also faced danger on land and sea. During the Spanish War he served as Major in Roosevelt's Rough-Riders, and in 1906-07 he was executive officer of the Wellman Polar Expedition. His sky journeys as a member of the aëro clubs of both France and America have been greatly facilitated by his practical knowledge of atmospheric temperatures and currents largely gained through his connection with the United States Weather Bureau.—THE EDITOR.

FLOATING softly up into the blue ocean of air, watching the earth sink slowly away beneath us and fade and change quietly to an immense map spread before our wondering eyes—such are the first impressions of balloon voyagers. The noisy shouts of those who come to wish us *"Bon voyage!"* become fainter and fainter until absolute quiet reigns about us. It is so still that the ticking of the clock in the barograph is heard noisily counting the seconds as it traces the line of our upward flight across the sheet.

Meanwhile the earth-map down below us stretches out larger and larger; but its details are fading and becoming blurred. High hills have changed to flat surfaces. A river winds and bends its way through the duller colors like a tangled ribbon of silver. A small lake sparkles in the sunshine, giving life and fire to the sober

shades about it. A railway train creeps slowly along, its trail of smoke streaming back over it; but as we look, it suddenly disappears from sight, apparently swallowed up before our eyes. Then we realize that it has plunged into a tunnel, through a hill which to us seems only a flat surface; now it appears again, coming out on the other side.

So the wonderful scenes come and go, ever changing, but ever grand and inspiring—scenes that come back to us real and vivid, that we may live them over again in later days. The cloud effects are at times the most beautiful of all. After having sailed up through these into the dazzling sunlight, we see the snowy billows just below our car, the shadow of our balloon falling upon their white surface. This shadow is often surrounded by a halo of rainbow colors of rare beauty. At such times one has the feeling of having left the earth completely, and to have reached some other planet. The white masses just below seem to be quite solid, and look as though one might step out of the balloon and take a stroll over them, if one only had snow-shoes. The air is wonderfully clear and pure, and gives one a feeling of exhilaration much greater than that enjoyed in mountain-climbing. Is it, then, surprising that ballooning is rapidly becoming a popular sport?

In America ballooning is in its infancy, but in France almost any pleasant day in the year there are several balloon ascensions. There is certainly no recreation more absorbing, or which will make a man forget his business cares and troubles to a greater degree than this. Nor can there be one more healthful, since the devotee is carried quickly to an atmosphere free from dust and germs, where he must drink in long, deep breaths of the purest air.

In Europe there are many clubs which have balloon houses arranged for the quick inflation of balloons and for proper storage of them between flights. A club member may telephone the manager to "have Balloon Number Six ready for ascension at three o'clock this afternoon." At the appointed hour he and his companions go to the club-house, where all is ready for a sail through the sky. On landing, the balloon is shipped back to the club, and the aëro party returns by train. Although we have several good aëro clubs in America,—notably at New York, Philadelphia, St. Louis, and Boston,—they have not, so far, succeeded in making suitable arrangements for the convenient inflation of balloons. This will probably be done in the near future.

Of course no fire of any kind can be used in a balloon, and for flights lasting overnight the lack of a hot lunch is a cause for complaint; but this lack is now remedied by the use of thermal bottles, which provide hot coffee or bouillon for from twenty-four to thirty-six hours. I first used this resource in the race from Paris in 1906, when I assisted Lieutenant Lahm. The coffee was put in bottles about eleven o'clock in the forenoon before starting, and the next morning, in passing over England, we had a cup of coffee that

was as hot as we could drink it. I used these bottles to good advantage in the St. Louis race; and on this trip we also had canned soups put up in a special double-can, with a filling of lime between the two cans. By pouring a little water into this lime, sufficient heat was generated to warm the soup in the inner can. These arrangements covered the food question satisfactorily; but the sky-voyager who is dependent on tobacco does not fare so well, since cigars and matches are contraband articles.

The pilot of a balloon does not have as good an opportunity as the passengers to enjoy the beautiful sights. He must watch carefully the barograph, which records automatically the height of the balloon above the earth, and the statoscope, which shows whether the balloon is ascending or descending; for, strange to say, one cannot tell by looking over whether the balloon is rising or falling. There is absolutely no sense of motion in either a horizontal or a vertical direction. To cause the balloon to rise it is necessary to throw out ballast, and to make it descend the gas is let out through a valve in the top. The pilot must know just how much ballast to throw out, and must decide when it is necessary to let out gas. These matters require constant attention, and the pilot is usually a busy man.

In a partly cloudy day it is very difficult to maintain the equilibrium of the balloon. The rays of the sun pass through its semi-transparent skin, sometimes raising the temperature of the gas to a point thirty or forty degrees higher than that of the surrounding air, in exactly the same way that the air in a hot-house is heated by the rays of the sun passing through its glass roof. Now, the heated gas has much greater lifting power, and the balloon climbs higher. If a cloud comes over the sun, the gas in the balloon cools rapidly, losing some of its ascensional force, and the balloon begins to descend. This must be checked by throwing out ballast; but good judgment must be exercised to prevent throwing out too much. Here is where the skill of the pilot is thoroughly tested. It is much easier to manage a balloon at night, as the effect of the sun on the gas does not have to be overcome, and frequently a balloon will sail through a whole night

Drawn by Arthur T. Merrick

ANCHORED TO A TREE IN A GALE AND SAVED BY THE "RIPPING CORD."

at a steady height with almost no loss of ballast.

In the St. Louis race, after getting our equilibrium for the night about 8 P.M., we used less than one sack of ballast up to sunrise the next morning, and our height above the ground was virtually steady at a little more than 300 feet. The guide-rope which swung down about 300 feet below the basket occasionally touched the tree-tops. The guide-rope, as it is called, is simply a piece of rope suspended from the balloon, and is of great assistance in keeping the balloon steady when near the ground. If it descends until the end of the rope drags on the ground, the weight of the rope that is on the ground is taken off the balloon, and this will check its descent. It is also valuable in a dense fog, giving warning that one is nearing the earth.

One of the chief difficulties met with by amateur balloonists is in making a good landing, especially in a strong wind. When the wind is light, it is comparatively simple ; but if the balloon is flying along at the rate of forty miles an hour, which is not unusual, to bring it to a sudden stop in a country where there are trees, rocks, or buildings, requires good judgment and a cool head to avoid at least a lively shaking-up. Even after the basket strikes the ground, the huge gas-bag is still in the air, presenting a large surface to the wind. Unless it can be deflated almost instantly, the basket will probably be dragged swiftly along, even with the anchor out. If the anchor can be thrown into trees, it will usually hold, but on the ground it is apt to drag without catching. For quick deflation, an excellent device called the "ripping-cord," or panel, has been introduced. From near the top of the balloon down to the equator a gash is cut. The sides of this cut are hemmed, and made strong with two thicknesses of cloth. A long patch or panel is then cemented over this cut, closing it and making it gas-tight. This panel terminates in a loop at the upper end, and to this loop is attached a cord, running down inside the balloon to the car. A sharp pull on this cord will tear the patch off, opening the side of the balloon for nearly a quarter of its circumference. Through this opening the gas rushes out in a few seconds, and the balloon collapses on the ground.

In my sixth ascension, which I made entirely alone, going up from Rueil, near

Paris, I had to make a landing in a wind blowing about forty miles an hour. I threw out the anchor as I was coming to a country road, with trees on each side of it. The anchor caught and held well in one of the trees, but the wind was so violent that the balloon stood out almost horizontally, and thrashed up and down frightfully, throwing things out of the basket. I succeeded in getting hold of the ripping-cord, and peeled off the panel in a hurry. Almost instantly the balloon settled down to the ground, giving no more trouble. This was my first experience in the use of the ripping-cord. Since then I have used it frequently, and have come to look on it as one of the greatest safeguards in ballooning. Of course one must be sure not to pull this cord by mistake up at a great height. For this reason the ripping-cord is colored red, to distinguish it easily from the valve-cord which hangs near it. The part of the cord coming down into the basket is now usually made flat, like a tape, so that it can be distinguished by feeling at night, when it is too dark to see the color. At one time, when practising alone in a small balloon, I tried the experiment of pulling the ripping-cord when I was about 150 feet in the air. I certainly got the hardest jolt I ever had in landing. The basket struck the ground with a terrific shock, and I was considerably dazed, though uninjured.

I have usually been lucky in making landings, but I had a rather exciting experience on one trip last May in France. I had gone up from Paris, taking with me Dr. W. N. Fowler, surgeon of the Wellman Polar Expedition, who wished to learn how to manage a balloon. We had gone about forty miles from Paris, and our experience had been very pleasant. As our ballast was nearly all used up, we were letting the balloon come down from an altitude of about four thousand feet. It was rather open country, with occasional small tracts of woodland. We floated down over one of these little patches of timber not much more than a hundred yards across. There were three or four poplar-trees that stood high above all the others, and I did not notice that the top of one of these had been broken off, leaving a sharp point. Our balloon came down a little faster than

we expected, and as our basket swung along a few feet from this tree, the gasbag, extending out above us, struck on this sharp stub, driving right through the balloon and tearing an opening ten feet in length. Our netting became entangled in the tree, while the gas poured out quickly. This left us hanging sixty feet above the ground, with almost no gas in the balloon, which threatened to tear loose. There was only one thing to do, and that was to get out as quickly as possible. The Doctor climbed out on the tree and descended to the ground. I then threw from the basket all the ballast and other loose material, and getting on the tree, climbed up to where the netting was caught, and succeeded in disentangling it, letting the balloon and the basket drop to the ground. The peasants had gathered round by this time, and cheerfully took hold and assisted us to get the balloon out and pack it up for shipment.

Free balloons, while in the air, have been considered to be safe from lightning; but last summer in Italy an aëronaut made an ascension at a big celebration, and was killed by lightning. The weather looked very threatening at the time, but as there was an enormous crowd, including the King and Queen of Italy, waiting to see the event, the aëronaut decided to start. He had gone only a short distance, and was being watched by the vast throng, when a flash of lightning struck the balloon, exploding the gas and killing the occupant instantly. This is said to be the only case on record of a free balloon being struck by lightning.

In my first ascension we had a rather exciting experience with lightning. We had gone up from the Aëro Club Park at St.-Cloud, near Paris, about eleven o'clock in the forenoon. The weather looked a little bad when we started, and there was scarcely any wind. The balloon was not a large one, and there were three of us in the basket, so we were able to take but little ballast. We went up about three thousand feet, and drifted lazily away from the park, changing direction from time to time, but not making any headway. Finally, when over the Seine, in the suburbs of Paris, a huge black cloud came rolling toward us from the west. Our pilot did not like the looks of it,

Drawn by Harry Grant Dart.   Engraved by C. W. Chadwick

MAJOR HERSEY'S BALLOON IMPALED UPON A POPLAR.

and it certainly did have a terrifying aspect. We did not have ballast enough to throw out and so go above it, so we decided to go down. The pilot pulled the valve-cord, letting out a lot of gas, and we went sliding down the sky at the rate of a thousand feet a minute. Just as we got well started, a vivid flash of lightning cut through the inky blackness of the cloud near us, followed almost instantly by a deafening roar of thunder, and the rain and hail came down in torrents. We were dropping straight toward a good-sized island in the middle of the Seine. We hoped to make a landing on this; but when we got within a few hundred feet of the earth, a little breeze sprang up, carrying us away from the island into the middle of the river. Our guide-rope was in the water and it looked like a swim for us; but throwing out what little ballast we had left, we stopped descending about thirty feet from the water. Then rising a little, we swept up the bank, across a street, over some low housetops, and down into a back yard, where we succeeded in making a fairly good landing. We were soon surrounded by an excited but good-natured Parisian crowd, anxious to help us. It was really a very busy few minutes; and as it was my first ascension, it was quite impressive to me. If we had been carrying plenty of ballast, we could have gone above the cloud, and then have come down later, after the storm had passed.

MAJOR HERSEY'S FIRST BALLOON ASCENSION FROM THE AËRO CLUB GROUNDS, PARIS

The pilot was Mr. F. H. Lahm (father of Lieutenant Lahm who won the Paris race in 1906). It is the moment of letting go and Mr. Lahm stands ready to empty a bag of ballast in case the balloon should not rise rapidly enough to clear the trees.

A GROUP OF BALLOONS IN THE TUILERIES GARDENS, PARIS

These are a few of the balloons which started in the Paris race of 1906, but the picture does not include the winner, the "United States," which was piloted by Lieutenant Lahm with Major Hersey as assistant.

I am often asked about the dangers of ballooning. With a balloon of standard quality, properly constructed and handled by a skilful, conservative pilot, the danger is very slight if the ascension is not made near any large body of water. There is a very decided element of danger in going up too close to the sea-coast. Even if the surface wind is away from the water, a higher current may be in the opposite direction, and one may get into a fog or cloud and not be aware of a change of direction until the balloon is out over the sea, with no means of getting back. If it is daylight, there is of course a chance of rescue by some passing ship; but if it is night, there is but little hope. Two young English officers were drowned last summer in this way. They were seen drifting toward the sea just before dark. A day or two later one of the bodies and the wreckage from the balloon were washed up on the beach.

The Great Lakes of this country have claimed their share of tribute. Professor John Wise, an experienced aëronaut, made an ascension from St. Louis in 1879, and came down in the southern end of Lake Michigan, where he and his companion, George Burr, were both drowned. In 1875, the veteran aëronaut Professor Donaldson made an ascension from Chicago with a young newspaper reporter for a companion. They were never again seen alive, both being drowned in Lake Michigan. Water is the only serious danger the balloonist has to encounter, and this can be avoided. If an ascension is made near a large body of water,—that is, one too large to attempt to cross,—the balloon should be kept at a low altitude, so that a quick descent can be made if the pilot finds that he is drifting dangerously close. If this is done, no great risk will be incurred.

All balloons taking up passengers should be managed by experienced pilots. This is a matter which has generally been insisted on by the various aëro clubs, and licenses are issued by them to competent persons who have fulfilled certain requirements. They must have made not less than ten ascensions. Of these, two must have been under the supervision of a licensed pilot, at least one must have been made entirely alone, and one must have been a night ascension. The applicant must also be recommended by two licensed pilots who are familiar with his work. There are very few licensed pilots in this country at present, but a number are going through the preparatory work. In all races held under the auspices of the International Aëronautic Federation, one of the requirements is that the balloons must be handled by licensed pilots.

It has been my good fortune to take part in two international races. In 1906 I accompanied Lieutenant Frank P. Lahm in the "United States" in the race for the Gordon Bennett cup. This opportunity came to me quite unexpectedly. I had just returned to Paris from the Arctic region, where I had been on duty with Mr. Walter Wellman's expedition in preparing for an attempt to reach the North Pole by means of a dirigible balloon or air-ship. Lieutenant Lahm had engaged a French aëronaut to assist him, but this had aroused a storm of protest from the French contestants. Learning of this, I immediately offered my services to Lieutenant Lahm, and they were accepted, although it was only about an hour before starting that the matter was definitely settled.

The experience in this race was very pleasant. The weather was perfect, and there was an enormous crowd out to see the start from the Jardin des Tuileries. There were sixteen balloons in the contest, representing France, England, Germany, Italy, Spain, and America, and the list of pilots included the names of the most famous aëronauts of the world. It had been expected that a westerly wind would prevail, carrying the air fleet over Germany, Austria, or Russia; but the wind was from the opposite direction, and we all sailed west, straight for the Atlantic. I had studied the French weather-chart pretty carefully, and believed that our course would change to northwest when we got out over western France, and give us a chance to cross the English Channel and reach the British Isles. We kept low out over France, and for the first fifty miles continued to travel straight west. A little later we began to veer slightly to the northwest. This was very encouraging, and we decided to go out

over the Channel. As we neared the coast, we could see the flash of a lighthouse, and a little after 11 P.M. we floated out over the water. We still kept low, as we were getting a strong breeze and a good direction. At 2:30 A.M. we sighted the intermittent red-and-white flash of a light-ship stationed east of the Isle of Wight. Our course was now nearly northwest, and at 3:30 A.M. we sailed in over the English coast near Chichester, having covered a distance of 125 miles in a little less than four and a half hours. We continued a northerly course over England, and as the sun came up, heating the gas in our balloon, we began to rise slowly, finally reaching an altitude of about 10,000 feet. Our course now changed to east of north, and at 3 P.M. we found we were getting close to the North Sea. We decided to make a landing as near the coast as possible. The wind was blowing about twenty-five miles an hour, and we were kept pretty busy for a few minutes, but we succeeded in landing in a smooth field about half a mile from the shore.

We had been in the air more than twenty-two hours, and were 402 miles in a direct line from Paris. We landed on the estate of a gentleman of the name of Barry, who was extremely kind to us. His men helped us pack the balloon, and we left at 5 P.M. for London. We went only as far as York that night, for on arriving there, and finding we must wait some time for a train, we decided to go to the hotel and get some much needed sleep. In the morning we learned that we had won the cup. It turned out that nine of the sixteen balloons had dropped down in France, not thinking it wise to attempt to cross the Channel.

It was due to Lieutenant Lahm's energy in preparing for and entering this race, and to his skilful handling of this balloon, that the race was held in this country, at St. Louis, in 1907. As he had won the cup, the American club which he represented had the right to say where the next contest would be held, and the management decided on St. Louis. This proved to be a wise decision. The St. Louis people took hold of the work of preparation in an energetic manner. An unusually good quality of coal-gas was secured, and the whole work of inflating and starting the balloons in the race was most efficiently done. It must be remembered that this was the first balloon-race ever held in America, yet everything was managed smoothly and efficiently. The Aëro Club of America and the St. Louis people certainly de-

Moore, chief of the bureau, special observations were made at noon in all parts of the country. These reports were telegraphed to the St. Louis office, and a special map was issued, showing the weather conditions existing at the time over the whole country. No other weather

MAJOR HERSEY (IN PROFILE) AND HIS ASSISTANT MR. ATHERHOLT,
READY FOR THE START IN THE ST. LOUIS RACE OF 1907

The net attached to the basket, at the right, holds a canvas cover for the protection of the
gas envelop, in shipping the balloon after the flight.

serve great credit for their excellent showing.

The work of the weather bureau in connection with this event is worthy of mention. Copies of the daily weather-map were placed at the disposal of the contestants every morning by the St. Louis office, and on the day of the race, under instructions from Professor Willis L.

service in the world could have done this, and it was looked upon by the foreign contestants as a wonderful achievement.

I entered the St. Louis race very unexpectedly. During the preceding summer I had again been in the Arctic with Mr. Wellman, and on getting back to Norway, in September, I found a letter from Lieutenant Lahm, in which he stated that

From a photograph by E. Frankl, Berlin

COUNT ZEPPELIN'S AIR-SHIP, MORE THAN FOUR HUNDRED FEET LONG, IN FLIGHT

he had entered the race, and had designated me as his alternate and asked me to assist him again. I immediately wired him that I should be glad to accept; but when I arrived in London, I found a letter from him saying that his recovery from a severe attack of typhoid fever had been so slow that he would not be able to take part in the race, and urging me to be sure to take his place.

I hurried across the Atlantic to make the necessary preparations, as the time was getting short. It was difficult to get an aide who had done any ballooning. There were plenty of applications from good men, but most of them had never been in a balloon. There was one application from a St. Louis girl, a very clever young newspaper writer. She could hardly be induced to take "No" for an answer, and I believe she would have been a really good assistant. I decided on Mr. Arthur T. Atherholt of Philadelphia. He had made only three ascensions, but had shown decided ability in the work he had done in these. I had no reason to regret my decision, as he proved to be not only a good assistant, but a very pleasant companion.

We went up in the "United States" from St. Louis at 4:05 P.M. Starting in a northwesterly direction, we soon crossed the Missouri River and a little later the Mississippi, near the mouth of the Illinois River. A small motor-boat was puffing saucily down the river in the faint light of the rising moon. We were less than 400 feet above the river, and we shouted down to them and learned just where we were. Our course now changed to about north, and we continued sailing along a little more than 300 feet above the earth. I had kept low in order to get as long a run to the north as possible, hoping to be able to reach the Atlantic coast as far north as New England the next night. The higher currents would have carried us east sooner, but they would have brought us to the Atlantic coast farther south.

All night long we floated silently through the moonlight at an even altitude. Mr. Atherholt, who had a rich tenor voice, sang several charming songs, and occasionally we had a shouted conversation with people as we passed over towns. We had recognized, in passing, several of the larger towns, including

Macomb and Galesburg, Illinois, and our course had gradually turned to the northeast. Just before sunrise we came sweeping down to Lake Michigan, and passed directly over Zion City of Dowie fame, about forty miles north of Chicago, and out over Lake Michigan. One solitary steamer was running down the west shore, and this was the only craft of any kind that we saw on the lake.

As the sun struck the balloon we began to climb steadily, and had attained an altitude of about 4500 feet when we reached the Michigan shore. We were now traveling about forty miles an hour in an easterly direction across the State of Michigan. At 1:20 P.M. we reached Lake St. Clair, with Detroit in full view to the south of us. Intermittent cloud and sunshine had made it necessary to throw over considerable ballast. We passed straight across Lake St. Clair, reaching Lake Erie near Rondeau, Canada. We sailed out over Lake Erie, expecting to reach the New York shore south of Buffalo, but when we were out in the middle of the lake the wind changed, carrying us northeast into Canada again. This brought us up to the

west end of Lake Ontario, with a direction which would take us the whole length of the lake, a distance of nearly 200 miles. As we had less than eight sacks of ballast left, we felt that it would not be wise to attempt this at a time of day when the balloon, due to the increasing coldness of the night, was losing its buoyancy.

We decided to make a landing, but as it was now getting dark and the country was very rough, it was not easy to do this in the heavy wind that was blowing. We finally succeeded in dropping down into a plowed field, and made a very gentle landing by use of the ripping-cord. Mr. Thomas Berry, a farmer living near by, kindly invited us to supper, which was all ready, and we enjoyed a delicious meal, after which, Mr. Berry hitched up his horse and drove us into Caledonia, the nearest town, a distance of seven miles. We had been in the air twenty-five hours and ten minutes, and had made a distance of 625 miles in a direct line from St. Louis, but had actually covered 750 miles or more, about 175 miles of which distance was over water.

Our balloon should have been rewar-

BIRD'S-EYE PHOTOGRAPH OF ST. PETER'S, THE VATICAN AND THE VATICAN
GARDENS, MADE FROM AN ITALIAN MILITARY BALLOON

BIRD'S-EYE PHOTOGRAPH OF THE COLOSSEUM, ROME, MADE
FROM AN ITALIAN MILITARY BALLOON

nished, but I did not have time before the race. If this had been done it would have held gas much better, and we would probably have been able to cross Lake Ontario and make a much better showing.

I had chosen the low current the first night because it carried us to the north. I wished to get well in the north so that when we went east we would have a chance for a long flight out over New England or possibly New Brunswick, but the condition of my balloon defeated this plan.

The winner of the race, Mr. Erbsloh in the German balloon "Pommern," and the close second Mr. Le Blanc in the French balloon "Islede France," had balloons that were in perfect condition, and they are both excellent aëronauts.

I believe that if Mr. Erbsloh had gotten as far north as we did that he would have been able to go east to the New Brunswick coast, not only winning the cup but breaking the world's record for long distance.

Much discussion is heard in regard to the future of ballooning and aërial navigation of all kinds. The spherical balloon, which is the simplest form of aircraft, can never be used to any great ex-

tent except for pleasure. It affords a delightful, quiet ride through the air, but no absolute point of landing can be determined on in advance, and this precludes its use in a business way to any great extent. The aëroplane or flying-machine, using no gas, but lifting itself into the air by its own power, is now being worked out all over the world by many ingenious minds. While a few short flights have been made, it is still far from being an established success. It is probable that an immense amount of experimental work, occupying a number of years, will be necessary before this means of air travel will become practicable. Indeed, I do not believe that any form of aërial locomotion will ever be able to compete in a commercial way with the present means of transportation.

The dirigible balloon, or air-ship, as it is usually called, is now an established success, and is sure to play an important part in future wars. The French government is taking the lead in the matter, and will soon have a whole fleet of aërial cruisers, capable of sailing over the enemy's defenses and dropping hundreds of pounds of dynamite into their fortifications; or of gliding quietly out at night over a battle-ship, and dropping down on her enough dynamite to send her, a shattered wreck, with all on board, to the bottom of the sea.

Germany is also making rapid strides in this work. Count Zeppelin, working under the patronage of the government, has built the largest and probably the most scientifically planned air-ship ever constructed. This ship, named the ——, is more than 400 feet in length, and has made a speed of thirty-five miles an hour in calm weather. Instead of one large gas-bag, it has an aluminum frame holding a dozen smaller gas envelops. In this way greater rigidity is secured, and one gas compartment may be pierced by cannon-shots without injury to the others. England is now working hard to keep pace with the advances in this feature of warfare, and has an air cruiser which has done good work. Italy, Spain, and all the European nations, in fact, are working at the problem.

Italy is paying great attention to the employment of the balloon for photographing and it is said that a branch of the military service has thus photographed the whole of the northern frontier, as well as a large part of the interior. Some of the pictures of Rome herewith presented are particularly interesting.

Our own government has done but little in ballooning except in the way of preparatory work. An aëronautic division has been organized in the signal corps, and a small body of picked men is being trained in aëronautics by use of the ordinary spherical balloon.

While we feel secure from war in our isolated position, and with our enormous resources, yet we should at all times be prepared, and no important advance in the art of war like the use of air cruisers should be neglected. We are a peaceful nation, but the very fact of our being fully prepared is the greatest safeguard against aggression which might involve us in war.

35.
The Safety of Flying
(1908)

THE SAFETY OF FLYING

By CLAUDE GRAHAME-WHITE

How Increased Knowledge and Better Construction Have Lessened the Dangers of the Air

THE aim of constructors of aeroplanes is to produce a machine which shall be generally more stable; they seek also for higher speeds even than those which have already been attained. Increased stability, accompanied by higher average speeds, promises to reduce very materially the risks of aviation. A study of these risks in the light of the aeroplane accidents which have been chronicled is an extremely useful and instructive occupation. Personally, as an airman and, therefore, as a very interested party, I have devoted much time to going over the data that are available concerning aeroplane disasters. One may learn a great deal in this way. In fact, it is the experience gained through the testing, and occasional breaking, of experimental machines that has taught the builder of air craft what he knows to-day.

In the first place, I think it is very necessary to dispel the popular illusion that the risks of aviation are appallingly great. The ordinary man regards the pilot of an aeroplane as an individual who runs a dreadful risk every time he makes an ascent. He is fostered in this belief by the great amount of space which has been devoted in popular journals to aerial catastrophes. It has become the habit to open a newspaper and exclaim, "Ah! Another airman killed!" Thus, the casual reader comes to form an opinion that the ranks of airmen are being so steadily depleted that there will soon be very few left.

As a matter of fact, quite the reverse is the case. The army of pilots is growing so rapidly that, even at the end of last flying season, there were estimated to be 6,000 men in the world capable of handling an aeroplane; nowadays the lists of men who have secured their pilot's certificates are augmented from week to week so rapidly that it is impossible to keep count of all the newcomers to the pastime. And the important point to be made in this connection is: all this flying is being accomplished with diminishing risk to the pilots taking part in it.

I was very greatly impressed, quite recently, by some invaluable statistics which were compiled by the Aero Club of France. This club, for some years past, has kept a record of the approximate number of miles flown by aeroplanes in that country. The result is that it is able to show, in a manner beyond question, that there has been only one aeroplane fatality in France for every 62,000 miles flown. This, I think, is a very significant fact, and one that cannot gain too wide a publicity. It puts matters in the true proportion.

In all risks which men take, the question of proportion enters largely, of course. Flying, being a new and very spectacular achievement, is naturally looked at very largely from the point of view of danger. And yet, through being accustomed to read of them, people get to disregard the perils of other sports and pastimes. Take mountaineering, for example. In one season alone—that of 1910—over one hundred people lost their lives while scaling mountains.

Concerning aviation, it must be remembered that the machines men have been called upon to fly have been very largely experimental; this fact has made the risk, in the past, appreciably greater than it is at the present time, when so many valuable data have been secured. Again, one should make clear the fact that the airmen have had everything to learn. They have been invading an unknown element and have been meeting—in the matter of unexpected wind gusts—an unseen and treacherous enemy. Now, however, pilots have learned very many definite lessons regarding the element they navigate. They have studied winds and have paid particular attention to the question of gusts and sudden eddies. In this connection, therefore, there is a growing factor of safety.

To me, this question of the risks of aviation and how they may be decreased is a very fascinating field for inquiry and research, and, as a practical airman, I have been able recently, in moments of leisure, to obtain reliable data concerning the causes of many aeroplane disasters. I find, for example, that I have been able to secure accurate details, from eyewitnesses and others, as to sixty-four of the fatalities which have already marred the progress of the science; and I think I shall be interesting my readers, and at the same time providing useful information, if I analyze these accidents, and show where risks lie and how they may be avoided. In the first place, I will make a list of these accidents, showing their causes:

Cause.	No. of Accidents.
Breakage of some part of machine....	18
Machine overturned by wind gusts....	13
Pilot's loss of control while flying....	11
Unexplained disasters	5
Accidents while on ground...........	4
Accidents in testing experimental machines	3
Sudden illness of pilot while flying....	3
Aeroplanes lost at sea................	2
Failure of motor	2
Pilots falling from machines while in flight	2
Running into obstruction while flying in fog	1

In regard to the accidents caused by the breakage of some portion of an aeroplane while in flight, one important point needs to be emphasized. The early manufacturers of aeroplanes built with what they considered to be a reasonable margin of safety. And for all ordinary flying their margin of strength was adequate. But, every now and then, an aeroplane would be suddenly subjected, while in the air, to an altogether abnormal strain. Whereupon, unable to withstand the stress placed upon it, some portion of the machine collapsed.

Let me take, for the sake of practical demonstration, three actual monoplane disasters. In the first, a pilot was flying on a very fast, powerfully-engined machine. The wind, at the time, was rather gusty. He was making excellent progress, however, until he was assailed by one particularly vicious gust of wind that eddied up near some sheds which he was passing. The monoplane quivered under the shock. Then the violently applied pressure put a breaking strain upon one of the wings. This wing suddenly buckled up, and the machine crashed down to the ground, utterly beyond control, and the unfortunate pilot was killed.

The second monoplane accident, which is typical of many, concerns a machine which was being piloted in a long *vol plane* by the airman in charge of it. This maneuvre, in which the pilot sweeps down to the ground, in a long, smooth glide, with his engine stopped, is a perfectly safe one, I may mention, provided the machine is handled carefully. In the case I am quoting, when comparatively near the ground, the airman sought to check the downward speed of his machine by a movement of his elevating planes. The action was somewhat abruptly made. The machine swung rapidly into a horizontal position. In doing so, a very severe strain was placed upon the two supporting wings, which were, so to speak, acting as brakes on the air. This strain was, indeed, more than the planes could stand, and they both folded back, allowing the machine to fall like a stone, with fatal results for the pilot.

In my third case, an airman was piloting a monoplane in company with a passenger. The machine was, therefore, fairly heavily laden. The wind was uncertain, and suddenly the machine passed into a lessening of pressure under its planes, which has been called an "air pocket," or "a hole in the air." Naturally, with this sudden diminution of "lift," the monoplane dropped downward. To practical flyers, this experience is not uncommon, although it is always very unpleasant, seeing that occasionally a machine will fall many feet, nearly jerking one off the driving seat, before it encounters normal pressure again.

In the instance with which I am dealing, the monoplane dropped so quickly and heavily, and its fall was then arrested again so violently, that one of its wings broke, with the result that there was another regrettable calamity to record. Naturally, however, the builders of aeroplanes were not oblivious to the lessons taught by these disasters—which were that existing margins of strength were not sufficient. Monoplane wings were promptly built upon a much stronger scale and each piece of wood entering into their construction was minutely tested to make sure that it concealed no hidden flaw.

Furthermore, when assembled, each wing was subjected to a pressure which was many times more than it would be likely to sustain when the machine was in flight. Again, the wings of monoplanes were stayed and supported, by wires above and below, in a thoroughly adequate and practical manner. As a matter of fact, constructors have so taken to heart the lessons that accidents have taught them that monoplane accidents of the nature I have described are now almost unknown. Thus one is again shown the value of practical experience, albeit, as is the case in almost every new industry, that experience is sometimes dearly bought.

It is certainly necessary, in this connection, to touch also upon the subject of biplane accidents. Here I may take three catastrophes, for the purpose of analysis. In the first, while being brought into a horizontal position at the conclusion of a dive, the tail planes of a machine—supported on four wooden booms—crumpled up and broke away. In the second case, while flying in a high wind, the pilot found that his front elevating plane, also carried on four wooden rods, bent back and collapsed. In the third instance, the controlling wires of a machine broke, while in flight, with the result that the biplane became quite unmanageable and dived to the ground.

In this connection I may, perhaps, cite an experience of my own. While flying at Blackpool, in England, the wire leading to the ailerons of my biplane, on one side, suddenly broke. I discovered, afterward, that the wire had been gradually fraying itself away in working through a guide. Fortunately I was near the ground at the time and was able to keep the machine properly balanced until I landed. But it was a lesson for me, as such accidents are to others, and the controlling wires of aeroplanes are now very safely duplicated and are, in addition, very carefully looked after by the mechanics. In general construction, also, the biplane is now improved. Such accidents as the breaking of elevating and tail-planes are now almost impossible. Improvements in design and greater efficiency in engines and propellors make it possible to strengthen the framework of machines. Thus the factor of safety is now a perfectly satisfactory one.

Metal vs. Wood Construction

The aeroplane is, indeed, rapidly ceasing to be a frail construction of wood and wire. Metal, in the form of steel, is now being used to an appreciable extent. Machines are becoming more powerful and able to lift greater loads. Thus we find, as a typical military biplane, a machine with a framework of steel and an engine developing 100 horsepower, capable of lifting a crew of three men into the air and traveling with them, at a high rate of speed, for several hours without descending.

It is now possible to turn to the accidents occasioned by aeroplanes being overturned by wind gusts. When one comes to examine the facts of the case, it is not surprising that there should have been a certain number of catastrophes through this cause. In the very earliest stages of aeroplaning, men flew only in dead calms. Soon, however, their skill increasing and their motors becoming more reliable, they began to ascend in light winds. Then, by degrees, they made flights in quite strong and gusty winds. But the danger was that no pilot knew exactly what would be the maximum strength of any wind gust which might suddenly assail him. It is known, in fact, that winds vary in strength, sometimes, from a few miles an hour to vicious, overpowering gusts. Here, then lay the peril, and it is to his ill-fortune in being struck by an unexpected gust of unusual velocity that more than one airman has owed the loss of his life.

Let me take a typical instance. A pilot is flying in a troublesome wind. Suddenly a treacherous gust catches his machine under one wing. Despite his efforts to right it, the machine tilts over sideways and then "side-slips" through the air, getting quite out of control. Again, it has happened more than once that a machine, when gliding down to the ground, has been struck by a sudden gust, with the result that the glide has been converted, in an instant, into a perilous, practically vertical drop.

I am glad to be able to say again, however, that such accidents are growing fewer every day. The reason lies partly in the growing skill of airmen, and mostly in the increase of knowledge regarding aerial conditions. Then the modern-type of aeroplane is much more stable than were the early machines. Refinements in construction and in the operation of its controlling planes have given it a surer equilibrium. Then the increased speed with which present-type machines fly is a factor to be considered. A fast-flying machine, when assailed by a gust, has its momentum to help it. It resists more effectually than a slow-flying machine the overturning impulses of ugly gusts. In this connection, it is interesting to note that a speed of more than a hundred miles an hour through the air has already been achieved by a racing monoplane.

To a pilot's loss of control, while flying, an appreciable number of fatalities have been due. Here, again, experience in airmanship is lessening risks. In more than one case, the over-daring feats of men who have only just learned to fly have brought about disaster. An instance is easily forthcoming. An airman who was still a novice, and who had not mastered the art of making a *vol plane,* insisted one day upon ascending to an appreciable altitude. Suddenly his motor gave trouble and then stopped. Instead of tilting his machine quickly downward and thus maintaining his control over it by setting it upon a glide toward the ground, he allowed it to lose its pace until it came practically to a standstill in the air. The result was that, having no steerageway upon it, the machine passed out of control and slid backward through the air, with the result that the pilot was killed.

Foolhardiness a Fruitful Cause of Disaster

More than once, also, inexperienced men have essayed to make flights in gusty winds, ignoring the warnings of their friends, and disaster has overtaken them. To the attempting of hazardous evolutions while in the air, more than one catastrophe has been due. The aeroplane, in unskilled and foolhardy hands is, indeed, a veritable instrument of danger. The man who flies learns quickly, if he has commonsense, to take no liberties with his craft. It is sufficient if he flies and flies carefully. Lack of judgment, or a careless, thoughtless action may very quickly get him into serious trouble.

Fortunately, in this connection, the tuition at the flying schools is becoming far more thorough. More is known about the art of aviation every day; therefore, more may be taught. In early days, a pupil had almost everything to learn himself. Nowadays, he finds himself in the hands of an instructor who knows what he is talking about and can lead him from step to step.

A matter of vital interest to the industry concerns unexplained aerial disasters. Of these, already, there have been a regrettable number. Loss of a life is sad enough, and it is doubly so when the cause of that loss cannot be traced. In a flying disaster, when the pilot is alone, or when he and his passenger may both be killed, there is no chance of obtaining the evidence of anyone actually in the machine. All that can be gained, therefore, is the statement of eyewitnesses, and, as these are not usually experts, confusion and contradictions frequently ensue.

As a rule, the lesson of the disaster lies in the machine. Although it may be badly shattered, its remains generally tell their tale to the expert eye of the investigator. But occasionally this resort fails, and no clue can be obtained from the wrecked machine. Then, if the testimony of eyewitnesses is also unreliable, the matter becomes a mystery. Frequently, no doubt, when an accident is written as being unexplained, the secret lies in the breakage of some part of the machine while in flight, or in the treacherous attack of a windgust. But it cannot be proved, of course, and this is the unsatisfactory point.

Difficulty of Determining the Cause of Accidents

I may quote a recent case in this regard—that concerning the death of Mr. Graham Gilmour, the well-known English airman. Flying under apparently safe conditions, his machine suddenly dived to the ground and he was killed. Spectators declared that they saw one of the wings of his monoplane buckle up, but an examination of the machine did not seem to bear out such a statement, and the fatality was written down as a mystery. So impressed is the English Aero Club by the need to clear up such mysteries of the air as these that a special committee has now been appointed, which will sift all available evidence and endeavor to place on record, for the benefit of those interested, a clear account of the cause or causes of any accident which may be in doubt. The work of such a committee should prove exceedingly valuable.

What may be considered a curious item, in my list of aeroplane fatalities, is that concerning accidents which happened while machines were on the ground. In explanation, I may set forth how several of these catastrophes occurred. In one case, after landing from a flight, a man's machine ran forward and fell into a ditch; in another, an aeroplane, while moving across an aerodrome, ran into a pylon, or mark-tower, and was wrecked, the top part of the wooden pylon falling upon the pilot and

killing him; in a third, the airman ran into a wall, or fence, after alighting, with disastrous results. Such accidents naturally suggested the use of some form of brake by which the airman could, after alighting, or when running along the ground, check the forward motion of his machine. As a matter of fact, a form of shoe or skid brake is now in use, and this point is likely to receive greater attention as the development of machines proceeds. Modern type monoplanes, being constructed so that their tail planes are low when the machines are on the ground, offer their two main wings more or less as a brake to the air; in consequence, they pull up quite quickly after landing from a flight.

Now we come to the accidents caused through the use of experimental machines. In this regard, we have again to deal with the man of little knowledge. Accidents under this heading would rarely happen if ordinary precautions were observed. In one instance of which I have knowledge a private experimenter built a machine which, although embodying good ideas, was condemned for its constructional weakness by several experts. But this did not deter the novice. He had determined to fly the machine, and fly it he did. At first he met with success. Several flights were accomplished, and then one day, without any warning, the machine buckled in the air and the misguided airman was killed.

The moral here is so self-evident that I need not labor it. An experienced, careful man is needed to build an aeroplane. Machines are surprisingly light, and yet at the same time they have to be astonishingly strong. The building of an aeroplane must, in fact, be in competent hands. An experimental machine, perhaps with one fatal weakness which will wreck it directly a heavy strain is thrown upon its structure, presents a fearful element of risk. I may mention in this connection that it has already been suggested that official examinations be made of all new machines. The idea is that some sort of certificate should be granted to the machine which passes reasonable tests. In this way, it is held that a dangerous machine would be weeded out, and would not be left to bring some ill-advised pilot to grief. There are a good many points of view to be considered before any such drastic rule is finally laid down, but the general idea of any such inspection of machines is an excellent one.

Several aeroplane fatalities have been attributed to the sudden illness of a pilot while actually steering his machine through the air. But the testimony, in this connection, has generally been somewhat unsatisfactory, and a good deal of doubt remains in several instances. In one case an airman was seen, apparently, to throw up his arms and release his controlling levers; in another, medical evidence suggested that the steersman had been overtaken by some form of fit, or seizure, while making a flight. The point in regard to this matter that should be made is this: an airman needs to be physically fit. It is dangerous for a man with organic weakness of any kind to be piloting a high-speed machine, whether it be aeroplane, motor car or railway engine. In the ordinary way, and under favorable weather conditions, there is no more strain in piloting an aeroplane than in driving a motor car; but emergencies arise in this, as in other sports, which demand that a man should have a sound physique and strong nerves.

Over-Sea Flying

The last items on my list can, with one exception, be dismissed briefly. Airmen who have been lost at sea have been driven out of their course by side winds, or have been enveloped in fogs. Only under favorable wind conditions, and with an absence of fog, are long over-sea flights reasonable, and even when the weather serves I consider it essential that there should be patrol boats ready to pick up the airman should his motor fail him. But foolhardy flights have unfortunately been made, occasionally with disastrous consequences.

I think it is a distinct tribute to the reliability of the aeroplane motor that only two accidents in my list should be put down to the failure of a power plant. As a matter of fact, of course, even when his motor does fail him there is no need, in nine cases out of ten, for the pilot to concern himself unduly. All he has to do, if he is flying carefully and at a reasonably safe altitude, is to plane down upon the nearest piece of ground that appears suitable for a landing.

The increased reliability of aeroplane motors has a great deal to do with the present safety of flying. In early days there were two elements of danger—the overheating of the motor or the breakage of some working part. Both causes of breakdown were due to the high rate of speed at which engines had to be run in order to keep an air craft aloft. Nowadays the overheating problem has been largely solved. In the engines themselves a great precision of manufacture is observed. They are no longer motorcar engines adapted to flying; they are aeroplane engines proper. All working parts have been specially designed and strengthened to meet the heavy and persistent strain that experience has shown is put upon them. Water-cooling has been made very much more efficient; and, as regards air-cooled engines, the revolving "Gnome" has achieved results that are astonishing. Greater general efficiency and perfection in workmanship have enabled other air-cooled engines also to make a good showing. It is no exaggeration to say that the aeroplane engine, when well looked after and reasonably driven, has become as reliable as that which is fitted to a motor car.

As regards my last two headings, little comment is necessary. An aeroplane plunges violently, occasionally, in wind gusts; and there is a risk, albeit rather a negligible one, of a pilot being thrown from his driving seat. Many airmen now fix themselves in their seats by means of a strap, made partly of leather and partly of India rubber, which can be easily thrown off when desired. Such a precaution lessens the risk of being thrown from one's seat in a bad landing.

As regards running into obstructions while flying in fog, all one can say is that there is always a serious risk in piloting a machine under such conditions, and particularly near the ground. Fog is, indeed, one of the airman's great enemies, particularly when he is attempting a long cross-country flight.

For a final word, I should like to touch upon the relative safety of biplanes and monoplanes. For the pupil, learning to fly, I think the biplane, on account of its slower controlling action, offers somewhat greater security than the monoplane. But that the latter is dangerous is an entirely wrong supposition. A good deal of skill is certainly required to pilot a monoplane. Its control is delicate, and its high speed makes sound judgment, on the part of the pilot, quite imperative. But a competent airman can achieve wonders with a monoplane.

Regarding the relative values of the two machines, one should look upon the biplane, I think, as the weight-carrying machine, and the monoplane as the craft for high-speed work. The former is safe, pleasant and easy to handle; the latter is invaluable when speed is essential, or when a flight needs to be made under very troublesome weather conditions.

36.
A Fall From the Sky
(1910)

THE STARTING PLACE AT SCHMARGENDORF IN THE
SOUTHWEST SUBURBS OF BERLIN

The "Conqueror" may be distinguished in the middle of the picture, by the
square upon it made by the American flag.

A FALL FROM THE SKY

HOW TWO AMERICANS IN AN EXPLODED BALLOON DROPPED
A THIRD OF A MILE, AND LIVED TO TELL THE TALE

BY AUGUSTUS POST

IN September, 1908, the first aëroplane tests for the United States Government were in progress at Fort Myer. It was these tests that started the present aviation excitement in this country, and set the newspapers talking confidently of "the conquest of the air." On this occasion I was representing the Aëro Club of America, stopping at the Cosmos Club in Washington, when a telegram from Mr. A. Holland Forbes broke into this absorbing occupation, and eventually brought me into the most exciting experience that I have ever shared.

Mr. Forbes was Vice-President of the Aëro Club of America, a sportsman such as only the word intrepid will describe, yachtsman, automobilist, balloonist of experience, and what was most to the purpose in this connection, owner and pilot of the "Conqueror," one of the largest and finest balloons in the country. His telegram invited me to act as his aide in the Gordon Bennett International Balloon Race, to take place at Berlin, Germany, on October 11 of that year. There was no

time for meditation; the telegram called me, should I accept, to meet him at once at the New York Yacht Club. Indeed, I needed no time for decision; the offer was attractive. I had had one experience already in a Gordon Bennett race, sailing with Mr. Alan R. Hawley from St. Louis almost to the Atlantic Ocean. Balloon races in general have a wonderful charm, and the German "meet" was to be an event of world-wide importance; while, for a companion in the car, no one could be more desirable than Mr. Forbes.

The successful make-up of a team in a long-distance balloon-race depends on many qualifications, mental almost more than physical. For many hours perhaps, two men, cut loose from the earth, sharing a profound solitude, must have one mind and one motive, and must act instinctively with a precision that admits of no hesitation and no discussion. In any event, a long-distance race is bound to be a great memory, and your companion must be one with whom you are willing to share a great memory—and that is in

463

itself something of a test of one's opinion of a man.

So I telegraphed Mr. Forbes without further delay that I accepted, and the next morning I started to meet the appointment. The aëroplane tests were going on beautifully; I shook hands with Mr. Orville Wright at parting with every prospect of his immediate success and every hope of mine; no one could know that within a few days the aëroplane upon which the attention of America was focused would be a battered mass with poor Selfridge dead under the wreckage, Mr. Wright wounded in the hospital, and our balloon, the "Conqueror," the victim of a fate more spectacular, if not so tragic. The conquest of the air was not so complete as the press of September, 1908, would have had the world believe.

At the New York Yacht Club Mr. Forbes explained to me in complete detail, so as not to take me afterward by surprise, the plan that he had in mind for conserving gas, and thus increasing our chance of prolonged flight. His plan was to lengthen the appendix of the balloon twelve feet, so that it would hang down into the basket, where he could close it with a rubber band. This point, upon which our whole subsequent action depended, requires a little explanation to make the matter clear to the non-professional reader.

The appendix is the neck, or pipe, at the bottom of the balloon through which gas is introduced during inflation, and out of which gas escapes when the balloon becomes expanded. This expansion of gas is caused by the sun's warmth during the day or by the heat radiated from the earth during the night, or by the decrease in pressure of the outside air as the balloon rises to a higher altitude. A balloon, technically known as an aërostat, seeks as its name implies, a point in the air where its weight just equals the weight of the air which its bulk displaces. The gas within the envelop being lighter than air at the surface of the earth, would naturally rise to a point where the air was just as light as it was, if it were not for the weight of sand ballast which is taken on board a balloon to keep it down. Putting out the sand, which is managed with the greatest delicacy, and regulating the out-flow of gas, make up the controlling process of the flight. Pure coal-gas lifts about forty pounds for each thousand cubic feet, and a large balloon of 80,000 cubic feet, like the "Conqueror," lifts about 3200 pounds. The varnished cotton envelop, basket, guide-rope, and baggage that we carried weighed about 1200 pounds, making it necessary to take on board a ton of sand ballast to prevent us from shooting up into the sky like a rocket.

The balloon is "balanced" with the utmost care before the start, sand being put on and taken off until the balloon weighs exactly as much as the air it displaces and floats without rising, poised like the pans of an apothecary's scales. This is technically known as the point of equilibrium. Now if the aëronaut spills ballast he rises and the gas expands and underflows from the neck or appendix, which is always open. It works like a bottle filled with liquid that if expanded would overflow; except that, as gas acts oppositely from liquid, you must imagine your bottle upside down. Every time a little ballast goes over, the balloon rises; a little gas escapes and then the balloon sinks somewhat, the momentum gained by the movement of the mass carrying it just beyond the point at which it should naturally stop, so that without care it may lose equilibrium altogether. In a racing balloon the sacks of ballast are tied so none of the sand can spill out, and canvas is stretched over the floor of the basket to prevent its getting out through the willow meshes, and to enable the aëronaut to gather up the very last grain by hand. The sand is handled by the skilful aëronaut with a small scoop, like so much gold-dust, for upon economy of ballast depends the length of the trip. Indeed the gold-dust simile is not inapposite, for it is like living on a fixed income, that can be spread out with more or less economy over a longer or shorter period, but cannot be increased.

The delicacy of this process is marvelous; the broken tip of a knife-blade thrown over is enough to start a balloon rising, even the huge "Conqueror," fifty feet in diameter, eighty feet high—quite as large as a good-sized building—and with a gas-capacity of 80,000 cubic feet. This is the largest size used in racing, the limit being originally determined by the strength of balloon material, which stands only just so much internal pressure.

It will be seen that Mr. Forbes's idea of lengthening the appendix so as to bring it down into the basket, where he could close it, would prevent the slopping over or underflow of gas when in this delicate state of equilibrium, and thus had great value in preventing small losses of gas and thus giving us a greater chance of winning. Of course when any considerable expansion of gas took place, the appendix was to be opened. In short, the control of the appendix, which was to be opened and closed from the basket, was a useful expedient— and, it must be added, in view of the possible *sudden* expansion, it was an expedient attended with undeniable risk.

However, the risk was not necessarily inevitable. The famous German aëronaut Oscar Erbslöh, who so tragically met his death this year, was the first to use a similar expedient in this country in a free balloon. When Erbslöh started in his balloon "Pommern" from St. Louis in the Gordon Bennett race of the year previous, 1907, he had a cord from the appendix reaching down into the basket by which the neck could be drawn up and partly closed. I had many talks with him then about methods of economizing gas, and the possibilities of bursting balloons, little thinking that each of us was to have an experience of this sort in time to come, his fatal, and mine so strangely fortunate. Mr. Forbes's plan, however, was to lengthen the appendix itself, instead of controlling it with a cord.

The plan of action once understood, there remained but a few days for the

A. HOLLAND FORBES, PILOT OF THE
BALLOON "CONQUEROR"

necessary preparations, and for what little "training" was to be done. For the preparation of the aëronaut differs from that of any other sportsman only in that he should never be out of training, for the balloonist, like his balloon, must keep in equilibrium, physical and mental, ready for anything.

A few days of cross-country runs and walks before we sailed, a few hours of brushing up Wise and Moedebeck on the steamer, and a hasty polish of my long-disused German, formed all the special preparation I was to make.

It was emphatically a trip with a purpose, and scarcely a moment passed that did not contribute to this. In Paris we saw the International balloon races, a preparation for the Berlin Coupe Internationale Gordon Bennett; all the French contestants for the latter event went up in one balloon—how they ever managed to run it I don't know. The enthusiasm there was the best sort of an impetus, had we needed more; every one was obsessed with balloons and balloon-racing. At Mallet's atelier at Puteaux, just outside Paris, that most interesting of shops, with envelops hanging about and baskets standing in rows, we saw the new balloon "St. Louis," looking beautiful with her cloth covered with composition and varnish on the outside, ready to be sent on to Berlin for the use of Mr. Arnold and Mr. Hewatt, and we picked out a medium-sized basket for her.

Balloon baskets are made of willow and rattan wicker-work, with wire and rope woven through, to enable them to withstand shocks and hard usage, and to protect the passengers, for though the passage through the air is without breath or motion, often in landing in a high wind the basket is dragged over fields or through trees, and is likely to receive many bumps. It is so strong, though apparently so frail, that it can go through even such an experience as that which awaited the "Conqueror" without being smashed.

Mr. F. S. Lahm and Mr. J. C. Mc-Coy, owner of the other contesting balloon, the "America II," went with us, and we discussed with Mr. Lahm at some length what would happen if a balloon should burst in the air. He maintained that it would form a parachute. Mr. Lahm is the Dean of the pilots of the Aëro Club of France, one of the most eminent of authorities, and his son, Lieutenant Frank P. Lahm, had won the Gordon Bennett Cup for America in 1906, an event commemorated by the founding of the Lahm Cup for long-distance flights in America. His opinion, therefore, had more than usual weight, reinforced as it was by his quotation from John

AUGUSTUS POST, AIDE TO MR. FORBES

Wise's experiences near Philadelphia in 1838. Wise, one of the pioneers of ballooning, made several ascents in order to experiment in this very matter, deliberately preparing his balloon so it could be ripped open after reaching a great height, so certain was his confidence that it would "parachute" down. At 1300 feet the balloon became so distended by the pressure of gas that was rushing out of the small neck that Wise was considering abandoning the experiment, when, taking the responsibility upon itself, the balloon exploded. The lower part doubled into the upper as he had expected, and though when the car struck Wise was thrown

ten feet and the basket landed upside down, his account concludes, with true sporting spirit, "Before many minutes had elapsed after this descent, I resolved to repeat the experiment at the first opportunity."

Arrived in Berlin—for we made but a flying visit to Paris—the final preparations for the long-distance race were at once under way. How elaborate these preparations were, and for how many contingencies it was necessary to provide, will be evident if it be borne in mind that we were embarking on what we hoped might be a three days' journey, literally at the will of the wind, across the continent of Europe. The record made by Count de la Vaulx stands at 1193 miles; we must therefore provide for a possible landing anywhere within that distance of Berlin. If you will take a map of Europe, and using a radius of 1193 miles, describe a circle around the German capital, you will see that it would have taken us over a tremendous range of territory—into Russia, as de la Vaulx had gone, over the Mediterranean, into the Desert of Sahara, into Turkey, Bulgaria, Asia Minor—indeed, from the Lofoten Islands to Africa.

The Deutsche Luftsschiffs Verein had provided us with phrase-books for all the probable and improbable countries in which we might land, with parallel columns of sentences for every sort of purpose, and in the case of certain strange and outlandish tongues, with phonetic pronunciation for the balloonist to use in addressing the illiterate. This is a sample of the foresight of the authorities, for it is apt to be among the peasants, far from civilization, that the foreign balloon trip ends. You ascend from the midst of a crowd, you usually descend in solitude. I remember especially the sentences in this book, "Don't all talk at once," "Show me on your fingers how many," and "You shall have a big tip." The questions and answers covered all the wants the aëronaut was supposed to have, and some that only Teutonic thoroughness would have suggested. The telegraph blanks with which we were provided were printed in a string of languages; so were the little slips that accompanied them. These "ballon-depeschen" were to be filled out from time to time, weighted with tiny bags of sand already attached, and dropped over the side, bearing a printed promise of reward for forwarding at once to Berlin.

Passports were of course a prime necessity. I recall that they made me take off my hat to a picture of the Czar at the consul's office before they would give me a Russian passport. Then there was clothing for every clime, eatables and drinkables for three days and more, for it was not impossible that we might have to camp out on landing. Among the provisions were hot drinks in patent bottles, and soups packed in lime so that opening the can and pouring water on the packing heated the contents. Comforts were not to be lacking above the clouds. We had drinking-water in case we came down in a desert, and life-preservers in case we came down in the sea. The statoscope and the barograph, delicate instruments so exquisitely adjusted that they record the slightest variation, electric lights by which one may take readings by night, all the scientific equipment for making and preserving the records of such a journey, all were in shape. And that nothing should be lacking to a proper start, a grocer's boy put some picture-postcards, addressed to himself, into the basket, with the request that we throw them out when at a distance, it being apparently impossible for the German mind to conceive of an excursion without *ansichtspostkarten* to be mailed on the way.

The meeting of contestants brought together some of the most eminent aëronauts of the world, among them Jacques Faure of France, whom we had already met, Moore-Brabazon of England, Erbslöh, the most celebrated balloonist of Germany, Captain von Abercron, Leblanc, and the Americans, McCoy, Arnold, and Hewatt. The great day of the meet, October 11, 1908, was perfect both for aëronauts and for sightseers, and as it was a Sunday, holidaymakers crowded every roof-top of Berlin. Within the inclosure, vast as it was, every inch of space for spectators was filled. Such crowds Berlin had never before brought together, surely never crowds so absorbed and intent, so vivid is the interest that all Germany takes in aëronautic matters to-day.

The word came down to us at last, "Start in five minutes." We were in our places in the car of the "Conqueror"; everything was going off like clockwork; at 3:40 exactly we were to rise. The "Conqueror" was "balanced" until it floated without rising; then a dozen German soldiers lifted the car upon their shoulders, the huge bulk swaying in its netting overhead, and carried us to the starting-place, where representatives of the Aëro Club of Germany and officers of the Imperial Army were sending off, one by one, the balloons of the various nations in their allotted order. An officer, watch in hand, stood, ticking off the last seconds.

This moment of equilibrium, just before the start of a long-distance race, must be something like the proverbial "last moment" of a drowning man. In the instant's pause—literally one of suspense— there flash through the mind, if not one's whole life, at least all the days and weeks of preparation that have now culminated. So, in that backward survey, taking account of everything, we honestly thought we had provided for every possible contingency; and so we had, for all save one —and that was the one that happened!

THE moment of departure had arrived, the officer commanded "Let go, all!" The men released their hold, and Mr. Forbes threw out a little sand. Curiously enough, there was a difference of fifty feet in the elevation of the starting-place and that of the spot where we had been balanced, and even this slight difference brought about a little heaviness in the start of several balloons. We were gently rising, when a puff of wind caught us, and whisked us toward a board fence against which the crowd was packed. For that matter, the crowd was packed everywhere, but this part of it had to scatter;

Drawn by W. T. Benda.   Half-tone plate engraved by H. C. Merrill

THE EXPLODED BALLOON "CONQUEROR" FALLING UPON THE ROOFS OF FRIEDENAU
IN THE SOUTHWEST SUBURBS OF BERLIN

The picture shows the aspect of the falling balloon after the burst envelop had folded into the top, forming a parachute.
Mr. Forbes and Mr. Post grasped the ring above the basket to ease the shock of the imminent impact with a roof.

the car tore through the fence as if it had been made of paper, and then, swaying from the force of the shock, began to swing like a giant pendulum far out on either side. Two bags of sand were knocked off, another split open, and the sudden loss of weight sent the balloon shooting up into the air high above the crowded tribunes, the field covered with vehicles of every sort, high over the streets and roofs black with gazers, and the meadows and farms that now stretched out under our view far on every side. The swaying stopped and the car settled into the characteristic calm that marks the passage of the free balloon. We got out the guide-rope, adjusted the instruments, and settled ourselves for a long voyage.

From far below came a faint murmur, all that we could hear, at this great height, of the roars of applause going up from the assembled million; far away in the distance we could see the balloons that had preceded us, eight of them, stretching in a long line like buoys at the entrance to a harbor. They drifted slowly, the farthest just disappearing in the haze over the horizon. Forbes was busily engaged in piloting the balloon, his eye on the statoscope, that showed us at a height of nearly 3000 feet and still rising rapidly. I entered the barometer reading in my log-book, and watched the neck of the balloon swell and become distended as the gas expanded under the decreased pressure at such a height and from the heat of the sun. Forbes said, "How nicely it works!" The expansion had come so quickly that the appendix was fully open and swelled by the gas that rushed out with a roar like the blowing off of a steam boiler. My pencil was on the log-book when I felt a distinct tremble of the basket, such as we sometimes feel when a wrinkle straightens out of the balloon-envelop.

I looked up. The bottom of the balloon was beginning to shrivel like an old dry apple. It was plain what had happened. I said to Forbes, "She's gone," and reached up just in time to slip the end of the appendix rope through the knot, so it could rise into the top of the balloon which then could form a parachute. Meanwhile the gas had escaped from the huge rent in the side, through which we could see the blue sky.

It is not pleasant to think what would have happened had not one of us caught and released the appendix rope just before it tightened, the rope that was intended to prevent exactly what was our only salvation,—the forming of a parachute. One second more, and it would have been as taut as an iron rod; in the time it would have taken to cut it, we should have been on the ground with even the knife-blade shattered to pieces. For the "Conqueror" would have come down like a stone with a rag tied to it.

As it was, the first speed of descent was terrific. Forbes took out his big knife that he carried in a sheath at his waist, and slashed the bags of sand that hung at the corners of the basket, and they dropped like apples from a tree roughly shaken. The last thing a balloonist does is to drop a bag whole, and I remember asking Forbes about it, and his replying that every one was looking at us and had plenty of chance to dodge. We were going down so fast that we passed some of the bags on the way,—but these were the empty ones that I had shaken over the side, making such a sandcloud that we seemed to be passing through a simoon in the desert. The empty bags made little parachutes of themselves, going down more and more slowly, just as we were beginning to do.

For the rush of the fall had sent the cloth of the lower part of the balloon up into the top with a snap; there it was held by the netting, though the strain stretched the stout cords to their utmost, and the cloth tried its best to get through the meshes. But they held, and the great top, now like a mushroom, began to check our descent and to slant with the wind.

However, it was clear that we were not to have any choice in the matter of landing. The city was coming up to meet us; it seemed as if some great giant was hurling buildings, streets, churches, up at us with all his might. It looked at one moment as if we were to land in the street, the next, our diagonal course took us straight for some tiled roofs with chimneys sticking up. The next instant we had crashed into one of these, scattering the bricks in a shower, the basket smashing down through the tiles of the roof as we hung from the concentrating ring over our heads, so that at the moment of impact we

Drawn by W. T. Benda.   Half-tone plate engraved by H. C. Merrill

THE BASKET OF THE "CONQUEROR" SMASHING INTO A TILED ROOF OF FRIEDENAU

The basket broke through the roof sufficiently to be held fast.   In a moment the top had settled over
ridges and chimneys and Mr. Forbes and Mr. Post, removing their coats, were
engaged in saving the instruments and materials of the balloon.

were still in the air. We had made this
last move with the same instinctive prevision that had guided our actions all the
way down; a certain intense concentration
of mind kept us just in advance of the
event.

Fortunately, the basket had made such
a deep, jagged hole in the roof that it
stuck there and by another of the extraordinary circumstances of the fall, we were
not dragged over the edge, for the fall
from roof to street would have damaged
us more than the three-thousand-foot drop
from the heavens, and it would have been
a pity to have spoiled it all in the last
forty feet.

The great envelop, now entirely collapsed, draped itself along the roofs, its
netting catching the chimneys and holding
it fast. We dropped into the basket, and
in a moment more had clambered out on
the roof. It was the house Number 7
Wilhelmstrasse, Friedenau, a suburb of
Berlin. Forbes had a little bruise where
he had been thrown against the side of the
basket, and we were both somewhat
shaken up, but neither of us noticed that
at the time. We threw off our coats and
Forbes started methodically unpacking the
instruments, clothes, and such things as
had not already gone overboard (only
three bottles of mineral water were

broken) while I unslung my camera and photographed the balloon from all directions, showing just where it landed, to complete my record of the trip.

These proceedings seemed to astonish the natives, who had reached the roof a few moments after we did, almost as much as our spectacular descent. All the newspaper accounts next day, all the "interviews with eye-witnesses" referred to Forbes, "a true American type," coolly fishing out his boots from the car, or my taking photographs "in aller Seelenruhe," as if the etiquette of the occasion demanded that we should have done something eccentric—just what I do not know. The episode of the boots was due to his having taken them off as soon as the balloon had mounted, and settled himself comfortably in his slippers for a possible three days' trip. Three days! It seemed three years since that moment.

I could not hear anything; the rapid change of pressure on the ear-drums made them feel as if the inside of my head were filled with cotton. Perspiration was starting from every pore. The whole world looked brilliant and beautiful; thoughts came rushing in sentences; I found myself speaking German with a fluency that I never had before, or have had since, answering questions with the greatest ease, replying to the greetings and congratulations that came from every side. The prevalent feeling was one of joy; they had believed us dashed to death and we were alive and unhurt; the revulsion of feeling brought out an expression of simple human love.

Meantime the excitement had spread over all Berlin. The fire-bell was ringing in Friedenau, an automobile full of ambulance men had started at full speed from the Startplatz. A lady told us next day that the instant the bag burst her two little girls dropped to their knees, put their hands together, and began to pray for our safety. The dear creatures were convinced that they had brought us down uninjured. One of the sand-bags that went over so unceremoniously had landed in a baby-carriage, from which, happily, the nurse had just removed the baby. Another struck between a gentleman and his wife, who were walking on a street at some distance from the grounds; neither was hurt, though the lady fainted from the shock, as he told us in a letter next day, asking for our autographs.

The only persons apparently unmoved were the balloonists who were to follow us, who in spite of a spectacle that might have been expected to unnerve them, kept leaving the ground without a moment's break in the schedule. Directly after us came Erbslöh, who started at the moment when it seemed certain that we were being killed, but went up without a quaver. Just before us the French balloon had ascended, with Jacques Faure, also a personal friend of ours. He saw our fall, but before he could make out the result, the wind had carried him out of sight. Later in the evening Erbslöh caught up with him, and as soon as they came within speaking distance Faure called through a megaphone, "What became of Forbes and Post? Are they killed?" Erbslöh shouted back, "Oh, they got down all right. I saw them through my glasses on the roof of a house in their shirtsleeves, so they must be all right." Then the wind carried them apart to opposite ends of the country, but Faure wrote us a touching note of congratulation, weighted it with a little bag of sand, and sent it down to the earth, where some one forwarded it to us. That very night we received his message from the clouds, together with those from across the sea, in answer to the cables we had sent from the roof of the house in Friedenau. One, I remember, congratulated me on my "successful downfall."

That was my last sight of Erbslöh; on July 13, just as this article was being prepared, he lost his life with four companions by a fall from an elevation as high as ours, with his own dirigible balloon near Opladen, Rhenish Prussia. It burst in mid-air, probably from a benzine explosion, and as there was no netting, as in a spherical balloon, to hold together the cloth and form a parachute, the mass of metal fell like a shot, just as the French dirigible "La République" had fallen with its officers and crew the year before.

The fire-company of Friedenau was on the roof almost as soon as the spectators that swarmed up the stairs. I had no lack of witnesses to sign the record, which was completed in proper form before we reached the ground below. Indeed the report was handed in almost before the last contestant in the race was clear of

ONE OF SEVERAL PAGES IN MR. POST'S BALLOON LOG-BOOK, RECORDING
THE TRIP OF THE "ST. LOUIS" IN 1907

This is part of the record of the ascent on October 21, 1907, from St. Louis in the balloon of that name, Mr. Alan R. Hawley, pilot, Mr. Augustus Post, aide, as contestants in the Gordon Bennett International Cup Race, which was won by the late Oscar Erbslöh, who landed near Asbury Park, New Jersey, 876 miles from the starting place. The "St. Louis" landed near Baltimore after a flight of 718 miles.

The first column of this page of the log records the time between 7:30 and 10:30 of the first night of the race; the second column records the altitudes at the stated times; the third column indicates the direction of travel; the fourth column gives first the temperature (Fahrenheit) and second the humidity, also an entry showing when the eighth bag of ballast was emptied (the remarkable fact being that between 9:37 P. M. and 8:39 A. M. no ballast was discharged).

The abbreviated remarks in the last column, if amplified, would read as follows: "Three balloons in sight. Hailed Leblanc at 7:30 P. M., who was at an altitude of 1100 meters (we being a thousand feet above him). At 7:40 three balloons still in sight. Conversation by megaphone with Brewer (in English balloon), with Mix (aide to Leblanc), and with Levee (aide to Gasnier) who said they had started with 40 bags of ballast and had so far used 8; their altitude 2000 meters (nearly level with us). At 8:17 two balloons in sight. Can read by moon; cast over envelop (giving record of progress). At 8:46, nothing in sight; 9:20, balloon in equilibrium; finished eighth bag of ballast; wind better (direction); balloon to the east of us; 10:10, lights (of some town) to the east. At 10:30 Post relieved Hawley as pilot.

the starting grounds, and the surprised officials were still considering the shortest official balloon report on record, when the "Conqueror" itself arrived in one of the fire company's wagons, badly torn from its various experiences, not the least damaging being its treatment at the hands of souvenir-hunters. I can fancy strips of it now, with suitable inscriptions, decorating the walls of some Friedenauer living-room.

Getting down from the roof, which we accomplished as soon as the packing was well under way and the official report drawn up, was an experience such as seldom falls to the lot of any one. It was a strange and an immensely moving experi-ence to pass through streets so packed that the automobile could hardly push its way, people shouting madly, almost hysteri-cally, fairly beside themselves with joy that two men were alive—two men about whom they had known nothing ten min-utes ago, and whose names at that mo-ment they did not know. The automobile sought for the less-frequented streets, but there were no less-frequented ways at all; every avenue of approach was filled solid with shouting people, and hands were con-tinually thrust over the side for us to grasp. The excitement followed us all through the meet, the "miraculously saved young Americans" were surrounded with

(handwritten balloon log-book record)

THE RECORD IN MR. POST'S BALLOON LOG-BOOK OF THE ASCENT, EXPLOSION, AND DROP OF THE "CONQUEROR" NEAR BERLIN ON OCTOBER 11, 1908

This record is not so symmetrical as the one on the opposite page, for reasons readily understood. It indicates that the "Conqueror" was to start officially at 3:40 P. M. At 3:25 the balloon was carried from the place where it was inflated, to the balancing place; at 3:35 soldiers carried it to the starting place. The start was made at 3:37; two sacks of ballast were thrown out; the basket hit a fence; at 3:40 the balloon had ascended 750 meters and was moving south; at 3:45, being 850 meters up, the word "tear" was immediately written to denote the explosion. After the fall, "drop" and "land 3 Kil(ometers) Parachute" were written to record the cause and method of landing. The lowest entry indicates that at 4:30 Mr. Post arrived by automobile back at the starting place, to deliver his record, followed by a detail of firemen with the damaged balloon and effects; while Mr. Forbes, in another automobile, proceeded to his hotel in order to send messages to allay the anxiety of Ambassador Hill, General James Allen, Chief of the United States Signal Corps, and friends in America.

an atmosphere of good-will; it even followed us to the Royal Opera, where, as visiting aëronauts, we were among the guests of the Emperor, sitting in a box opposite His Imperial Majesty. We saw him looking at us as some one beside him was evidently, from the gestures, describing the fall, and it did give us a sort of subconscious chuckle to think that for once in our lives, instead of our looking at the Emperor, the Emperor was looking at us. The play was the gorgeous pantomime of "Sardanapalus," the Emperor's own project, which he had staged with the utmost magnificence, seemingly an expression of the power and the glory of the German Empire. It was given, as I have said, in honor of the visiting aëronauts; but we were the only contestants in the Gordon Bennett race that circumstances had enabled to attend. The others were scattered all over the map; Captain van Schaick, in the balloon "Helvetia," after breaking all endurance records by a flight of seventy-three hours' duration, came down so low over the North Sea that he was towed in by officious boat-men, who could not be made to understand that all he wanted was to be let alone. However, after some discussion, he was awarded the trophy, so that he insured the next international race for Switzerland, while his trip gave the race of 1908 the longest balloon journey on record in point of time, while we gave it the shortest. The "Banshee" (British), the next competitor for the trophy, came down in Schleswig Holstein; the "Condor" (French) and the "Belgica" (Belgian) not so far away. Neither the French "Ile de France" or the "Brise d'Automne" went so far, nor the Belgian "Utopie" or the Swiss "Cognac." The Spanish balloon "Castilla" with Señor Montojo as pilot came down near Mintzen. Mr. McCoy landed in Mecklenburg, after a very circuitous course, during which he had the doubtful pleasure of revisiting Berlin. He came down in a tree-top near Wismar, on the shores of the Baltic, within ten yards of the steep cliffs. But the other American balloon, the "St. Louis," that we had seen in Paris looking so pretty in Mallet's shop, with its new

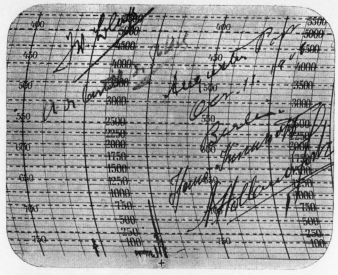

BAROGRAPH RECORD OF THE ASCENT AND FALL OF THE
BALLOON "CONQUEROR" ON OCTOBER 11, 1908

A + is placed under the line which registered the ascent to 850 meters (about 3000
feet). There the explosion took place, and the drop was so sudden that the
marker followed the line down three fourths of its length, where the parachute-like
top had arrested the descent, and then made a heavier line a little to the right.
The entire fall occurred in less than two and a half minutes. The signatures to attest
the record are by Mr. Forbes, Mr. Post, and three officials of Gordon Bennett race.

varnish and its new basket, came down in
the North Sea, and the navigators, Messrs.
Arnold and Hewatt, were saved by a life-
boat from a pilot ship as they were being
dragged through the waves at the rate of
twenty miles an hour.

The Americans, it will be seen, furnished plenty of thrills. But so far as the
contestants themselves were concerned,
the thrills came afterward. We at the
time, as I very well know, were altogether
too busy for them.

The one question we are asked everywhere, even to this day, just as we were
asked it on the roof at Friedenau, is "How
did it feel?" If you want to know how it
felt to pass through the experience we
did, think first of what we had to do.
We had to move a ton of sand out of the
car, and we had to do it in less than two
minutes and a half. If you want to know
how that feels, go down into the cellar
and move a ton of coal from one side to
the other while some one holds a watch
and tells you when two minutes and a
half goes by. Then try to see how much
you have felt and remembered while you
were doing it. It will give you a better
idea if you move the coal while you are in
a state of intense, vivid mental concentra-

tion, compressing years as it were into
moments. If we had had but those two
and a half minutes for the rest of our
lives, as it looked at first, they would have
been at least very good measure.

Like Wise, who "resolved to repeat the
experiment as soon as possible," we were
neither of us in the least inclined to follow
the advice of some of the timid souls who
greeted us on our return with the hope
that now we had come down we would
stay down. Since then Mr. Forbes has
won the Lahm Cup for long-distance
flight in America, and made many balloon
trips, one of which landed him and his
companion, Mr. Yates, on the ground in
Kentucky with a violence that would have
put an end to the career of any one not
under his lucky star. I kept at it as well,
and with Mr. Clifford B. Harmon in his
balloon, the "New York," reached the
highest altitude yet made in America, estimated at 24,200 feet, although the barograph needle went above the card at its
limit of 16,200 feet, and the surplus had
to be computed. On this same trip, in
the Centennial races of 1909, we made
the duration record for America, of 48
hours, 26 minutes in the air.

The air must have its martyrs as well

as the sea; it is greedy of success. It is a hard master; its laws must be obeyed, and always obeyed, or it will enforce them at our expense. Air is our best friend and our worst enemy. Go with it, and this power and force of nature will do more than ever the sea has done; but man can never conquer the air: he can only conquer himself enough to adapt himself to it. When he knows it better, he will be its friend, worthy of its strength, its help, in time of pleasure or of need.

Drawn by W. T. Benda

THE "CONQUEROR" AFTER THE FALL,
SPREAD OVER THE HOUSETOPS
OF FRIEDENAU